A Journey to Paris In the Year 1698

No. 4

Facsimile Reprints in the history of science, sponsored by
the History of Science Society of the University of Illinois

UNIVERSITY OF ILLINOIS PRESS

Urbana, Chicago, and London, 1967

A
JOURNEY
TO PARIS
In the Year 1698

BY MARTIN LISTER

Edited, with Annotations, a Life of Lister,
and a Lister Bibliography, by
RAYMOND PHINEAS STEARNS

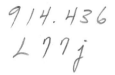

ACKNOWLEDGMENTS

For the various editions of Martin Lister's *A Journey to Paris In the Year 1698* I am indebted to the University of Illinois Library, especially to the Acquisition Librarian, Miss Helen Margaret Welch (Mrs. Preston Tuttle), and to the Assistant Reference Librarian, Mr. Richard G. Smith. In turn, we are all indebted to The Library Company of Philadelphia and to the Library of the University of California at Davis, particularly to the latter's Head of the Department of Special Collections, Mr. Donald Kunitz, who generously lent the Davis copy of the third edition of Lister's *Journey* for reproduction.

No well-authenticated picture of Martin Lister appears to be available, and our intention to reproduce one as a frontispiece has been thwarted. However, I wish to acknowledge the assistance of those who helped in the search, especially Mrs. John A. Quinn, of Champaign, Illinois; Miss Christine Stocker, Librarian, Department of Chemical Engineering and Chemical Technology, Imperial College, London, S.W. 7, England; and Arthur Lister, Esq., F.R.C.S., 56 Wimpole Street, London, W. 1, England. In addition to his aid in the vain search for a likeness of Martin Lister, Mr. Lister also supplied me with a copy of the account of Martin Lister as it appeared in the family

v

genealogy, Henry Lyttelton Lyster Denney's *Memorials of an Ancient House: A History of the Family of Lister or Lyster* (Edinburgh, 1913).

I am particularly grateful to Mr. John D. Krugler, my research assistant by the grace of the Graduate College Research Board of the University of Illinois, for his intelligent assistance in gathering materials for the notes to Lister's *Journey;* and to Mr. John Dagres, whose researches in France on Joseph Pitton de Tournefort he has generously placed at my disposal. The biographical and bibliographical materials gathered about Martin Lister were part of my researches on a larger subject, and I wish to thank the staff at the Library of the British Museum, London, especially those of the Manuscripts Division; at the Bodleian Library, Oxford; at the Library of the Ashmolean Museum, Oxford; at the Rare Book Room of the University of Illinois Library; and at the Library of the Royal Society of London, to whose President, Council, and Fellows I express my further gratitude for the privilege of quoting from the Royal Society's Archives.

Lastly, I wish to acknowledge the expert assistance of the University of Illinois Press, especially that of its Editor, Mr. Donald D. Jackson, and of its Assistant Editor, Mrs. Elizabeth Gjelsness Dulany.

The helpful cooperation of all those mentioned above has added immeasurably to the zestfulness with which I have been able to complete the preparation of this edition of Martin Lister's *A Journey to Paris In the Year 1698.* But they are in no wise accountable for any errors which may have crept into the following pages. Those are, however unintentionally, my own.

R.P.S.

CONTENTS

INTRODUCTION

I. *A Journey to Paris In the Year 1698*

When Dr. Martin Lister arrived in Paris on the first of January 1697/98,[1] he was no stranger to France. He tells us that he had visited France "three several times before."[2] It appears impossible to pinpoint each of these visits, but at least one of them had extended to about three years, 1663-66, when, as a young Cantabrigean who recently (1662) had received his M.A., he studied medicine at Montpellier and made the acquaintance of a number of young Frenchmen, some of whom, by 1698, had become physicians with appointments in high places at the French court.[3] Obviously he could speak French, although he had trouble at the opera, "not being so good a Frenchman, as to understand them when Sung."[4] Obviously, too, he liked

---

[1] See *A Journey to Paris In the Year 1698* (3rd ed., London, 1699), p. 4 (hereafter cited as *A Journey*). Presumably Lister referred to the Old Style (Julian) calendar, still in use in England. Accordingly, the date by the New Style (Gregorian) calendar, currently employed in France, would have been January 11, 1698.

[2] *Ibid.*

[3] Harcourt Brown, *Scientific Organizations in Seventeenth Century France, 1620-1680* (Baltimore, 1934), pp. 210-11; *A Journey*, pp. 244-45. Lister states that he had seen Louis XIV in 1666. *Ibid.*, p. 201.

[4] *Ibid.*, p. 174.

France. But his affection wavered in regard to some aspects of the monarchy of Louis XIV and also in regard to the Gallican Church, especially to monasticism, of which he violently disapproved.[5] He found the French climate salubrious, and, as he says, he longed to return, his "chiefest reason" for going to France in 1698 being to improve his health.[6] Accordingly, when, in 1697, he was invited to accompany William Bentinck, the Earl of Portland, on a diplomatic mission to France, he quickly seized the opportunity.

The Earl was to represent the English king, William III, in negotiations regarding the succession to the Spanish throne, in which nearly all of Europe held a vital interest, and the negotiations concluded with the short-lived First Spanish Partition Treaty (October 11, 1698).[7] Lister evidently took no part in the diplomatic negotiations, and it is equally evident that he had very little to do of an official nature. The members of Portland's delegation re-

[5] Cf. *ibid.*, p. 224. Lister considered the Court of Versailles "the most magnificent in Europe," but he no longer relished it as he had thirty years before (*ibid.*, p. 206), and his anti-Catholicism (especially his disapproval of monastic institutions) crops up repeatedly in his book. See especially pp. 75, 133-36.

[6] *Ibid.*, p. 4.

[7] Earlier editors of Lister's *Journey* asserted that the negotiations were relative to the Treaty of Ryswick. But the latter treaty was signed September 20, 1697, and while the Earl of Portland had a finger in the negotiations, he left France before the treaty was concluded. Both the time sequence and the role of Portland point to the First Spanish Partition Treaty, for the negotiation of which Portland went to France with Lister as physician to the English delegation in 1698. For the earlier accounts, see especially *A Journey to Paris. An Account of Paris at the close of the seventeenth century . . . now revised . . . with a sketch of the life of the author*, by G. Henning (London, 1823). The French editors of Lister's book followed Henning closely. See *Voyage de Lister À Paris en MDCXCVIII Traduit pour la première fois, publié et annoté Par La Société des Bibliophiles François . . .* (Paris, 1873).

quired little medical attention, and Dr. Lister had almost six months' time on his hands (from January 1 to about mid-June, 1698).[8] Moreover, he had no interest in politics or court affairs in general. In his "Introduction to the Reader" Lister wrote:

... I promise you not to trouble you with Ceremonies either of State or Church, or Politicks; for I entred willingly into neither of them. ... I incline rather to Nature than Dominion; and that I took more pleasure to see Monsieur *Breman* [Jean Brémant] in his White Wastcoat digging in the Royal Physick Garden ... than Monsieur *de Saintot* making room for an Ambassador; and I found my self better disposed, and more apt to learn the Names and Physiognomy of a Hundred Plants, than of Five or Six Princes. ... I was no more concerned in the Embassy, than in the sailing of the Ship which carried me over. ... .[9]

Lister's book, then, is about neither politics nor diplomacy. He was vitally interested in French learning and technology, especially in every aspect of the new "experimental philosophy," embracing, besides his own profession of medicine, natural history, the entire gamut of antiquities (including numismatics), demography, city planning, arts and manufactures, gardening, horticulture, and all the other facets of the "new science" to which the Royal Society of London — of which Lister was an active and prominent Fellow — had dedicated itself since its formal chartering in 1662. In consequence, he visited the French virtuosi, both great and small, the libraries, both public and private, the gardens, both formal and experimental, the collections, both of natural "curiosities" and of antiquities, the factories and the quarries, the great buildings, the hospitals (especially the surgical rooms), and the great

[8] According to James Petiver, Lister returned to London a few days before June 21, 1698. See *Sloane 3333*, fol. 146b (British Museum).
[9] *A Journey*, pp. 2-3.

public works in Paris and environs. He observed and commented upon Parisian streets, public conveyances, water supply, fuel supply, street lighting, medicine, surgery, foods, promenades and parks, and, to some extent, paintings, sculpture, and architecture. He found much to wonder at and admire, and much to criticize. And, although he states in his dedication to John, Lord Somers, that his are the "short Notes of an unprejudiced Observer," his occasional biases, especially in the arts, are evident to every reader. In general he is a classicist, with little taste for the rococo of Louis XIV's France. And, despite his admiration for France, he is English and Protestant to the core.

Lister wrote his *Journey to Paris*, as he says, "to satisfie my own Curiosity," and "to spare the often telling my Tale at my return."[10] His choice of subjects rendered his book a rather unusual one at the time, for it was not belles lettres, literary criticism, philosophy, theology, history, politics, biography, or polemics. Neither was it a guidebook for travelers in the usual sense of the term. It was not even a work on natural philosophy except as a work of scientific reporting. As such, it *was* a travel book, but its emphasis upon the scientific and technical scene, and its conscious avoidance of great princes and "high society" in general in favor of less well-known collectors, bibliophiles, and virtuosi, together with manufactories, and even nurserymen and gardeners, offended the literary tastes of some Englishmen. It was charged that Dr. Lister dealt with trivia and had written a foolish, garrulous book of no possible interest or value to persons of literary taste and pretensions.

Shortly after the appearance of Lister's *Journey to Paris*

[10] *Ibid.*, pp. 1, 2.

in 1698, William King, a clever but shiftless writer of miscellaneous items, mostly of a polemical nature, published a travesty on Lister's *Journey to Paris* entitled *A Journey to London In the Year, 1698. After the Ingenuous Method of that made by Dr. Martin Lyster to Paris, in the same year &c. Written originally in French, By Monsieur Sorbière, and Newly Translated into English.*[11] Samuel Sorbière had nothing to do with the book, although he had published earlier (in 1664) a book on his brief travels in England well known and much maligned for the author's ignorance and misinformation about English manners and customs.[12] Obviously King intended that some of the infamy of Sorbière's book would rub off on Lister's work, and in his phony introduction labeled "Monsieur Sorbeir To The Reader" King referred sarcastically to Lister's "clearness of Expression, the Elegancy of his Descriptions, as well as Ingenuous Choice of his Subjects [which] deserves a Particular *Salutation* from all the Admirers of the *Belles Lettres* in the Universe."[13]

The remainder of King's *Journey to London* consists largely of a mockery of Lister's book designed to emphasize the triviality of it. The imaginary French traveler describes the kennels and gutters of London, the "Tad-

---

[11] London, 1698. William King (1663-1712) was an Oxford graduate (B.A., 1685; M.A., 1688; B.C.L. and D.C.L., 1692), Advocate of Doctors' Commons. He was a Tory and High Church man, perhaps a Jacobin. He appears to have had a prejudice against the new science and scientists, as he wrote attacks upon Hans Sloane, the *Philosophical Transactions,* and a later parody of Dr. Lister which will be cited herein. He appears to have belonged to the "Ancients" as opposed to the "Moderns" in the long controversy so well described in Richard Foster Jones's *Ancients and Moderns* (St. Louis, 1936).

[12] Samuel Sorbière (1615-70) was a French physician, pseudo-clergyman, and literary hack.

[13] "To The Reader," unpaged.

poles & Stickebacks" of English collections, a "Calf with a Top-Knot," and "Play-things and Rattles," and Lister's proclaimed *"Relish* being not for *Art* but *Nature": "I found myself better dispos'd, and more apt to learn the physiognomy of a hundred Weeds, than of five or six Princes."* Similarly, King chided Lister's criticism of French monasticism and suggested that his preference for "Naked Statues," as opposed to the curiously draped figures of French rococo sculptures, demonstrated his obscene mind.[14]

But if Lister's *Journey to Paris* provoked jeers from such defenders of the bellelettristic tradition as William King, it evidently attracted other readers in considerable numbers. At least it ran to a third edition within a year, all by the same publisher, Jacob Tonson. Each of these editions differs from the others, and each is a new printing. The differences between the first and second editions are of small consequence. They are of the same number of pages (245), with the same six engravings; the principal alterations consist of correcting, in the second edition, the errata listed after the dedication in the first edition, together with changing the expressions involving numbers from the written words to arabic numerals.[15] But the third edition is considerably altered, principally by enlargement. As printed, it is three pages longer than the earlier editions, and Lister has added new words, new lines, and occasional whole paragraphs while omitting nothing from

[14] King's *Journey to London*, pp. 1-2, 5, 9-10, 12-13, 18, 22. The entire work is only 38 pages long.
[15] Cf. p. 3, ll. 8-9 (both eds.), "Five or Six Princes" to "5 or 6 Princes," and so on throughout. A few other words are altered, as, p. 6, l. 18, "Lords" becomes "peers," and, p. 8, l. 2, "ruined" becomes "damaged" in 2nd ed. With these minor exceptions, the two editions are the same.

the earlier editions.[16] Moreover, the illustrations, though the same as before, were placed at the end of the third edition whereas before they had been scattered through the text. Obviously the author reworked his manuscript considerably before the third and last edition to appear during his lifetime, and for this reason it is selected for reproduction herein.

Undeniably Lister's *Journey to Paris* contains trivia. But, equally undeniably, it also contains a considerable amount of material of rare historical value. The reader of these pages is taken on a unique tour of the principal col-

[16] Major additions to the third edition are:

> p. 5, ll. 9-25, not in 1st and 2nd eds.
> p. 11, ll. 1-15, not in 1st and 2nd eds.
> p. 12, ll. 6-10, not in 1st and 2nd eds.
> p. 19, l. 25–p. 20, l. 10, not in 1st and 2nd eds.
> p. 57, ll. 1-13, not in 1st and 2nd eds.
> p. 74, l. 8–p. 75, l. 5, not in 1st and 2nd eds.
> p. 107, ll. 8-19, "The Reader . . . Purse," not in 2nd ed.
> p. 138, ll. 8-18, not in 1st and 2nd eds.
> p. 147, ll. 5-15, not in 1st and 2nd eds.
> p. 150, ll. 9-26, not in 1st and 2nd eds.
> p. 158, ll. 16-22, not in 1st and 2nd eds.
> p. 167, l. 12–p. 168, l. 2, not in 1st and 2nd eds.
> p. 172, ll. 18-30, not in 1st and 2nd eds.
> p. 173, ll. 20-23, not in 1st ed.
> p. 177, ll. 11-24, not in 1st and 2nd eds.
> p. 178, l. 18–p. 179, l. 12, not in 1st and 2nd eds.
> p. 180, ll. 5-22, not in 1st and 2nd eds.
> p. 181, ll. 19-31, not in 1st and 2nd eds.

Various other lesser alterations also were made: the numbers were written out as in the 1st ed. throughout; the corrections made in the 2nd ed. were retained in the 3rd; other word changes: p. 31, l. 17, (3rd ed.), "or naked" added, l. 30, "things" read "matters" in earlier eds.; p. 38, l. 30, "in all" added; p. 42, l. 3, "thereby" previously "hereby"; p. 43, l. 26, "except" read "without" in earlier eds.; p. 45, ll. 2-3, "and . . . before" added; p. 68, l. 17, last two words and next two lines added; p. 112, l. 22, parenthetical expression added; p. 142, ll. 8-10, "I . . . with us" added; and p. 226, l. 22 added.

lections of natural history, including zoological specimens
and fossils as well as botanical collections, gardens, and
nurseries; of antiquities, including ancient manuscripts,
coins, medals, and inscriptions; of factories and quarries;
of medicine, surgery, and dissection rooms; and of art
collections and architecture — all belonging to (or presided
over by) the principal savants of the foremost city of
Christendom. Here are word pictures, duplicated by no
other writer of the time, of the virtuosi of Paris in their
native habitats, spiced with occasional accounts of scientific discussion, speculation, and even gossip reported by a
sympathetic, learned, and inquiring observer whose own
breadth of interests and knowledge were remarkable. In-
evitably, of course, Lister's own particular areas of special
knowledge — shells, fossils, anatomy, medicine, botany,
and antiquities — stand forth; but, like the other virtuosi
of the time, there are few limits to his inquiries. He frequently compares the Parisian scene with that of London.
Clearly, he feels that the long hard wars of Louis XIV had
left their mark upon the French intellectual and economic
development, and that, relatively speaking, the English
were advancing more rapidly than the French in natural
philosophy. Lister is aware, too, of the differences in
emphasis and in approach to scientific problems between
France and England, the results, in part at least, of the
different political, social, and economic developments in
the two states and stemming from the shortcomings (and
occasional advantages) of the absolutism of the French
king.

It becomes evident, further, that in spite of the long
wars which had alienated and, to a degree, isolated the
English and the French prior to the Treaty of Ryswick in
1697, the intellectual and scientific communities of both

countries had retained contact and were warmly disposed to enlarge and improve their intercourse as more peaceable circumstances might permit. Perhaps, if the War of Spanish Succession had not intervened, the accelerated French-English intellectual exchange that began soon after the Treaty of Utrecht in 1713 might have dated from about the time of Lister's *Journey*.[17] Everywhere, if we can accept Lister's word for it, he was received cordially and without reserve. Obviously he neither saw nor felt any significant restraint between himself and his hosts.

If other portions of Lister's work are less valuable — such as his descriptions of Paris and Parisian life, the streets, the conveyances, the street lighting, the promenades, the water supply, the foods, and the wines — it is largely because we have other, and in some instances better, contemporary sources to which to turn. Even so, Lister still provides a precision in detail that is sometimes unique,[18] and until private and public archives became available (generally, within the past seventy-five years), Lister was the sole authority for much that he related. On certain subjects, such as the pottery of St. Cloud (pp. 139 ff.) and the origin of King Charles's drops (pp. 245 ff.), Lister is still the principal source of contemporary information.

[17] Cf. Gabriel Bonno, "La Culture et la Civilisation Britannique devant l'Opinion Française de la Paix d'Utrecht aux Lettres Philosophiques, 1713-1734," *Transactions of the American Philosophical Society*, n.s., XXXVIII, pt. I (1948), 1-184. The author quotes (p. 123) a French journalist writing in 1717: "Avec quelle ardeur les Anglais cultivent-ils les sciences, et principalement la physique, les mathématiques, la médecine. Témoins les Harvées [*sic*], les Willis, les Boyles, les Sydenhams, les Listers, les Lowers et taut d'autres; en sort que les savants des autres nations se font une gloire d'être associés à l'Académie Royal de Londres."
[18] See, for example, pp. 158-59, with reference to oysters cut from the shell. Cf. the French edition, p. 143, n. 2.

Since Martin Lister's death in 1712, his *Journey to Paris* has been thrice republished, each time, unhappily, in a somewhat garbled form. The first republication was in *A General Collection of the best and most interesting Voyages and Travels in all parts of the World . . .* edited by John Pinkerton in 1809.[19] No indication is given as to which edition was reprinted, there is essentially no editing or annotation, and the entire performance smacks of a hasty scissors-and-paste job. The second republication was in 1823, edited by George Henning and entitled *An Account of Paris at the close of the seventeenth century . . . by Martin Lister, M.D., now revised. . . .*[20] Again the editor gives no indication of which edition he employed, although it is evident from the contents that he used the second edition, without the author's revisions and additions. Unfortunately, too, the editor "revised" the book by making minor alterations in it, especially by dividing it rather arbitrarily in chapters with titles supplied by the editor. Even the original title of the book itself was changed. Still, Henning presented the essence of Lister's *Journey* without serious damage to the contents; and he added an introductory sketch of Lister which has colored every other biographical account of the Doctor to the present day. Moreover, he annotated the work to some extent, initiating the error that Lister had accompanied the Earl of Portland to Paris to negotiate the Treaty of Ryswick of 1697. All in all, Henning's edition was a good one for its day, and the next editors of *A Journey to Paris* used Henning's copy as the basis for their work. This, the last edition to date, was a French translation entitled

---

[19] 12 vols., London, 1809. Lister's *Journey to Paris* appears in IV, 1-76.
[20] London, 1823. Published by subscription, which bespeaks a more than passing interest in Lister's work — or in George Henning!

Voyage de Lister À Paris en MDCXCVIII Traduit pour la première fois, publié et annoté Par La Société des Bibliophiles François. . . .[21] Unfortunately the Society did not trouble carefully to check the various editions of Lister's work, and the editors (of whom there were several) simply translated Henning's edition (i.e., the second edition), with Henning's introduction, sketch of Lister, arbitrary chapter headings, and, to some extent, his annotations. However, the French editors added further annotations to the text of Lister's *Journey*, some of which have proved useful to the present editor, especially in the identification of persons and places mentioned by Lister in his work.

The present book presents the third edition of Lister's *Journey to Paris* as revised and enlarged by the author. It is presented in its entirety, by photographic process, thereby eliminating the possibility of error in its transmission. This leads to a certain clumsiness in the annotations, which must be presented by page and line at the end of the text — although for those readers who resent footnotes at the bottom of the page this process enables them to read the whole of Lister's *Journey* without interruption, if they choose. However, for those readers who may desire them, rather full notes follow the text to identify persons, places, and scientific specimens insofar as possible.

II. Martin Lister, 1638-1712

Martin Lister belonged to a family well known in the annals of English medicine and science, as a glance at any of the major English biographical dictionaries will con-

[21] Paris, 1873. The book also includes extracts from the works of John Evelyn relative to his journey in France between 1648 and 1661.

firm. Two of his uncles — or more probably great-uncles[22] — were court physicians: Edward was Physician in Ordinary to Queen Elizabeth I and to James I; Sir Matthew was physician to Anne, queen of James I, and later to Charles I. Martin's father, Sir Martin Lister (knighted in 1636), was, however, neither a physician nor a scientist. Rather, he entered the King's service and became a member of the Long Parliament until he was secluded by Pride's Purge (December 6-7, 1648). In the meantime, he had married Susannah, daughter of Sir Alexander Temple. Susannah had been maid of honor to Anne of Denmark, James I's queen, and was highly esteemed at court for her beauty. Martin Lister was born of Susannah Temple and Sir Martin Lister about 1638 at Radclive, near Buckingham, in Buckinghamshire. His early education was under the direction of Sir Matthew Lister, physician to Charles I, and on June 12, 1655, he entered St. John's College, Cambridge, as a pensioner. He graduated B.A. in 1658, became a Fellow of St. John's by royal mandate in 1660, and won the M.A. degree in 1662. Obviously, Martin Lister and his family survived the English Civil Wars and the Protectorate of Oliver Cromwell without shattering losses — and Martin's fellowship in 1660 bespoke royal favor at the hands of the restored Stuart king. Indeed, Martin Lister indicates that he had attended the court of Charles II and was personally known to the King.[23]

---

[22] *Dictionary of National Biography,* "Edward Lister" (1556-1620), and "Sir Matthew Lister" (1571?-1656). The dates suggest that if these two men were brothers, as the *D.N.B.* affirms, they were not likely to have been brothers of Martin Lister's father, Sir Martin Lister, who, dying in 1670 at the age of sixty-seven, must have been born about 1603. It seems unlikely that three brothers (even half-brothers) would have been born, respectively, in 1556, 1571[?], and 1603[?]. See S. Wood, "Martin Lister, Zoologist and Physician," *Annals of Medical History,* n.s., I (1929), 87-89.

[23] *A Journey,* pp. 29, 246-47.

Shortly after he had graduated M.A. from Cambridge, Martin Lister proceeded to France, where, between 1663 and 1666, he studied medicine and such related subjects as anatomy and botany at Montpellier. Montpellier was a favorite resort of English medical students at the time and there was an academy to which Lister belonged in association with other foreign students and the French.[24] Precisely with whom Lister studied and with whom he associated at Montpellier are uncertain. As a foreigner and a Protestant, Lister could not formally enroll at the University and become a candidate for a degree, but his associations in the academy enabled him to become familiar with the scene and to observe closely what was taking place in medicine, botany, and allied studies. One "Dr. Chiquenau" was botanic professor, anatomy reader, and Chancellor of the University, but Pierre Magnol (1638-1715), then a young man but destined to become a prominent French physician and botanist, was already reputed to be the better herbarist.[25] The great Niels Stensen (1638-86) ("Steno," as he was known by his Latinized name), the Danish geographer and anatomist, was also at Montpellier, and Lister probably observed him while he dissected an ox's head and demonstrated the existence of the "ductus salivaris," or the "duct of Steno," which was Stenson's great discovery.[26] If we judge by Lister's re-

[24] Sir Kenelm Digby, Sir Robert Southwell, and Henry Oldenburg had all been recent sojourners at Montpellier. Brown, *Scientific Organizations in Seventeenth Century France*, pp. 208 ff.
[25] Was "Dr. Chiquenau" Dr. Chicoyneau, father of François Chicoyneau (1672-1752), Prefect of Montpellier Gardens? Philip Skippon's "An Account of a Journey Made Thro' Part of the Low-Countries, Germany, Italy, and France," in *A Collection of Voyages and Travels* . . . (6 vols., London, 1732), VI, 714-35, tells of Montpellier, Lister, and the latter's associates shortly before Lister left Montpellier in 1666.
[26] Made at Amsterdam and published in his *Observationes Anatomicae* in 1662. The "duct of Steno" is the duct of the parotid, or largest salivary gland.

marks in *A Journey to Paris,* he greatly enjoyed his years
at Montpellier. Evidently he became thoroughly familiar
with the environs for miles around — a familiarity which,
one is led to surmise, was the result of frequent botanizing
trips in the Languedoc villages and countryside and ex-
tending at least as far as Pézenas in nearby Hérault.[27]
His English associates at Montpellier included several men
soon to become famous as physicians or scientists, or both:
William Croone (1633-84), physician; Clopton Havers
(d. 1702), physician and anatomist; Henry Sampson
(1629?-1700), physician; Francis Jessop (1638-91), naturalist and mathematician; Sir Thomas Crew (later Second
Baron Crew of Stene, 1679-97), ornithologist; Peter
Vivian, a Fellow of Trinity College, Cambridge; and many
others.[28]

In August, 1665, a trio of Cantabrigeans whom Lister
may have known at Cambridge arrived in Montpellier on
a tour of the Continent. These were John Ray, destined
to become England's greatest natural scientist before
Darwin, Ray's former pupil, Philip Skippon, and Na-
thaniel Bacon, also a former Cambridge student.[29] During

---

[27] See Lister's references in *A Journey,* pp. 3, 214-16, 244-45.

[28] Philip Skippon ("An Account of a Journey," *loc. cit.,* p. 714) related
that, as of early August, 1665, the following English persons were at
Montpellier: "My lord *Clinton,* the Earl of Lincoln's son, Mr. *Withers*
his governor; Sir *Thomas Crew,* lord *Crew's* son; two Mr. *Harveys* . . .
Mr. *Peter Vivian* fellow of *Trinity* college in *Cambridge;* Mr. *Martyn
Lyster,* fellow of *St. John's* college, *ibid.* Mr. Ward, student of *Christ-
church;* Mr. *Whitcombe,* Mr. *Tanner,* Mr. *Spicer,* of the Temple; Mr.
Sampson, formerly of *Pembroke-Hall* in *Cambridge;* Mr. *Jessop;* earl
of *Alisbury,* and lord *Bruce,* his eldest son, with a great train, his lady
and daughters being with him; Mr. *Havers,* formerly of *Trinity College;*
Mr. *Ol*[iver] *St. John,* formerly lord chief justice, who went by the
name of monsieur *Montagne,* and his lady; Mr. *Ellock;* Mr. *Abdy;* Dr.
Downes; Mr. *Poley;* Dr. *Croone;* Mr. *Howlett;* Dr. *Moulins,* a *Scotch-
man;* Mr. *Norwood;* Mr. *Deane;* Mr. *Duckwood;* and Dr. *Jeanes."*

[29] C. E. Raven, *John Ray* (Cambridge, 1950), pp. 131 ff.

the next five or six months these three, with Lister and several of his Montpellier friends, toured about in southern France observing plants, animals, insects, and other natural phenomena together with the various manufactures of the communities which they visited. Then on February 1, 1666, Louis XIV, about to enter upon the War of Devolution, ordered all Englishmen out of France within three months. In consequence, the English at Montpellier moved out. Lister, Jessop, Sampson, Crew, and others moved to Lyons, where they met Ray, Skippon, Vivian, and others in early March. From Lyons, Lister, in company with Ray, Skippon, and "Dr. Moulins,"[30] moved by horseback to Paris, arriving there on March 16. There they stayed for about a fortnight of sightseeing, including a glimpse of Louis XIV *en promenade* at Versailles. On April 1 (o.s.), Lister and Skippon, separating from the others of their company,[31] traveled by coach to Calais, where they took ship and arrived at Dover on April 8, 1666. Lister's principal stay in France had come to an end.

There is ample evidence that Lister both enjoyed and profited from his studies and travels in France. He had studied at one of the foremost centers of intellectual life and of natural history, and he had come to know some of the prominent Europeans of his generation in medicine, anatomy, and natural history. Still, perhaps the most immediately important aspect of his French tour was the

[30] Probably James Molins, M.A., of Aberdeen.
[31] Ray and two others went to Calais in a fishcart (*chasse marée*), but Lister and Skippon demanded more comfortable means of travel. This entire reconstruction of Lister's travels in 1665-66 is derived from Skippon, "An Account of a Journey," *loc. cit.*, pp. 714-35. There is no evidence that Lister completed his medical studies at Leyden, as Henry Lyttelton Lyster Denny states in his *Memorials of an Ancient House: A History of the Family of Lister or Lyster* (Edinburgh, 1913), pp. 218-23. I am indebted to Mr. Arthur Lister of 56 Wimpole Street, London, W. 1, for excerpts from this rare volume.

friendship and mutual regard which developed during his last months there with John Ray. From this there sprang up a scientific correspondence and mutual exchange of specimens, information, and opinion that ran for several years, during which Lister blossomed into prominence as a scientist and an active member both of the scientific circle at Oxford and of the Royal Society of London.

At Dover, or possibly at London, Lister parted company with Philip Skippon and made his way to his uncle's house at Burwell, "nere Louth," in Lincolnshire. There, during the winter of 1666-67, he entered into correspondence with Ray and devoted himself to natural history.[32] In the summer of 1667 he moved back to St. John's at Cambridge, where evidently he remained until the spring of 1669. Then, in April or early May, he married Hannah Parkinson and took up temporary residence at Carleton Hall in Craven, Yorkshire.[33] The following summer (1670) he moved to York, to a house "without Michael's-gate Barr," where he settled down to the practice of medicine and the pursuit of natural science and antiquities for the next thirteen years.

LISTER AS A PHYSICIAN

Martin Lister devoted the remainder of his life, professionally, to the practice of medicine. Evidently he was a

---

[32] Lister's letters to Ray are the principal means of tracing his movements for the next several years. See Edwin Lankester, ed., *Correspondence of John Ray* (London, Ray Society, 1848), pp. 11 ff. (hereafter cited as *Ray Correspondence*), and R. T. Gunther, ed., *Further Correspondence of John Ray* (London, Ray Society, 1928), pp. 111 ff. (hereafter cited as *Further Correspondence*).

[33] Ray congratulates him on his marriage and sends his "service to the new lady Lister" on May 7, 1669. *Further Correspondence*, pp. 122-23. Lister had nine children by this marriage (see n. 118 herein). Hannah Lister died in 1694.

successful practitioner.[34] But his success appears to have attracted more social and political attention than it achieved professional acclaim. He was well trained by one of the best European medical faculties, and his works attracted sufficient attention that, on March 5, 1683/84, he was awarded the Doctor of Medicine degree by diploma at Oxford.[35] He became a candidate for the Royal College of Physicians in 1684, a Fellow in 1687 (by action of King James II, March 11, 1686/87), and was elected Censor in 1694.[36] In 1702 he was appointed Second Physician in Ordinary to Queen Anne, a position he held until his death in 1712.[37] By the material and social standards of his time, Martin Lister rose to a high place in his profession.

In the meantime he published half a dozen books and nearly a dozen articles about medical matters.[38] Half of his books dealt with the medical waters and baths of England, with which he performed a number of experiments

[34] Wood, "Martin Lister," *loc. cit.*

[35] Joseph Foster, *Alumni Oxoniensis* (early ser., 4 vols., Oxford, 1891), III. Doubtless Lister's extensive gifts to the Ashmolean Museum, together with his gifts to the Bodleian Library, helped to effect this action on the part of the University. He was recommended for the degree by the Chancellor, the Duke of Ormonde, who cited him as a person of exemplary loyalty, of high esteem among the most eminent of his profession, and of singular merit to the University. Wood, "Martin Lister," *loc. cit.*; R. T. Gunther, "Life and Letters of Edward Lhwyd," in *Early Science at Oxford*, XIV (Oxford, 1945), 62.

[36] Wood, "Martin Lister," *loc. cit.*; Sir George Clark, *A History of the Royal College of Physicians of London* (Oxford, 1964), p. 421. At the same time the King named Edward Lower, Hans Sloane, and Tancred Robinson as Fellows of the Royal College.

[37] Denny makes clear (*Memorials of an Ancient House*) that Lister had been angling for an appointment as Royal Physician since about 1699, and he was assisted in winning the appointment in 1702 by his niece, Lady Sarah Churchill.

[38] See the Lister bibliography in the Appendices herein.

to distill mineral salts; but neither the chemistry nor the physiology of his time had advanced to a point by which he was able to offer significant medical contributions.[39] In general, he was conservative in his approach to medical problems and cautious in the adoption of new methods in medicine and surgery — although he was not consistent in this attitude. He was said to have disputed bitterly with some of the most advanced practitioners of his day, especially with Thomas Sydenham and Fredrik Ruysch, although he appears to have held considerable agreement with the former in regard to the value of Peruvian bark in the treatment of agues and in the use of clinical observation instead of theory. When his book *Sex Exercitationes Medicinales De Quibusdam Morbis Chronicis . . .* appeared in 1694 Edward Lhwyd wrote to him that "Dr. Sherard and others informed me yt your book had given great offense to ye London physicians" and ascribed their offense to "malice and absurd prejudice."[40] But some of the offense appears to have arisen from the fact that Lister described specific venereal cases of female patients in a manner that shocked his colleagues — and one section dealt with hydrophobia, which, as Lister's colleagues complained, seldom occurred.[41] In one instance, however, Lister's medical conservatism may have cost him dearly. In 1698 one Joseph Lister, a "Sea-faring man" who

[39] Lynn Thorndyke, "Newness and Novelty in Seventeenth-Century Science and Medicine," in *Roots of Scientific Thought*, eds. Philip P. Cuiener and Aaron Noland (New York, 1957), p. 454.

[40] Gunther, "Life and Letters of Edward Lhwyd," *loc. cit.*, pp. 253-54. The book was republished in Richard Morton's *Opera Medica* (London, 1697), so evidently some medical men valued it highly.

[41] Lister, however, had had experience with it at York and, perhaps, in London. See his articles in the *Philosophical Transactions*, XIII, no. 147 (May 10, 1683), 162-70; XX, no. 242 (July, 1698), 246-48. Cf. also Lynn Thorndike, *A History of Magic and Experimental Science*, VIII (New York, 1958), 261.

claimed kinship with the Doctor, wrote from Fort St. George in Madras to offer his services as a collector of plants, seeds, shells, and information from the Far East. Two years later he sent from Amoy, in China, a fairly viable description of the Chinese method of inoculation for smallpox.[42] This was nearly fifteen years before Dr. Emanuel Timoni communicated to the Royal Society of London the Near Eastern method of inoculation from Constantinople (1714) and more than twenty years before the method was successfully put to the test in England.[43] Lister, however, took no effective action, and his friend Dr. Clopton Havers, perhaps using Lister's source of information, brought the Chinese practice to the attention of the Royal Society only a few weeks after Lister had been appraised of it.[44] It seems possible that if Lister had espoused the matter with enthusiasm, the wide benefits of smallpox inoculation might have been experienced in England twenty years or so before the practice was actually projected. Martin Lister may have sacrificed fame and uncounted English lives because of his incredulity.[45]

[42] The letters are in *Lister 4*, fol. 80, *15*, fol. 15, and *37*, fol. 15 (Bodleian Library). For Joseph Lister, see also Henry Davison Love, *Vestiges of Old Madras* (Indian Records ser., 4 vols., London, 1913), II, 65; Denny, *Memorials of an Ancient House*, p. 278.

[43] R. P. Stearns, "Remarks upon the Introduction of Inoculation for Smallpox in England," *Bulletin of the History of Medicine*, XXIV (1950), 103-22.

[44] *Journal-Book*, Feb. 14, 1699/1700 (MS in the Library of the Royal Society of London). This and subsequent materials from the Royal Society Library are cited with the permission of the President and Fellows of the Royal Society of London.

[45] Lister had, curiously enough, demonstrated a particular interest in smallpox. See his *Exercitatio-Anatomica altera . . . His accedit Exercitatio medicinalis de variolis* (2 pts., London, 1695). The disquisition on smallpox was republished separately in 1696 and twice reprinted afterwards, in 1696 (Geneva) and in 1737 (London). See the Lister bibliography in the Appendices herein.

Still, Lister's tendency toward conservative medicine was by no means constant. Although he was steeped in the medical classics from the ancient Hippocrates to the medieval Rhazes, and while he often rejected the medical theories of his colleagues, he frequently set forth medical hypotheses of his own and kept himself well informed about the medical opinions and discoveries of his own generation. He accepted and employed the two best new drugs of the day, Peruvian bark (quinine) and ipecac. He endorsed Leeuwenhoek's account of the spermatozoa, and, as he recounts in *A Journey to Paris,* he was vitally interested in new surgical methods for removing the stone and had himself proposed the method of "cutting above the *Os Pubis*" (with which he had become familiar in France) in "A Proposall of a New Way of Cutting for the Stone of the Bladder," presented before the Philosophical Society of Oxford on April 28, 1685.[46] He despised medical quackery in all its forms and deplored the popular notion, as prevalent in France as in England, that medicine was considered to be "a Knack, more than a Science or Method."[47]

Men are apt to prescribe to their Physician [he wrote], before he can possibly tell what he shall in his Judgement think fitting to give . . . and *our Men,* who ought to Converse with the Patient and his Relations with Prognosticks only, which are the honour of Physick; and not play the Philosopher by fanciful and precarious Interpretations of the Nature of Diseases and Medicines, to gain a sort of Credit with the Ignorant; and such certainly are all those that have not studied Physick thoroughly, and in earnest.[48]

[46] R. T. Gunther, "Dr. Plot and the Correspondence of the Philosophical Society of Oxford," in *Early Science at Oxford,* XII (Oxford, 1939), 291.
[47] *A Journey,* pp. 245-46.
[48] *Ibid.,* p. 246.

After all, said Lister, who prescribed moderation in all things, "the best Rule of Health and long Life is to do little to our selves."[49]

LISTER EMERGES AS A SCIENTIST

Edwin Lankester remarked in 1846 that Lister's "labours in natural history are of more value than those in medicine,"[50] and in that judgment there is universal concurrence. No concrete evidence remains to explain why and by whom Martin Lister became disposed toward natural philosophy; but the medical traditions in his family, his Cambridge years during the time that, as Raven has said, all Cambridge was turned toward natural philosophy by John Ray and his friends and pupils (the latter including Francis Willughby and Philip Skippon)[51] — all these factors must have combined to incline Lister toward the new science. His years in France clearly quickened these impulses, and before he left Montpellier Lister was making observations in natural history and exhibiting the interests and the methods of a natural philosopher.

His chosen profession contributed further to these interests and methods, especially in botany and anatomy, and many of his instructors and fellow students — not to mention his colleagues in later life — strengthened his dedication to the new science. Whether he had previously known John Ray at Cambridge, or Henry Oldenburg at Montpellier, there is no record; but both of these men contributed greatly to Lister's early career as a scientist. His as-

[49] *Ibid.*, p. 35.
[50] *Memorials of John Ray* (London, Ray Society, 1846), p. 17n.
[51] Raven, *John Ray, passim.*

sociations with Ray in France led to a warm mutual
regard between the two men. Within a year after their return to England, they had entered into a philosophical correspondence and scientific exchange which continued for
many years. Lister wrote to Ray to express his interest in
natural history, including animals as well as plants. By
June, 1667, he was adding items to Ray's *Cambridge Catalogue of Plants;*[52] the next month he described some insects
in his collection;[53] and the correspondence continued, often
at monthly intervals. In June, 1667, Ray advised Lister
"to see with your own eyes, not relying lazily on the dic-
tates of any master but yourself, comparing things with
books, and so learning as much as can be known of
them."[54] It seems likely, however, that Ray's words only
reinforced Lister's proclivities. In December, 1669, after
urging a more careful analysis of old works, Lister wrote:

For my part, I think it absolutely necessary that an exact and
minute distinction of things precede our learning by particular experiments, what different parts each body or thing may consist
of; likewise concerning the best and most convenient ways of sep-
aration of those parts, and their virtues and force upon human
bodies as to the uses of life; all these, besides the different tex-
tures, are things subsequent to natural history, unless you make
the last assistant, as indeed all the rest are, were they truly
known. . . .[55]

By 1670 Lister's scientific correspondence had widened
so that he was becoming well known as a member of the
English circle of natural philosophers. Henry Oldenburg
had entered the picture with John Ray, Francis Willughby,

[52] *Catalogus Plantarum Cantabrigiam nascentium* (Cambridge, 1660).
[53] *Ray Correspondence*, pp. 11-15.
[54] *Ibid.*, p. 14.
[55] *Ibid.*, p. 49.

Francis Jessop, John Brooke, and others, and Oldenburg, as Secretary of the Royal Society of London and publisher of the *Philosophical Transactions,* soon emerged as the pivotal figure.[56] He passed on information about the meetings of the Society, about the activities of the French Academy, and reports of other events of scientific interest in Holland, Italy, and the German states. Lister had turned his attention more and more to insects, especially spiders and flies, and on January 3, 1670/71, Oldenburg asked him to submit a paper on the subject. Lister responded on January 25 with a letter "About the hatching of certain bees . . ." which was read before the Royal Society on February 9. Already, on February 4, Oldenburg had written him an encouraging letter and asked permission to propose Lister as a Fellow of the Royal Society. This was done on May 18, and on the following November 2, 1671, Lister was formally elected Fellow. There followed an astonishing series of almost weekly letters from Lister to Oldenburg on scientific subjects throughout 1671, 1672, and 1673, all of which were read before the Society and nearly all of which were published in the *Philosophical Transactions.* The frequency was reduced after 1673 but continued at a more moderate rate until the summer of 1676.[57] They reflected Lister's exchanges with Ray and Willughby (largely botanical), his medical practice, and his growing interest in insects, which soon included snails and other mollusks.

[56] See *Lister 34,* fols. 1, 5, 23, 35, 73, *et seq.* (Bodleian Library); *Letter-Book,* IV, *passim* (MS in Royal Society Library).
[57] See *Lister 34,* fols. 1, 5, 23, *et seq.* Lister's letters to Oldenburg are in *Guard-Book L 5-6,* fols. 20-80 (MS in Royal Society Library). Those published in the *Philosophical Transactions* are listed in the Lister bibliography in the Appendices herein.

For reasons by no means clear, Martin Lister's scientific correspondences were punctuated by three periods of relative inactivity during each of which he appears to have largely withdrawn from the scene. As each of these interims are evident both in his extant correspondence and in his contributions to the Royal Society, it appears reasonable to conclude that they were genuine withdrawals and not the chance result of unknown or lost correspondence and other literary remains. In general Lister's active periods ran from about 1669 to 1676, from 1683 to 1685, and from 1693 to 1701. Between 1676 and 1683 his productivity (in terms of scientific correspondence and contributions to the Royal Society) was almost nil. Again, between 1685 and 1693 a similar hiatus occurred; and after 1701 he accomplished almost nothing of scientific import.

C. E. Raven, in his superb life of John Ray,[58] viewing Lister's scientific exchange with his fellow savants from the standpoint of Ray alone, suggested that Lister was piqued with Ray and broke off his correspondence because of it. Lister's pique occurred, according to Mr. Raven, because Ray credited Edward Hulse with being the first close observer of gossamers (spiderwebs) when, actually, both Hulse and Lister had made similar observations independently and simultaneously. There is no doubt that Lister was momentarily taken aback by this episode (which occurred in 1670-71), but Mr. Raven overlooks the fact that Lister continued to correspond freely and friendlily with Ray for at least the next five years with no hint of continuing pique, withdrawal, or diminution in the

[58] *John Ray*, p. 139 *et passim*.

exchange.[59] Lister had a much warmer dispute with Nehemiah Grew in 1673,[60] but it, too, passed quickly without permanent estrangement. The conclusion is inescapable that the hiatuses in Lister's scientific corre-

---

[59] *Ray Correspondence*, pp. 61-63 ff. Lister's complaint to Ray does not appear. On July 17, 1670, Ray takes note of Lister's dissatisfaction, saying: "The observation [about spiders projecting their webs] is yours as well as his, and neither beholden to other (that I know of) for any hint of it, only he had the hap to make it first. . . ." Lister appears to have misunderstood Ray. He wrote (March 21, 1670/71) that he believed that he was the first to acquaint Ray with an account of spiders "sailing and mounting up into the air . . . but that is best known to yourself." He admitted that others "may many of them light upon the same observation"; and he added that he preferred all to be "free and communicative that we may, if possible, considering the shortness of our lives, participate with posterity." Ray replied (April 13, 1671): "The flying or sailing of spiders through the air is, for aught I know, your discovery; from you I had the first intimation and knowledge of it. Dr. Hulse acquainted me with no more than the shooting out their threads." He went on to assure Lister that he would rob no man, especially Lister, of proper credit — which, as Mr. Raven demonstrates, was characteristic of Ray. The correspondence thereafter continued with no restraints until the summer of 1676. There is a sharp decline thereafter, and the correspondence was never resumed except in desultory fashion. Other evidence, however, supports the conclusion that Lister continued to hold Ray in high regard and to assist him at several points in his work. Lister's interruption in his Ray correspondence coincided so closely with his general inactivity between 1676 and 1683 that it is clearly part of a more general pattern and not confined to Ray alone. But it offers no clue as to the reason for the general collapse during that period.

[60] *Sloane 1929*, fols. 1-3, 4-8b, Oct.-Dec., 1673 (British Museum). Grew was much annoyed by Lister's "animadversions upon my last book." Grew said that Lister wrote "not with Ink, but with Aqua fortis, designing to obliterate all yt lyes before them; as if their pens were nothing els but arrows, nor yr words but bullets; yt to be a Philosopher, were only to be a good ffencer, & ye seat of ye Muses were but a Martial field." Grew went on to express "odius resentment" for "a contentious person" and sorrowfully conceived that Lister was such a one (Grew, himself, did not do badly!). But later both men worked harmoniously together in the Royal Society with every sign of mutual respect and friendliness.

spondence were not the result of personal piques and injured pride, although, undeniably, Lister was stubborn in his opinions. Lacking the perspectives of twentieth-century scientific achievements, he cannot fairly be castigated for failing to comprehend the towering greatness of some of his colleagues in the seventeenth century, when, after all, nearly every aspect of natural science was in flux and nothing had been fixed upon with any finality.

Lister's first outburst of scientific activity (*c.* 1669-76) encompassed a wide variety of subjects. Some of them obviously stemmed from his cooperation with John Ray and Francis Willughby, especially his concern with botany, birds, and fishes; but others — insects (especially spiders), minerals, fossils, and mollusks — grew out of his own interests for the most part. Ray and Willughby were pushing forward studies in botany, ornithology, and ichthyology (although their interests and competence, particularly Ray's, ranged over the whole of natural history). Willughby's untimely death in 1672 left Ray with a mass of materials which, partly out of loyalty to his friend and patron, he felt constrained to bring to completion. Lister, among others, contributed to Ray's efforts — and it was a tribute to him that Ray accepted him so widely (though not uncritically) in his work. At the outset Ray was engaged in the preparation of his *Catalogus Anglicae* (1670), and Lister contributed collections of English plants and made observations on "the Bleeding of the Sycamore," on "the Motion of Sap in Trees," "On the Motion of Juyces in Vegetables," on "Vegetable Excrescencies," on "Veins . . . in Plants," and related aspects of plant physiology which were pioneering studies in the field.[61] Unfortunately, however, Lister identified the bleeding of wood in winter with the weeping of vines and other woody plants in spring, which, as was learned later, depends on entirely different causes. He showed that it is possible to force water out of the wood of a portion of branch cut in winter by warming it artificially, and then to cause the water to be absorbed again by cooling it. But it was reserved for later physiologists to demonstrate that this phenomenon has nothing to do with the bleeding of cut stems caused by root pressure.

After Willughby's death, Ray pushed forward his studies in ornithology. Again Lister sent specimens of birds and made observations and experiments. In their correspondence Ray and Lister discussed a wide variety of birds, the means of their differentiation, the extraordinary abilities of woodpeckers "to shoot out and retract their tongues" in search of insects and larvae for food, and various structural peculiarities of the bird family.[62] On one occasion, Lister saved Ray from "a notable error" when he pointed out differences between the snipe and a similar bird known in Yorkshire as a gid, and so prevented Ray from confusing the two. In February, 1676, Lister sent Ray a variety of notes on his observations about birds. Among them was the following: "One and the same Swallow I have known by the subtracting daily

---

[61] All of these were read to the Royal Society, 1670-72. Cf. *Guard-Book L 5-6*, fols. 24, 26, 29, 41, 42. On Lister's contributions to Ray, see *Ray Correspondence*, pp. 43-46, 46-48, 53-54, 57, 64-65, 82-83. Lister's letters to the Royal Society on plant physiology excited Henry Oldenburg in 1672 to ask for more. *Lister 34*, fol. 73, Dec. 12, 1672. Lister did submit observations "On Juices of Plants" in 1676. *Guard-Book L 5-6*, fol. 77.

[62] Raven, *John Ray*, pp. 315 ff.

of her eggs to have laid nineteen successively and then to have given over."[63] Ray was instantly aware of the remarkable significance of this fact and published it both in the English version of the *Ornithology* (1678) and in his *The Wisdom of God* (1691). But, as Mr. Raven says, the physiological interest of Lister's observation escaped attention for more than a century and received no scientific study until 1936.[64] How much Lister appreciated the importance of his experiment is unknown; but, as a physician, he must have been dimly aware of it or he would not have performed it.

Lister's interest in insects appears to have been his own,[65] though Ray, Oldenburg, and others encouraged him in its purusit. His correspondence with Ray from 1668 onward is filled with observations and speculations about "the darting of Spiders," the manner in which spiders spin their webs, and comments regarding the habits of ants, pismires, and other insects.[66] Indeed, Lister's first formal contribution to the Royal Society (as opposed to letters) concerned "the odd Turn of Some Shell-snailes, and the darting of Spiders," and two more of his letters to Oldenburg were about insects. Soon he was preparing a catalogue of spiders which he sent to Ray and Willughby in 1670. After receiving their comments he increased his number of species and continued to add to his collections and to revise his catalogue. In January, 1671, he inquired

---

[63] *Ray Correspondence*, p. 117.

[64] Raven, *John Ray*, pp. 478-80. After Ray's *Ornithology* appeared, Lister suggested various additions for a new English edition — suggestions which Ray adopted. *Ray Correspondence*, pp. 116-18; *Philosophical Transactions*, XV, no. 175 (Sept.-Oct., 1685), 1159-61.

[65] As early as 1667, while he was still at St. John's College, he referred to his collection of insects. *Ray Correspondence*, p. 15.

[66] *Ibid.*, pp. 54-55, 55-56, 57-59, 60-61, 65-67, 78-80, 82-83, 83-85, 88-90, 99-100.

about Francesco Redi's *Esperienze intorno alla generazione degl'insetti* (1668) and, with Redi, quickly aban-
doned the classical belief in the spontaneous generation of
insects in putrid matter. Here again, Lister's innate conservatism gave way to new opinion based upon experiment
and close observations — observations which closely coincided with his own. His studies of kermes certainly
pointed in this direction — a study which appeared to be
as much utilitarian as scientific. Lister was concerned with
the kermes as a source of dyestuffs and as a possible
source of medicine, as well as with the life cycle and the
curious feeding habits of the kermes itself.[67]

Simultaneously, he was investigating minerals, fossils,
snails, and other mollusks. In Lister's time these items
were generally looked upon as "formed stones," whether
they included fossil remains, shells, crystals, corals, pyrites,
gallstones, or stalactites. All were *sui generis* in nature.
No doubt, too, Lister, as a medical man who was familiar
with bladder stones and with "a Stone cut out from under
the tongue of a Man" at York,[68] as well as with fossil
remains, crystals, corals, belemnites, and the like, was
readily disposed to accept the current opinion that all were
"formed stones" by nature. Hence, minerals, fossils, and
shellfish were all of a kind to be studied together. Lister's
interest in minerals appears to have had a utilitarian back-
ground, as he hoped to develop mines (probably iron
mines) on his properties at Craven in Yorkshire.[69] Subsequently, as his publications show, he was active in collect-

[67] See his "Extracts of Two Letters . . . concerning the kind of Insect
hatched by the English Kermes . . . ," *Philosophical Transactions,* VI,
no. 73 (July 17, 1671), 2196-97.
[68] See his account of it in *ibid.,* VII, no. 83 (May 20, 1672), 4062-64.
[69] *Ray Correspondence,* pp. 48-51, Dec. 22, 1669.

ing materials from mines and in the results of borings into
the earth at various places. At the same time, he gathered
specimens and prepared a catalogue of snails, land snails
at first, then fresh-water snails, and finally marine snails.
Other mollusks also attracted his attention in the course
of time.

Out of these manifold observations and studies Lister
prepared his first major book and fell into disagreement
with John Ray. The disagreement arose early in 1672
over the "origin of those stones which we usually call
petrified shells."[70] Lister argued that petrified stones and
the like found in the earth were "formed stones," whereas
Ray was of the opinion that they were "originally vegetables" — although, as he wrote to Lister, "you want not
good ground for what you assert."[71] Lister found star-
stones to be branched like St.-Cuthbert's-beads, and when
Ray argued that they were organic remains of creatures
formerly living, Lister replied that he did not believe that
St.-Cuthbert's-beads had been the backbone of any living
creature, "because I find of them ramous and branched
like trees."[72] He published in the *Philosophical Transactions* "A Description of certain Stones figur'd like Plants
. . ." with illustrations, but Oldenburg added a note from
John Ray asserting "that these Stones were originally
pieces of Vegetables."[73] And so the two men differed on
the origin of fossils, both vegetable and animal. Ray, of
course, was far ahead of his time in this matter, although
he had support from prominent sources, notably Niels
Stensen, Marcello Malpighi, Robert Hooke, and some

[70] Ray's expression, March 2, 1671/72. *Ibid.*, pp. 94-95.
[71] *Ibid.*, pp. 94-95, 99-100, 103-4, 104-5.
[72] *Ibid.*, pp. 99-100.
[73] VIII, no. 95 (June 23, 1673), 6181-91.

others among his English friends.[74] Lister soon found firm support for his views in Edward Lhwyd; in fact Lhwyd became more dogmatic on the issue than Lister, and, with the support of such well-meaning theologians as Thomas Burnet, the belief in *lapides sui generis* largely carried the day.[75] Here was a point in which the old philosophy and the new conflicted head on, and until geology became a serious subject of study more than a century later there was little cause to desert the cosmogony of the Book of Genesis. Still, while Lister inclined toward the conservative view, he felt the need for more data and remained open to conviction. When he visited the stone pits near Paris and viewed the "Shell-stones" brought up there, he commented: "Fanciful Men may think what they please of this matter; sure I am, until the History of Nature, and more particularly that of Minerals and Fossils is better look'd into, and more accurately distinguish'd, all Reasoning is in vain. It is to be observed, where Men are most in the dark, there Impudence reigns most, as upon this Subject: They are not content fairly to dissent, but to insult every body else."[76]

---

[74] Tancred Robinson reported in 1684 that he had visited Malpighi and "once he took occasion to be a little angry with Dr. Lister (whose history he had by him), for his opinion of the origin of stones and shells resembling animal bodies." *Ray Correspondence*, pp. 141-43. In answer to Robinson, Ray took occasion (Oct. 22) to write one of his most convincing and pregnant statements to prove the organic origins of fossils. *Ibid.*, pp. 151-56.

[75] See Raven, *John Ray*, p. 428.

[76] *A Journey*, p. 231. Perhaps Lister's open-ended statements account for the misstatements about his attitude toward fossils by the *Dictionary of National Biography* (which states that he agreed with Ray!), by Raven (who goes too far in identifying Lister with the conservative faction), by Sir Charles Singer (who said that Lister "wrote the first book devoted to fossils which accepted their organic nature"[*The Story of Living Things, a Short Account of the Evolution of the Biological Sciences* (New York, 1931), p. 241]), and by Abram Wolf [*A History*

Out of his various collections, observations, and studies
in the years before 1678, Martin Lister fashioned his first
book, *Historiæ Animalium Angliæ Tres Tractatus: Unus
de Araneis, alter de Cochleis tum terrestribus tum fluviatilibus; tertius de Cochleis Marinia* . . . , published by the
Royal Society of London in 1678 and republished at York
in 1681. This book presented the first systematic descriptions and figures of spiders, snails, and fossils in England.
The section on spiders was promptly translated by Johann
August Ephraim Goeze and published in Germany,[77] and
John Ray relied upon it almost exclusively when he prepared his *Methodus Insectorum* (1704) and his *Historia
Insectorum* (posthumously published in 1710).[78] The
book described and illustrated the anatomy of English
spiders and their distribution by species and genera as
well as their food and habits. In his treatment of snails,
Lister argued that snail shells were "bred like other stones,
in the Earth." His mollusks and fossils were largely Yorkshire in origin, but the book demonstrates that he had
collected specimens from the carboniferous forms from
the districts about Craven, Leeds, and Halifax; from
jurassic forms about Scarborough and Whitley; and from
chalk species from Speeton.[79] He gave the earliest English

of Science, Technology, and Philosophy in the 16th and 17th Centuries,
new ed. by Douglas McKie (London, 1950), p. 362] and Karl Alfred
von Zittel [*History of Geology and Palaeontology to the End of the
Nineteenth Century,* trans. Maria M. Ogilvie-Gordon (London, 1901),
p. 17] (who both stated flatly that Lister's views were reactionary).
Sir Charles Lyell read Lister more accurately [*Principles of Geology;
or the Modern Changes of the Earth and its Inhabitants Considered as
Illustrative of Geology* (11th ed., 2 vols., London, 1872), I, 39].
[77] See the Lister bibliography in the Appendices herein.
[78] Craven, *John Ray,* p. 404.
[79] J. Wilfrid Jackson, "Martin Lister and Yorkshire Geology and
Conchology," *The Naturalist* (Jan.-March, 1945), pp. 1-11.

description of ammonites and (after Dr. Robert Plot) of belemnites, one of the latter of which was later named after him.[80] Indeed, this book, together with his later publications in the field, led subsequent scholars to refer to Lister as the "Father of British Conchology." In less than a decade, while actively engaged in the practice of medicine, Martin Lister had established himself firmly among the savants of the new natural philosophy.

LISTER AND THE ROYAL SOCIETY OF LONDON

Whatever the causes, Martin Lister's scientific activity as reflected in his extant correspondence and contributions to the *Philosophical Transactions* fell off shortly before the publication of his first book.[81] He had offered, after the death of Francis Willughby (1672), to take Willughby's place as John Ray's patron if Ray would move to York — an offer which Ray declined.[82] In February, 1678, Nehemiah Grew, who succeeded Henry Oldenburg as Secretary of the Royal Society upon the latter's death in 1677, wrote to Lister saying that the Society had "given me order to acquaint your self . . . That the Continuance of that Correspondence with me which you began with Mr. Oldenburge, will be most acceptable to them. . . . Nor shall I be wanting on my part in a reciprocal Communication of what is here done amongst us."[83] But Lister did

---

[80] *Neohibolites listeri* (Mantell), 1822.

[81] There simply is no evidence to explain it. One can speculate that he was ill, that his medical practice suddenly absorbed nearly all his energies, or that the work of seeing his book through the press twice consumed most of his time.

[82] Sir William Jardine, "Memoir of Francis Willughby, Esq., F.R.S.," *The Naturalist's Library*, V (Edinburgh, n.d.), 92 ff.

[83] *Lister 34*, fol. 202.

not immediately respond. Instead, he presently entered
into correspondence with members of the Oxford Philosophical Society, especially with Dr. Robert Plot, soon to
become the first "custos" of the newly founded Ashmolean
Museum at Oxford. In consequence of this new relation-
ship Lister developed an interest in the Ashmolean Museum, to which he presented a large collection of books,
manuscripts, and specimens in natural history which, as
Dr. Gunther has stated, "scientifically speaking, far out-
shone the benefice of [Elias] Ashmole," by whose original
gift the Museum had been founded.[84] There can be little
doubt that this newly formed connection swayed the University at Oxford to grant Lister the degree of Doctor of
Medicine by diploma in 1683. About this time Lister also
presented a number of papers to the Oxford Philosophical
Society, including: a "compendious way" of observing the
barometer (March 10, 1683/84), in which he proposed a
chart, or graph, whereby wind directions, barometric pres-
sures, and temperatures would appear side by side; a number of experiments on freezing (February 9, 1684/85);
"A Proposall of a New Way of Cutting for the Stone of
the Bladder" (April 28, 1685); and two papers about the
improvement of agriculture (the second was read on July
5, 1686, by Sir Richard Bulkley and received "great acclaim").[85] Soon, too, Lister was in active correspondence
with Edward Lhwyd, who later (1690) succeeded Dr.
Plot as Keeper of the Ashmolean Museum and became,

[84] Gunther, "Dr. Plot and the Correspondence of the Philosophical
Society of Oxford," *loc. cit.*, p. 39 *et passim;* Gunther, "Life and Letters
of Edward Lhwyd," *loc. cit.*, pp. 62 ff. Lister's gift included a collection
of beetles, a list of which was appended to Ray's *History of Insects.*
Cf. Raven, *John Ray,* p. 405.
[85] Gunther, "Dr. Plot," *loc. cit.*, pp. 39, 136, 138, 163, 194, 291. Some
of these papers were reported to the Royal Society of London and
appeared in the *Philosophical Transactions.* See the Lister bibliography
in the Appendices herein.

successively, a naturalist, a fossil expert, and a Celtic scholar.[86]

Late in 1683 Lister embarked on the practice of medicine in London, where he took up residence at "ye Old Pallace Yard in Westminster."[87] On October 31 he presented himself to the Royal Society, and a week later he signed "the obligation" and was formally admitted Fellow of the Society, to which he had been elected in 1671.[88] Immediately he threw himself into the work of the Society, which welcomed him warmly. On November 30, 1683, he was elected to the Council of the Society, on which he served during 1684, 1685, and 1686.[89] In 1685 he was elected Vice-President of the Society and, as the President, Samuel Pepys, was often absent, Lister served as chairman at Council meetings about half of the time and in a similar capacity at the regular meetings of the entire Society nearly all of the time in 1685.[90] On January 23, 1683/84,

[86] Lister refers to Lhwyd in *A Journey*, p. 99. The following year (1699), Lhwyd dedicated to Lister his *Lithophylacii Britannici Ichnographia* (London, 1699).

[87] Most authorities have stated that Lister moved to London in 1684. But as he was present at a meeting of the Royal Society on October 23, 1683, and at successive meetings thereafter, I believe that he made the move late in 1683. *Journal-Book*, Oct. 23, Nov. 30, Dec. 12, 1683, Jan. 16, 1683/84, *et seq.*

[88] Full fellowship in the Royal Society required personal attendance and signing "the obligation" (to pay contributions for the support of the Society's work). Provincial and colonial Fellows were excused the obligation unless and until they attended the Society in person, when they were *formally* admitted Fellow even though their election had occurred previously. See R. P. Stearns, "Colonial Fellows of the Royal Society of London, 1661-1788," *Notes and Records of the Royal Society of London*, VIII, no. 2 (April, 1951), 178-84.

[89] *Council Minutes*, Nov. 30, 1683 (MSS in Royal Society Library). Lister was present at Council meetings six times in 1684, ten times in 1685, and three times in 1686. He was not re-elected in November, 1686. *Ibid., passim.*

[90] The minutes show Lister in the chair at twenty-six of the twenty-seven meetings held in 1685. *Journal-Book*, Jan. 14, 1684/85–Nov. 25, 1685.

he volunteered to put the minerals in order in the Society's
"Repository of Rarities" if the Council would provide a
cabinet for them. The Council agreed and ordered
Nehemiah Grew to assist Lister in the task. It was at this
time, too, that the Royal Society was straining its finances
to publish both Francis Willughby's *History of Fishes*
(which Ray had completed) as well as Ray's magnum
opus on the *History of Plants*. Since 1682 Lister had urged
the Society to publish Willughby's *History of Fishes*, which,
he said "was made ready for the Press to my knowledge
4 years agoe by Mr. Ray. . . ."[91] Now, in 1685, with the
aid of Tancred Robinson, his former protégé at York,
arrangements were completed by the Royal Society for the
book's publication by the Oxford University Press and
Lister oversaw the illustrations for it. After many initial
difficulties,[92] the *History of Fishes*, sumptuously illustrated
and produced, appeared in 1686.

At the same time, Ray was engaged in completing his
History of Plants, an enterprise enthusiastically endorsed
and forwarded by his friends.[93] It, too, was approved for
publication (May 5, 1685) by the Council of the Royal
Society, and the first volume was ready in June, 1686; the
second volume appeared about two years later. As in the
History of Fishes, Lister had a hand both in assisting Ray
in the collection of material and in helping to guide the
book through the press. But the financial condition of the
Royal Society could not be expanded to permit illustrations in the *History of Plants*, and thus, unfortunately,
Ray's greatest work appeared without plates. The political confusion of the nation contributed to the difficulties.

[91] *Letter-Book*, VIII, 177-78, Feb. 11, 1681/82.
[92] A summary of them is in Raven's *John Ray*, pp. 349-50, 353-58.
[93] *Ibid.*, pp. 212 ff.

Beginning about 1683 with the Rye House Plot, continuing through 1685 with Monmouth's Rebellion, and culminating in the Revolution of 1688-89, the times were unsettled. The Royal Society was at a low ebb, forced to suspend publication of the *Philosophical Transactions* for a time (1687), and, for the last half of the decade of the 1680's, science suffered. And during this same period Martin Lister fell into his second period of relative unproductivity in the new science.[94]

Between 1682, the year before he moved to London, and 1686, when he again withdrew into relative obscurity, Lister published a translation of Johannes Goedaertius' *De Insectis*, two medical books about English medicinal waters and baths, a collection of his papers previously presented to the Royal Society, two books on conchology, which, when completed in four parts with an appendix, were drawn together in his greatest work, *Historia sive Synopsis Methodica Conchyliorium* (London, 1692), and sixteen papers in the *Philosophical Transactions*.[95] His translation of Goedaert, entitled *Johannes Godartius of insects. Done into English, and methodized. With the addition of notes [by M. Lister]*, was published at York in 1682. The figures were made from copper plates prepared at Lister's expense, and several of them were handsomely and accurately done. But the book lacked adequate descriptions, and its scientific value was slight.[96] At his first personal appearance at the Royal Society (October 31, 1683), Lister gave a modified version of his "compendi-

[94] The records of the Royal Society show that Lister abruptly broke off attendance, including meetings of the Council, of which he was an elected member, in March, 1686.
[95] See the lists in the Lister bibliography in the Appendices herein.
[96] A Latin edition, with Lister's notes, and appendices of Lister's beetles and other English insects, was published at London in 1685.

ous way" of observing the barometer, which he had presented to the Oxford Society the previous March. But, as
the Royal Society Secretary recorded, "The observation
seemed new to all that present."[97] From that time on
until late January, 1686, the minutes of the meetings of
the Royal Society show that Lister was taking an active
part. On December 12, 1683, he was still denying that
shellfish petrify — or, at least, that any of the "rock shells"
were identical to the known species of English shellfish.[98]
But he had left a door open to Ray and the opposing
opinion when he said, in 1678, "Either these [rock shells]
were terriginous, or, if otherwise, the animals they so exactly represent *have become extinct*."[99]

Already, in January, 1683, he had resumed his contributions to the *Philosophical Transactions* (the last article
from his pen had appeared in March, 1676). Several of
these were obvious by-products of his medical practice, but
in March, 1683, with "An Account of a Roman Monument
found in the Bishoprick of Durham . . . ," he began a
series of contributions on antiquities, an interest which he
had not formerly publicly displayed.[100] Without doubt,
however, Lister's most important article in the *Philosophical Transactions* was "An Ingenious proposal for a new
Sort of Maps of Countrys together with Tables of Sands
and Clays."[101] This "Ingenious proposal" not only reflected Lister's long interest in and observations relating
to minerals, mines, and fossils, but also demonstrated that

[97] *Journal-Book*, Oct. 31, 1683.
[98] *Ibid.*, Dec. 12, 1683.
[99] Quoted in Sir Charles Lyell, *Principles of Geology*, I, 39. The italics
were by Sir Charles.
[100] Subsequent articles on antiquities are listed in the Lister bibliography
in the Appendices herein.
[101] XIV, no. 164 (Oct. 20, 1684), 739-46.

he could think boldly and set forth scientific hypotheses.
For what he proposed was a geological map, some sixty-
two years before Jean Étienne Guettard presented his
famous *Mémoire et Carte Minéralogique* (1746) in France
and 131 years before William ("Strata") Smith constructed the first geological map of England in 1815.
Lister referred to it as a *"Soil or Mineral* map," and he
emphasized the correlation between different kinds of
rocks and their fossil contents, pointing out that "quarries
of different stone yield us quite different sorts or species
of shells." If one were with "great care . . . very exactly
to note upon the *Map* where such and such *Soiles* are
bounded . . . I am of the opinion such upper *Soiles* if
natural, infallibly produce such *under Minerals*, and for
the most part in such order." He manifested an excellent
knowledge of living conchylia and, while he was reluctant
to identify fossils with living animals, he illustrated living
and fossil conchylia side by side in order to demonstrate
their resemblance. He observed that certain rocks are
present over a definite extent of earth surface, so that
maps might be constructed with regard to the distribution
of different kinds of rock. And, as the fossil bivalves and
snails differed in the various kinds of rocks, he set forth
for the first time the basic geological principle that different rocks might be distinguished from one another according to their particular fossil contents. Obviously, as in
the case of Hero of Alexandria, Leonardo da Vinci, and
many others both before and after Lister, the concatena-
tion of intellectual, economic, technological, and social
events in the world was not yet ready to follow up Lister's
"Ingenious proposal," as the mere enunciation of the principle did not, as it did with William Smith in 1815, make

Lister the "Father of British Geology." But he had fore-
cast a basic principle in modern geology.[102]

LISTER'S PRINCIPAL WORKS ON CONCHOLOGY

From the early months of 1686 through the events leading up to and including the Revolution of 1688-89, Martin
Lister appears to have had little, if any, direct contact with
the Royal Society of London. James II named him as a
Fellow of the Royal College of Physicians (March 11,
1686/87), together with his friends Hans Sloane, Tancred
Robinson, and Edward Lower, and perhaps his member-
ship in this professional society distracted his attention
from the Royal Society to some extent. During these
years, however, and throughout the decade of the 1690's,
his scientific correspondence assumed new dimensions.
Not only did he engage in a continuing exchange with
members of the Philosophical Society of Oxford, but also
his correspondence expanded into the New World and the
Far East. Letters in the Bodleian Library at Oxford[103]
illustrate a wide circle of scientific correspondents, both
with such former communicants as John Ray, Nehemiah
Grew, Dr. Robert Plot, Jacob Bobart, and Samuel Dale,
and with a host of newcomers and *their* correspondents,
such as Edward Lhwyd, Dr. Tancred Robinson, Richard
Waller (who became Secretary of the Royal Society in
1687), Hans Sloane, Sir Richard Bulkley of Dublin, Henry
Compton, Bishop of London, and the ubiquitous James

---

[102] See Jackson, "Martin Lister and Yorkshire Geology and Conchology,"
loc. cit.; von Zittel, *History of Geology and Palaeontology,* p. 17;
Raymond Furon, "Naissance de la géologie," in *La Science Moderne
(de 1540 à 1800),* ed. René Taton (3 vols., Paris, 1958), II, 412-13;
Charles R. Longwell, "Geology," in *The Development of the Sciences,*
ed. L. L. Woodruff (2nd ser., New Haven, 1949), p. 155.
[103] Especially *Ashmole 1816, passim* (Bodleian Library).

Petiver, London apothecary of whom Ray wrote that "he hath the greatest correspondence both in East and West Indies of any man in Europe."[104] Through the good offices of these men, in turn, Lister entered into correspondence and received natural history specimens and information from Dr. Thomas Towne of Barbados,[105] John Banister of Virginia,[106] William Byrd of Virginia (whom Lister met in London in 1687),[107] Robert Stephens of Goose Creek,[108] South Carolina, the Reverend Mr. Hugh Jones of Maryland,[109] Joseph Lister of Fort St. George, Madras,[110] and perhaps others. Lister's overseas scientific correspondence never reached the proportions of that of Sloane or Petiver, but he developed wide-ranging communicants in foreign parts and in the English colonies in North America and the West Indies and in the English trading posts in the Far East.

From these new correspondents he enlarged his collections of shellfish, insects, and plants, and his knowledge of the natural history of distant parts of the world. And it was with these benefits that he published his greatest works, those related to conchology. These consisted of a

[104] Raven, *John Ray*, p. 233. For a particular account of Petiver's correspondence in the New World, see R. P. Stearns, "James Petiver, Promoter of Natural Science," *Proceedings of the American Antiquarian Society*, LXII (Oct., 1952), 243-365.
[105] Doubtless established by means of John Ray. *Ray Correspondence*, pp. 111-12; *Philosophical Transactions*, X, no. 117 (Sept. 26, 1675), 399-400.
[106] This contact could have been through Leon Plukenett, John Ray, William Byrd, or others. *Ray Correspondence, passim; Sloane 4067*, fol. 105 (British Museum); *Ashmole 1816, passim.*
[107] *Sloane 4062*, fol. 226, *4067*, fol. 105 (British Museum).
[108] *Lister 36*, fol. 161 (Bodleian Library); *Sloane 3330*, fol. 846, *3333*, fols. 108, 266v-67 (British Museum).
[109] By means of Petiver. See Stearns, "James Petiver," *loc. cit.*, pp. 293-303.
[110] *Lister 4*, fol. 80, *37*, fol. 15.

series of volumes which appeared from 1685 to 1696. The first two were published in 1685, entitled, respectively, *De Cochleis, tam Terrestribus, quàm Fluviatilibus Exoticis, seu, quæ non omino in Anglia inveniantur, liber [I]*, and *De Cochleis, tam Terrestribus quàm Fluviatilibus Exoticis; item de iis quæ etiam in Anglia inveniantur, libri II.* A third volume appeared in 1687, a fourth in 1688, and a separate Appendix in the same year. All of these were drawn together in the sumptuous *Historia sive Synopsis Methodica Conchyliorium* published in two volumes in London (1692). These were succeeded in 1694 with *Exercitatio Anatomica in quâ de Cochleis maximè Terrestribus et Limacibus agitur* . . . and with *Dissertatio Anatomica Altera de Buccinis Fluviatilibus et Marinis* . . . (1695), *Exercitatio-Anatomica altera, in qua · maximè agitur de Buccinis fluviatilibus et marinas* . . . (published with a medical discussion of smallpox in 1695), and *Exercitatio Anatomica Conchiliorum Bivalvium utriusque Aquæ* . . . (published with a medical essay on bladder stones in 1696).[111]

The works on conchylia were a family effort. They presented the shells in Lister's collection, the largest in England at the time, with illustrations made from copper plates etched by Lister's daughters Susanna and Anna.[112] More than a thousand shells were illustrated, including some forty-four species of marine shells and many other marine varieties. Since the works were published at Lis-

---

[111] For a more complete listing of these works see the Lister bibliography in the Appendices herein.

[112] Because of the occasional identification of the names Anna and Hannah, the Lister womenfolk may have been Lister's wife (Hannah) and daughter. There is uncertainty on this point. Lhwyd wrote to Lister (Feb. 18, 1691/92) that "I do not wonder your workw[omen] begin to be tired; you have held them so long to it. Gunther, "Life and Letters of Edward Lhwyd," *loc. cit.*, p. 155.

ter's expense, the outlay must have been considerable — as he suggested in his visit to the Royal Library in Paris.[113] Lister was inconsistent in acknowledging the source of his specimens. Most of them he had collected himself, both in England and on the Continent, especially in France, but he indicated specific items from Jamaica, acquired from Hans Sloane and his Jamaican correspondents; from Guinea and Bengal, supplied by James Petiver from his correspondents in the Far East; from Virginia, sent by John Banister or perhaps Thomas Glover, an early correspondent with Philip Skippon; from Hugh Jones in Maryland; from Robert Stephens in South Carolina; from Gibraltar, supplied by one Mr. Brown, a Petiver communicant; from Dr. Towne in Barbados; and other unnamed correspondents in Madagascar and Africa. For his colonial specimens Lister was obviously most heavily indebted to Hans Sloane and James Petiver. For English items he had, for the most part, made his own collection, but Edward Lhwyd had also contributed significantly.

Most of the shells were illustrated for the first time and, on the whole, Lister proved himself to be an accurate observer. Indeed, the illustrations were more impressive than the descriptions, for many of the specimens were figured with no specific description at all. There were, however, some dissections which, inaccurate as they were almost bound to be, considering the current knowledge of physiology and chemistry, were the earliest of their kind.[114] In fact, there was no further significant work on the anat-

[113] *A Journey to Paris*, pp. 106-7. No doubt such personal outlays in behalf of natural science explain his somewhat envious statements about the French scientists, whose works were generally paid for out of the royal purse.
[114] Lister published an account of "The Anatomy of the Scallop" in *Philosophical Transactions*, XIX, no. 229 (June, 1697), 567-70.

omy of mollusks until Cuvier's *L'Anatomie des Mollusques* appeared in 1816.[115] Lister's "method" in arranging the mollusks depended principally on the configurations of the shell alone, in which, again, he was a close observer. Newer principles, depending upon the structural points of the animal, have altered classifications, though not as greatly as in most other parts of natural history. Still, Lister described and figured a number of brachiopods under the name of *Anomia* which, until the present century, were regarded as mollusks.[116]

However, in spite of its shortcomings in the light of present-day knowledge, Lister's works on conchology became the standard of reference for many years. Martin Lister became the authority to whom his colleagues in natural philosophy deferred, both in England and on the Continent. Linnaeus proclaimed him to be the "richest conchologist of his time," and among his English successors he became known as the "Father of British Conchology."[117]

LISTER'S LAST YEARS

Martin Lister's medical practice prospered and he sank a considerable portion of his wealth in his scientific collections and publications. He also acquired a suburban house in Clapham and it was there that his first wife, Hannah

[115] Leopold Chrétien Frédéric Dagobert Cuvier (1769-1832), French anatomist, better known by his adopted nom de plume, Georges Cuvier.
[116] S. F. Harmer and A. E. Shipley, eds., *The Cambridge Natural History* (10 vols., London, 1913), III, 244, 464. In *A Descriptive Catalogue of Recent Shells arranged according to the Linnæan Method; with Particular attention to Synonymy* (2 vols., London, 1817), Lewis Weston Dillwyn incorporated Lister's shells.
[117] *Biographie Universelle* (30 vols., Paris, n.d.), XXIV, 608-9; Jackson, "Martin Lister and Yorkshire Geology and Conchology," *loc. cit.*, *passim*.

Parkinson, died (in 1694) and was buried in St. Paul's Church, of which Lister was a benefactor.[118] Evidently his health became impaired in the late 1690's — which, as he stated, was one of his principal reasons for going to France in 1698 — and his scientific endeavors dwindled to the point where, shortly after 1700, he wrote little of scientific consequence and his correspondence fell away to almost nothing.[119] On October 24, 1698, only a few months after his return from France, he remarried. His second wife, Jane Cullen, of St. Mildred, Poultry, whom he married at St. Stephen's, Walbrook, outlived him.

In his later years, Lister appears not only to have withdrawn permanently from scientific activity but also to have retreated professionally more and more into classical medicine. His *Hippocratis Aphorismi, cum commentariolo* . . . , published in 1703, was more of a performance in humanism than in the new science. And his edition (1705) of Apicius Caelius (Marcus Gavius Apicius, *c.* 14-37), the Roman epicure to whom *De Opsoniis et Condiméntis sive Arte Coquinariâ* was attributed, excited ridicule — even though it ran to a second edition in 1709. Lister's old adversary, William King, who had parodied Lister's *Journey*

[118] Wood, "Martin Lister," *loc. cit.* The Reverend Mr. Denny lists (*Memorials of an Ancient House*) nine children of Martin Lister by his first marriage, six daughters and three sons. Besides Susanna and Anna, mentioned above, were: Jane (d. 1688), Dorothy, Barbara, and Frances. The eldest son was Captain Martin Lister, later of Charles Churchill's Regiment of Foot; the second son, Michael, died in 1676; and the third son, Alexander, matriculated at Balliol College, Oxford, in 1696, and was still living at the time his father's will was drawn in 1704. Martin Lister had no issue by his second wife.

[119] See the Lister bibliography in the Appendices herein for his later works. His last contributions to the *Philosophical Transactions* were, for the most part, based either upon earlier experiments with medicinal waters, cases from his medical practice, or letters from his correspondents.

to Paris, published (London, 1710) *The Art of Cooking, in imitation of Horace's Art of Poetry. With some letters to Dr. Lister and others: occasion'd principally by the title of a book published by the Doctor, being the works of Apicius Coelius, concerning the soups and sauces of the antients. With an extract of the greatest curiosities contained in that book.* Writing with tongue in cheek, King addressed an imaginary friend to request Lister's book, because, he said,

Consider, dear Sir, in what Uncertainities we must remain at present; you know my Neighbor Mr. *Greatorix* is a learned Antiquary. I shew'd him your Letter, which threw him into such a Dubiousness, and indeed Perplexity of Mind, that the next Day he durst not put any *Catchup* in his *Fish Sauce,* nor have his beloved *Pepper, Oyl,* and *Limon* with his *Partridge,* lest before he had seen Dr. *Lister's* Book he might transgress in using something not common to the *Antients.*

Dispatch it therefore to us with all Speed, for I expect Wonders from it. . . . I hope, in the first place, it will, in some measure, remove the Barbarity of our present Education: For what hopes can there be of any Progress in Learning, whilst our Gentlemen suffer their Sons at *Westminster, Eaton,* and *Winchester* to eat nothing but *Salt* with their *Mutton,* and *Vinegar* with their *Roast Beef* upon Holidays?[120]

After such caustic comment on Lister's first seven books of "Soups and Sauces," King stated that Lister had but "two Books more, one of Sea, the other of River Fish, in the account of which he would not be long, seeing his memory began to fail him almost as much as my Patience."[121] And he wrote the following doggerel:

> Oh could that poet live, could he rehearse
> Thy journey Lister, in immortal verse —
> Muse! since the man that did to Paris go,
> That he might taste their soups, and mushrooms know.

If, as appears likely, Lister had developed a taste for French cuisine, it was not an uncritical one, as his comments in *A Journey to Paris* demonstrate.[122] But he suffered the disparagement common to all who would imply criticism of the diet of their countrymen.

Still, if Lister incurred the disfavor of the coffeehouse hacks, he retained favor at court. From the time he received his fellowship at St. John's College, Cambridge, in 1660 until his death, Martin Lister received repeated evidence of royal favor at the hands of the Stuarts, culminating, as we have seen, in his appointment (1702) as Physician in Ordinary to Queen Anne.[123] He held this position until his death. But his own health was failing badly, and he often retired to Epsom for rest and treatment. There, on February 2, 1711/12, he died at the age of seventy-four. In his will he bequeathed all his books and copper plates to Oxford University, and decreed that "My body shall without pomp in a private manner be carried in a hearse attended only by one mourning coach to Clapham and there be buried in the grave of my late deceased wife Hannah."[124] There, in St. Paul's Church, Clapham, his body lies with a memorial stone erected nearby.

Martin Lister adopted the new science and made notable contributions to geology and zoology. No doubt he was overshadowed by such towering intellects as John Ray and Isaac Newton in his generation, but he was a respected colleague whose work, especially in conchology, led many naturalists to beat a path to his door. His ac-

---

[122] *A Journey to Paris*, pp. 160-72.
[123] Dr. Arbuthnot was Primarius Medicus.
[124] Wood, "Martin Lister," *loc. cit.* Petiver sorrowfully noted his passing in a letter of August 7, 1712. *Sloane 3338*, fol. 90 (British Museum).

ceptance of the new natural philosophy was constantly tempered, however, by his caution and by his inborn regard for the learning of antiquity. In consequence, he received new scientific interpretations with less ready enthusiasm than many of this fellows, and was prone to adopt a "wait-and-see" attitude. This was not so much a rejection of new hypotheses in science as it was a tentative acceptance, final reception depending upon the gathering of further, definitive evidence. This was his attitude with regard to the question of the origins of fossils. And this was his attitude toward the new science in general. He made this clear when, having discussed magnetism with Michael Butterfield in Paris, he wrote: "the way to find out the Nature of those *Magnetick Effuvia,* seems to be to enquire strictly into the Nature of [them] . . . and not to run giddily into Hypotheses, before we are well stocked with a Natural History . . . and a larger quantity of Experiments and Observations . . . with all the Differences and Species of them; which I think has hitherto been little heeded. For Nature will be its own Intepreter, in this, as well as in all Matters of Natural Philosophy."[125]

[125] *A Journey to Paris,* pp. 92-93.

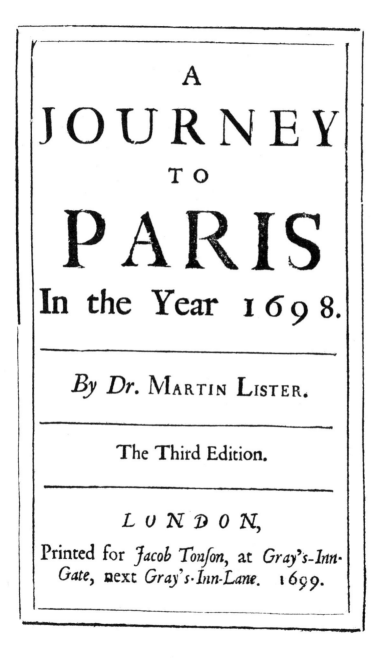

A

JOURNEY

TO

PARIS

In the Year 1698.

By Dr. MARTIN LISTER.

The Third Edition.

LONDON,

Printed for *Jacob Tonson,* at *Gray's-Inn-Gate,* next *Gray's-Inn-Lane.* 1699.

To His Excellency,

JOHN

Lord *Sommers*, Baron of *Evesham*, Lord High Chancellor of *England*, and one of the Lords-Justices of *England*.

My LORD,

VVIsdom is the Foundation of *Justice and Equity*, and it *seems not to be perfect, without it com-*

prehends also Philosophy and
Natural Learning, and whatever is of good Relish in Arts.
It is certain, my Lord, for the
Honour of your High Station,
that the greatest Philosopher of
this Age was one of your Prede-
cessors ; nor is your Lordship in
any thing behind him ; as tho'
nothing inspired People with
more Equity, than a true Value
for Useful Learning and Arts.
This hath given me the Boldness
to offer your Lordship this short
Account of the Magnificent and
Noble City of Paris, and the
Court of that Great King, who
hath given Europe so long and
vehement Disquiet, and cost
England in particular so much
Blood

Dedication.

Blood and Treasure. 'Tis pos-sible, my Lord, you may find a leisure Hour to read over these few Papers for your Diversion, wherein I promise my self you will meet with nothing offensive, but clean Matter of Fact, and some short Notes of an unprejudiced Observer. But that I may no longer importune you, perpetually busied in so laborious and useful an Imployment, I beg leave to subscribe my self,

My LORD,

Your Lordship's

Most Humble, and
most Obedient Servant,

Martin Lister.

A

JOURNEY

TO

PARIS

In the Year 1698.

Introduction to the Reader.

THIS Tract was written chiefly
to satisfie my own Curiosity,
and to delight my self with the
Memory of what I had seen.
I busied my self in a place where I had
little to do, but to walk up and down ;
well knowing, that the Character of a
Stranger gave me free Admittance to Men
and Things. The French Nation value
themselves upon Civility, and build and
dress mostly for Figure : This Humour

makes

makes the Curiofity of Strangers very eafie and welcome to them.

But why do you trouble us with a Journey to *Paris*, a Place fo well known to every body here ? For very good Reafon, to fpare the often telling my Tale at my return. But we know already all you can fay, or can read it in the *Prefent State of France*, and *Defcription of Paris* ; two Books to be had in every Shop in *London*. 'Tis right, fo you may ; and I advife you not to neglect them, if you have a mind to judge well of the Grandeur of the Court of *France*, and the immenfe Greatnefs of the City of *Paris*. Thefe were Spectacles I did indeed put on, but I found they did not fit my Sight, I had a mind to fee without them ; and in Matters of this Nature, as vaft Cities and vaft Palaces, I did not care much to ufe Microfcopes or Magnifying Glaffes.

But to content you, Reader, I promife you not to trouble you with Ceremonies either of State or Church, or Politicks ; for I entred willingly into neither of them, but only, where they would make a part of the Converfation, or my Walk was ordered me. You'll eafily find by my Obfervations, that I incline rather to Nature than Dominion ;

and

and that I took more pleafure to fee Monfieur *Breman* in his White Waftcoat digging in the Royal Phyfick Garden, and fowing his Couches, than Monfieur *de Saintot* making room for an Ambaffador ; and I found my felf better difpofed, and more apt to learn the Names and Phyfiognomy of a Hundred Plants, than of Five or Six Princes. After all, I had much rather have walked a Hundred Paces under the meaneft Hedge in *Languedoc*, than any the fineft Alley at *Verfailles* or *St. Clou*, fo much I prefer fair Nature and a warm Sun, before the moft exquifite Performances of Art in a cold and barren Climate.

Another Reafon, that I give you little or no trouble in telling you Court Matters, is, that I was no more concerned in the Embaffy, than in the failing of the Ship which carried me over : 'Tis enough for me, with the reft of the People of *England*, to feel the good Effects of it, and to pafs away this Life in Peace and Quietnefs. 'Tis a happy Turn for us, when Kings are made Friends again. This was the end of this Embaffy, and I hope it will laft our Days. My Lord Ambaffador was infinitely careffed by the King, his Minifters, and all the Princes. 'Tis certain the French are the

moft

moſt Polite Nation in the World, and
can Praiſe and Court with a better Air
than the reſt of Mankind. However the
generality of the Kingdom were through
great neceſſity well diſpoſed to receive
the Peace : The Bigots and ſome diſ-
banded Officers might be heard at our
firſt going, to grumble, but thoſe alſo
gave over, and we heard no more of
them when we came away. But to the
Buſineſs.

I happily arrived at *Paris*, after a tedious Journey in very bad Weather ;
for we ſet out of *London* the 10th of
December, and I did not reach *Paris* till the
firſt of *January* ; for I fell ſick upon the
Road, and ſtay'd Five Days at *Bologne*, behind the Company, till my Fever aba-
ted ; yet notwithſtanding ſo rude a Journey, I recovered, and was perfectly
cured of my Cough in Ten Days; which
was the chiefeſt reaſon of my leaving
London at that time of the Year, and
never had the leaſt return of it all the
Winter, though it was as fierce there as
I ever felt it in *England*. This great benefit of the French Air I had experienced three ſeveral times before, and had
therefore long'd for a Paſſage many
Years ; but the continuance of the War
was an inſuperable Obſtacle to my Deſires.
There-

Therefore the firſt opportunity which offered it ſelf I readily embraced, which was my Lord *Portland's* Acceptance of my Attendance of him in his Extraordinary Embaſſie; who ordered me to go before with one of my good Friends, who was ſent to prepare Matters againſt his Arrival.

There was nothing in the Road to *Paris* which pleaſed me, at that dead time of the Year, ſo much as the high Plains by *Chantillie*, a Seat of the Prince of *Conde's*, bordered by a Ridge of little wooddy Hills on one ſide, and a deep and noble Valley on the other. It extends it ſelf ſome Miles, and is planted with a great number of Copſes of Bruſh-wood, at large diſtances : Theſe are ſtored with plenty of Partridges, Pheaſants, and all ſorts of *Gibier*, which we ſaw in great Covies, ſpread over the Plain in the Evening, and feeding, as it were, tame. Betwixt the Copſes are here and there plowed Grounds, ſowed on purpoſe for them, and never reaped, but left for the Fowls and Hares.

Now that I might not wholly truſt my Memory in what I ſaw at *Paris*, I ſet down my Thoughts under certain Heads.

I. *Of* Paris *in General.*

THough I had much fpare time the fix Months I ftaid in that City, yet the rudenefs of the Winter Seafon kept me in for fome time. Again, I believe I did not fee the Tithe of what deferves to be feen, and well confidered; becaufe for many things I wanted a relifh, particularly for Painting and Building; However I viewed the City in all its parts, and made the round of it; took feveral Profpects of it at a diftance, which when well thought on, I muft needs confefs it to be one of the moft Beautiful and Magnificent in *Europe*, and in which a Traveller might find Novelties enough for fix Months for daily Entertainment, at leaft in and about this Noble City. To give therefore a ftrict and general Idea of it, and not to enter far into the vain Difputes of the number of Inhabitants, or its bignefs, compared to *London*; fure I am, the *ftanding Croud* was fo great, when my Lord Ambaffador made his Entry, that our People were ftartled at it, and were ready the next Day to give up the Queftion, had they not well confidered the great Cu-

rioſity

riofity of the *Parifians,* who are much
more delighted in fine Shows than the
People of *London,* and fo were well near
all got into the way of the Cavalcade.
One thing was an evident Argument of
this Humour, that there were fome Hundreds of Coaches of Perfons of the beft
Quality, even fome Bifhops and Lords,
which I faw, who had placed themfelves in a file to line the Streets, and had
had the patience to have fo remained for
fome hours.

'Tis alfo moft certain, that for the quantity of Ground poffeffed by the common
People, this City is much more populous
than any part of *London*; here are from
four to five and to ten Menages, or diftinct Families in many Houfes; but this
is to be underftood of certain places of
Trade. This difference betwixt the two
Cities alfo is true, that here the Palaces
and Convents have eat up the Peoples
Dwellings, and crouded them exceffively
together, and poffeffed themfelves of far
the greateft part of the Ground; whereas
in *London* the contrary may be obferved,
that the People have deftroyed the Palaces, and placed themfelves upon the
Foundations of them, and forced the Nobility to live in Squares or Streets in a
fort of Community: but this they have

done

done very honeftly, having fairly purchafed them.

The Views alfo which it gives upon
the River are admirable : that of the
Pont-neuf downwards to the *Tuilleries*, or
upwards from the *Pont-Royal* ; and in fome
other Places, as from *Pont St. Bernard*,
the *Greve*, &c. The River *Seine* which
paffes through the midft of the City, is
all nobly bank'd or key'd with large
Free-ftone; and inclofes in the Heart of
the City two Iflands, which caufes many
fine Bridges to be built to pafs over
them. One of thefe Iflands, called
l' Ifle de Palais, was all *Paris* for fome
Ages.

The Houfes are built of hewen Stone
intirely, or whited over with Plaifter ;
fome indeed in the beginning of this Age
are of Brick with Free-ftone, as the *Place-
Royal*, *Place-Dauphin*, &c. but that is
wholly left off now ; and the White
Plaifter is in fome few places only coloured after the fafhion of Brick, as part
of the Abbey of *St. Germain*. The Houfes every where are high and ftately ;
The Churches numerous, but not very
big ; The Towers and Steeples are but few
in proportion to the Churches, yet that
noble way of Steeple, the *Domes* or *Cu-
pola's*, have a marvellous effect in profpect ;

fpect; though they are not many, as that of *Val de Grace, des invalides, College Mazarin, De l' Aſſumption,* the *Grand-Jeſuits, La Sorbonne,* and ſome few others.

All the Houſes of Perſons of Diſtinction are built with *Porte-cocheres,* that is, wide Gates to drive in a Coach, and conſequently have Courts within; and moſtly *Remiſes* to ſet them up. There are reckoned above 700 of theſe great Gates; and very many of theſe are after the moſt noble Patterns of ancient Architecture.

The lower Windows of all Houſes are grated with ſtrong Bars of Iron; which muſt be a vaſt Expence.

As the Houſes are Magnificent without, ſo the Finiſhing within ſide and Furniture anſwer in Riches and Neatneſs; as Hangings of rich Tapeſtry, raiſed with Gold and Siver Threads, Crimſon Damask and Velvet Beds, or of Gold and Silver Tiſſue. *Cabinets* and *Bureau's,* of Ivory inlaid with Tortoiſhell, and Gold and Silver Plates, in a hundred different manners: Branches and Candleſticks of Cryſtal: but above all, moſt rare Pictures. The Gildings, Carvings and Paintings of the Roofs are admirable.

Theſe

Thefe things are in this City and the Country about, to fuch a variety and excefs, that you can come into no private Houfe of any Man of Subftance, but you fee fomething of them ; and they are obferved frequently to ruine themfelves in thefe Expences. Every one that has any thing to fpare, covets to have fome good Picture or Sculpture of the beft Artift : The like in the Ornaments of their Gardens, fo that it is incredible what pleafure that vaft quantity of fine things give the curious Stranger. Here as foon as ever a Man gets any thing by Fortune or Inheritance, he lays it out in fome fuch way as now named.

Yet after all, many Utenfils and Conveniences of Life are wanting here, which we in *England* have. This makes me remember what Monfieur *Juftell*, a *Parifian*, formerly told me here, that he had made a Catalogue of near Threefcore things of this Nature which they wanted in *Paris*.

The Pavement of the Streets is all of fquare Stone, of about eight or ten Inches thick; that is, as deep in the Ground as they are broad at top; The Gutters fhallow, and laid round without Edges, which makes the Coaches glide eafily over them.

Every

Every Stone cofts Six-pence before it is layed in the Pavement ; fo that the Charge hath been very great to have fo vaft a City paved with them, and alfo *all the Roads* that lead to it for fome Leagues together.

This Pavement is not flippery from the nature of the Stone, which is a fort of courfe and very hard *Sand-ftone.* There is plenty of this very Stone in the North of *England* ; and of it thofe little narrow Caufeys are made in the Weft-Riding of *Yorkfhire* ; where Strangers are afraid, but the Natives will freely gallop on them.

However it muft needs be faid, the Streets are very narrow, and the Paffengers a-foot no ways fecur'd from the hurry and danger of Coaches, which always paffing the Streets with an Air of hafte, and a full trot upon broad flat Stones, betwixt high and large refounding Houfes, makes a fort of Mufick which fhould feem very agreeable to the *Parifians.*

The Royal Palaces are furprifingly ftately ; as the *Louvre* and *Tuilleries*, *Palais Luxembourg, Palais Royal.*

The Convents are great, and numerous, and well-built ; as *Val de Grace, St. Germains, St. Victor, St. Genevieve,* the *Grand Jefuits,* &c.

The

The Squares are few in *Paris*, but very beautiful; as the *Place Royal*, *Place Victoir*, *Place Dauphine*, none of the largest, except the *Place Vendofme*, not yet finifh'd.

The City Gates are very Magnificent, and moftly new, as erected to the Honour of this King : That of *St. Dennis*, *St. Barnard*, *St. Antoine*, *St. Honor*, *des Conferences*.

The Gardens within the Walls, open to the publick, are vaftly great, and very beautiful as the *Tuilleries*, *Palais Royal*, *Luxembourg*, the *Royal Phyfick Garden*, of the *Arfenal*, and many belonging to Convents, the *Carthufians*, *Celeftins*, *St. Victor*, *St. Genevieve*, &c.

But that which makes the dwelling in this City very diverting for People of Quality, is the facility of going out with their Coaches into the Fields, on every fide; it lying round, and the Avenues to it fo well paved, and the Places of Airing fo clean, open or fhady, as you pleafe, or the Seafon of the Year and time of the Day require: As the *Cour de la Reyne*, *Bois de Bologne*, *Bois de Vincennes*, *les Sables de Vaugerarde*, &c.

But to defcend to a more particular Review of this great City, I think it not amifs

mifs to fpeak firft of the Streets and publick
Places, and what may be feen in them :
Next of the Houfes of Note, and what
Curiofities of Nature or Art, alfo of Men
and Libraries, I met with : Next of their
Diet and Recreations: Next of the Gardens,
and their Furniture and Ornaments ; and
of the Air and Health. We fhall conclude
the whole with the prefent State of Phyfick and Pharmacy here.

To begin with the Coaches, which are *Coaches.*
very numerous here, and very fine in
Gilding : But there are but few, and
thofe only of the great Nobility, which
are large, and have two Seats or Funds.
But what they want in the Largenefs,
Beauty, and Neatnefs of ours in *London,*
they have infinitely in the eafinefs of
Carriage, and the ready turning in the
narroweft Streets. For this purpofe they
are all *Crane-neck'd,* and the Wheels before very low, not above two Foot and a
half Diameter ; which makes them eafie
to get into, and brings down the Coach-
Box low, that you have a much better
Profpect out of the foremoft Glafs; our
high-feated Coachmen being ever in the
point of View. Again, they are moft,
even Fiacres or Hackneys, hung with
double Springs at the four Corners, which
infen-

infenfibly breaks all Jolts. This I never was fo fenfible of, as after having pra-ctifed the *Paris* Coaches for four Months, I once rid in the eafieft Chariot of my Lord's, which came from *England*; but not a Jolt but what affected a Man; fo as to be tired more in one Hour in that, than in fix in thefe.

Befides the great number of Coaches of the Gentry, here are alfo Coaches *de Remife*, by the Month; which are very well gilt, neat Harnefs, and good Horfes: And thefe all Strangers hire by the Day or Month, at about three Crowns Englifh a Day. 'Tis this fort that fpoils the Hacknes and Chairs, which here are the moft nafty and miferable Voiture that can be; and yet near as dear again as in *London*, and but very few of them neither.

Yet there is one more in this City, which I was willing to omit, as thinking it at firft fight fcandalous, and a very Jeft; it being a wretched Bufinefs in fo Magnificent a City; and that is, the *Vinegrette*, a Coach on two Wheels, dragg'd by a Man, and pufh'd behind by a Woman or Boy, or both.

Befides thofe, for quick Travelling there are great number of *Poft-Chaifes* for a fingle Perfon; and *Roullions* for two

Per-

Perfons : Thefe are on two Wheels only,
and have each their double Springs to
make them very eafie; they run very
fwiftly : both the Horfes pull ; but one
only is in the Thilles. The Coach-man
mounts the *Roullio.* ; but for the *Chaife*,
he only mounts the fide Horfe. I
think neither of thefe are in ufe in *England* ; but might be introduced to good
purpofe.

As for their *Recreations and Walks*, there *Recreati-*
are no People more fond of coming to- *ons and*
gether to fee and to be feen. This *Walks.*
Converfation *without-doors* takes up a
great part of their time : And for this
purpofe, the *Cour de la Reyne* is frequented by all People of Quality. It is a
treble Walk of Trees of a great length,
near the River-fide, the middle Walk having above double the breadth to the two
fide ones ; and will hold eight Files of
Coaches, and in the middle a great open
Circle to turn, with fine Gates at both
ends. Thofe that would have better and
freer Air, go further, and drive into the
Bois de Bologne, others out of other Parts
of the Town to *Bois de Vincennes*, fcarce
any fide amifs. In like manner thefe
Perfons light and walk in the *Tuilleries*,
Luxembourg, and other Gardens, belonging

ing to the Crown and Princes, (all which
are very fpacious) and are made convenient, with *many* Seats for the Entertainment of all People, the Lacquies
and Mob excepted. But of this more hereafter.

Biſhops.   No fort of People make a better Figure
in the Town than the *Biſhops*, who have
very fplendid Equipages, and variety of
fine Liveries, being moſt of them Men of
great Families, and preferred as fuch,
Learning not being fo neceſſary a Quali-
fication for thofe Dignities, as with us;
though there are fome of them very Deferving and Learned Men. I fay, they
are moſt Noblemen, or the younger Sons
of the beſt Families. This indeed is for
the Honour of the Church; but whether
it be for the good of Learning and Piety
is doubtful. They may be Patrons, but
there are but few Examples of Erudition
among them. 'Tis to be wiſh'd, that they
exceeded others in Merit, as they do in
Birth.

Abbots.   The *Abbots* here are numerous from
all Parts of the Kingdom. They make a
confiderable Figure, as being a gentile
fort of Clergy, and the moſt learned;
at leaſt were fo from the time of Cardinal

nal *Richlieu*, who preferred Men of the greateſt Learning and Parts to theſe Poſts, and that very frankly, and without their knowing it before-hand, much leſs folliciting him for it. He took a ſure way, peculiar to himſelf, to enquire out privately Men of Deſert, and took his own time to prefer them. This filled the Kingdom of *France* with learned Men, and gave great Encouragement to Study ; whereof *France* yet has ſome feeling.

'Tis pretty to obſerve, how the King *Signs in the* diſciplines this great City, by ſmall in-*Streets.* ſtances of Obedience. He cauſed them to take down all their Signs at once, and not to advance them above a Foot or two from the Wall, nor to exceed ſuch a ſmall meaſure of ſquare ; which was readily done ; So that the Signs obſcure not the Streets at all, and make little or no Figure, as tho' there were none ; being placed very high, and little.

There are great number of *Hoſtels* in *Hoſtels.* *Paris*, by which Word is meant *Publick Inns*, where Lodgings are lett ; and alſo the Noblemen and Gentlemens Houſes are ſo called, moſtly with Titles over the Gate in Letters of Gold on a Black Mar-

C   ble.

ble. This feems, as it were to denote, that they came at firft to *Paris* as Strangers only, and inn'd publickly; but at length built them Inns or Houfes of their own. 'Tis certain, a great and wealthy City cannot be without People of Quality; nor fuch a Court as that of *France* without the daily Infpection of what fuch People do. But whether the Country can fpare them or not, I queftion. The People of *England* feem to have lefs Manners, and lefs Religion, where the Gentry have left them wholly to themfelves; and the Taxes are raifed with more difficulty, inequality, and injuftice, than when the Landlords live upon the Defmaines.

The City re-built. It may very well be, that *Paris* is in a manner a new City within this forty Years. 'Tis certain fince this King came to the Crown, 'tis fo much altered for the better, that 'tis quite another thing; and if it be true what the Workmen told me, that a common Houfe built of rough Stone and plaiftered over, would not laft above twenty five Years, the greateft part of the City has been lately rebuilt. In this Age certainly moft of the great Hoftels are built, or re-edified; in like manner the Convents, the Bridges and Churches,

Churches, the Gates of the City ; and the great alteration of the Streets, the Keyes upon the River, the Pavements ; all thefe have had great Additions, or are quite new.

In the River amongft the Bridges, both above and below, are a vaft number of Boats, of Wood, Hay, Charcoal, Corn and Wine, and other Commodities. But when a fudden Thaw comes, they are often in danger of being fplit and crufht to pieces upon the Bridges ; which alfo are fometimes damaged by them. There have been great Loffes to the Owners of fuch Boats and Goods. *Boats upon the River.*

It has been propofed to dig near the City a large *Bafin* for a Winter Harbour ; but this has not had the Face of Profit to the Government ; fo they are ftill left to execute their own Project. There are no Laws or Projects fo effectual here, as what bring Profit to the Government. Farming is admirably well underftood here.

It is a wonder in fharp and long Winters, fuch as are often here, how fo great and populous a City can be fupplied with one fort of Fuel Wood, and that by Land and frefh-water Carriage only: Whereas *London* hath Coal and Wood

too

too both by Sea and Land. 'Tis certain, had it not been for the Canal of *Briare* which runs fome hundred of Miles into the Heart of the Country, they had been hard put to it. Alfo there is great care taken in that Affair by the City ; the Wood-Merchants having a conftant and ftrict *Affize* fet them ; and are oblig'd to have always in ftore fuch a quantity of Fuel before-hand.

Lawyers.   Amongft the living Objects to be feen in the Streets of *Paris*, the Counfellors and chief Officers of the Courts of Juftice make a great Figure : They and their Wives have their Trains carried up; fo there are abundance to be feen walking about the Streets in this manner. 'Tis for this that Places of that Nature fell fo well. A Man that has a right to qualifie a a Wife with this Honour, fhall command Fortune ; and the carrying a great Velvet Cufhion to Church is fuch another Bufinefs. The Place of a Lawyer is valued a third part dearer for this.

Monks.   Here are alfo daily to be feen in the Streets great variety of *Monks*, in ftrange unufual Habits to us *Englifhmen :* Thefe make an odd Figure, and furnifh well a Picture. I cannot but pity the miftaken Zeal of thefe poor Men ; that put themfelves

felves into Religion, as they call it, and renounce the World, and fubmit themfelves to moft fevere Rules of Living and Diet ; fome of the Orders are decently enough cloathed, as the Jefuits, the Fathers of the Oratory, &c. but moft are very particular and obfolete in their Drefs, as being the ruftick Habit of old times, without Linnen, or Ornaments of the prefent Age.

As to their meager Diet, it is much againft Nature, and the improved Diet of Mankind. The *Mofaic* Law provided much better for *Jews*, a chofen People; That was inftituted for Cleanlinefs and Health. Now for the Chriftian Law, though it commands Humility and Patience under Sufferings, and Mortification and Abftinence from finful Lufts and Pleafures; yet by no means a diftinct Food, but liberty to eat any thing whatfoever, much lefs Naftinefs; and the Papifts themfelves in other things are of this mind; for their Churches are clean, pompoufly adorned and perfumed. 'Tis enough, if we chance to fuffer Perfecution, to endure it with Patience, and all the miferable Circumftances that attend it; but wantonly to perfecute our felves, is to do violence to Chriftianity, and to put our felves in a worfe State than the *Jews*

C 3   were;

were; for to choose the worst of Food, which is sowre Herbs and Fish, and such like Trash; and to lie worse, always rough, in course and nasty woollen Frocks, upon Boards; to go bare-foot in a cold Country, to deny themselves the Comforts of this Life, and the Conversation of Men : This, I say, is to hazard our Healths, to renounce the greatest Blessings of this Life, and in a manner to destroy our selves. These Men, I say, cannot but be in the main Chagrin, and therefore as they are out of humour with the World, so they must in time be weary of such slavish and fruitless Devotion, which is not attended with an active Life.

The great Multitude of *poor* Wretches in all parts of the City is such, that a Man in a Coach, a-foot, in the Shop, is not able to do any business for the numbers and importunities of Beggars; and to hear their Miseries is very lamentable; and if you give to one, you immediately bring a whole swarm upon you. These, I say, are true Monks, if you will, of God Almighties making, offering you their Prayers for a Farthing, that find the Evil of the Day sufficient for the Day, and that the Miseries of this Life are not to be courted, or made a mock of. These worship, much against their Will, all rich
Men,

Men, and make Saints of the reſt of Mankind for a Morſel of Bread.

But let theſe Men alone with their
miſtaken Zeal : It is certainly God's good
Providence which orders all things in
this World. And the Fleſh-Eaters will
ever defend themſelves, if not beat the
Lenten Men : Good and wholſom Food,
and plenty of it, gives Men naturally
great Courage. Again; a Nation will
ſooner be peopled by the free Marriage of
all ſorts of People, than by the additional ſtealth of a few ſtarved Monks, ſuppoſing them at any time to break their
Vow. This limiting of Marriage to a
certain People only, is a deduction and an
abatement of Mankind, not leſs in a Pa-
piſt Country, than a conſtant War. A-
gain, this leſſens alſo the number of
God's Worſhippers, inſtead of multiply-
ing them as the Stars in the Firmament,
or the Sand upon the Sea Shoar : Theſe
Men wilfully cut off their Poſterity,
and reduce God's Congregation for the fu-
ture.

There is very little noiſe in this City *Publick*
of *Publick Cries* of things to be ſold, or *Cries.*
any Diſturbance from Pamphlets and
Hawkers. One thing I wondered at, that
I heard of nothing loſt, nor any publick

Ad-

Advertifements, till I was fhewed printed
Papers upon the Corners of Streets,
wherein were in great Letters, *Un*, *Deux*,
Cinq; *Dix jufq*; *a Cinquante Louis à a gagner*,
that is, from One to Fifty Louifes to be
got ; and then underneath an account of
what was loft. This fure is a good and
quiet way ; for by this means, without
noife, you often find your Goods again ;
every Body that has found them repairing
in a Day or two to fuch places. The *Ga-
zettes* come out but once a Week, and but
few People buy them.

'Tis difficult and dangerous to vend a
Libel here. While we were in Town, a
certain Perfon gave a Bundle of them to
a blind Man, a Beggar of the Hofpital of
the *Quinzevint*, telling him he might get
five Pence for every Penny ; he went to
Noftredame, and cried them up in the
Service time , *La vie & Miracles de
l'Evefq*; *de Reims*. This was a Trick that
was play'd the Archbifhop, as it was
thought, by the Jefuits, with whom he
has had a great Conteft about *Molinas* the
Spanifh J. Doctrines. The Libel went off
at any Rate, when the firft Buyers had
read the Title further, and found they were
againft the prefent Archbifhop, Duke, and
firft Peer of *France*.

The

The Streets are lighted alike all the Winter long, as well when the Moon fhines, as at other times of the Month; which I remember the rather, becaufe of the impertinent ufage of our People at *London*, to take away the Lights for half of the Month, as though the Moon was certain to fhine and light the Streets, and that there could be no cloudy Weather in Winter. The Lanthorns here hang down in the very middle of all the Streets, a-bout twenty Paces diftance, and twenty Foot high. They are made of a Square of Glafs about two Foot deep, covered with a broad Plate of Iron; and the Rope that lets them down is fecured and lockt up in an Iron Funnel and little Trunk faftned into the Wall of the Houfe. Thefe Lan-thorns have Candles of four in the Pound in them, which laft burning till after Mid-night.

As to thefe Lights, if any Man break them, he is forthwith fent to the Gallies; and there were three young Gentlemen of good Families, who were in Prifon for having done it in a Frolick, and could not be releafed thence in fome Months; and that not without the diligent Application of good Friends at Court.

The Lights at *Paris* for five Months in the Year only, coft near 50000 *l. Sterling.*

This

This way of Lighting the Streets is in ufe
alfo in fome other Cities in *France.* The
King is faid to have raifed a large Tax by
it. In the Preface to the Tax it is faid,
That confidering the great danger his Subjects were in, in walking the Streets in the
Dark, from Thieves, and the breaking
their Necks by falls, he for fuch a Sum of
Money did grant this Priviledge, that
they might hang out Lanthorns in this
manner.

Streets
clean.

    I have faid, that the Avenues to the
City, and all the Streets, are paved with
a very hard *Sand Stone*, about eight Inches
fquare; fo they have a great care to keep
them clean; in Winter, for Example,
upon the melting of the Ice, by a heavy
Drag with a Horfe, which maks a quick
riddance and cleaning the Gutters; fo
that in a Days time all parts of the Town
are to admiration clean and neat again to
walk on.

    I could heartily wifh their Summer
Cleanlinefs was as great; it is certainly
as neceffary to keep fo populous a City
fweet; but I know no Machine fufficient,
but what would empty it of the People
too; all the Threats and *Infcriptions up-*
on Walls are to little purpofe. The Duft
in *London* in Summer is oftentimes, if a
Wind

Wind blow, very troublefome, if not intolerable ; in *Paris* there is much lefs of it, and the reafon is, the flat Stones require little Sand to fet them faft, whereas our fmall Pebles, not coming together, require a vaft quantity to lay them faft in Paving.

But from the People in the Streets, to *Bufto's.* the dead Ornaments there. There are an infinite number of Bufto's or Heads of the Grand Monarque every where put up by the Common People; but the Noble and intire *Statues* are but few, confidering the Obfequious Humour and Capacity of the People to perform.

That in the *Place-Victoire* is a-foot in *Statues.* Brafs, all over gilt, with *Victoirie*; that is, a vaft Winged Woman clofe behind his Back, holding forth a Laural Crown over the King's Head, with one Foot upon a Globe. There are great exceptions taken at the Gilding by Artifts; and, indeed the fhining feems to fpoil the Features, and give I know not what confufion; it had better have been all of Gold braffed over; which would have given its true Lights and Shaddows, and fuffered the Eye to judge of the proportions. But that which I like not in this, is the great Woman perpetually at the Kings Back; which is a fort of Embarras, and inftead of giving
Victory,

Victory, seems to tire him with her Company. The *Roman Victory* was a little Puppit in the Emperours Hand, which he could dispose of at pleasure. This Woman is enough to give a Man a Surfeit.

The other are Statues of Three of the last Kings of *France*, in Brass a Horse-back.

That on the *Pont-neuf* is of *Henry* the Fourth in his Armour bare-headed, and Habited as the Mode of that time was.

The other of *Lewis* the Thirteenth in the *Palace-Royal*, Armed also after the Mode of the Age, and his Plume of Feathers on his Headpiece.

The third is of this present King *Louis* the Fourteenth, and designed for the *Place Vendosme*. This Colossus of Brass is yet in the very place, where it was cast; it is surprisingly great, being 22 foot high, the Foot of the King 26 inches in length, and all the proportions of him and the Horse suitable. There was 100000 pound weight of Metal melted, but it took not up above 80000 pounds; it was all cast at once, Horse and Man. Mons. *Girardon* told me, he wrought diligently, and with almost daily application at the Model 8 years, and there were two years more spent in the Moulding, and Furnaces, and Casting of it. The King is in the Habit of a *Roman* Emperor, without Stirrups or Saddle, and

on

on his Head a French large Periwig *A-la-mode.* Whence this great Liberty of Sculpture arifes, I am much to feek.

'Tis true, that in building precifely to follow the ancient manner and fimplicity is very commendable, becaufe all thofe Orders were founded upon good Principles in Mathematicks : but the Cloathing of an Emperor was no more, than the weak fancy of the People. For *Louis le Grand* to be thus dreffed up at the head of his Army now a-days would be very Comical. What need other Emblems, when Truth may be had ; as though the prefent Age need be afhamed of their Modes, or that the *Statua Equeftris* of *Henry* the Fourth or *Louis* the Thirteenth were the lefs to be valued for being done in the true Drefs of their times. It feems to me to be the effect of Miftaken Flattery ; but if regarded only as a Piece of meer Art, it is methinks very unbecoming, and has no Graceful Air with it.

I remember I was at the *Levee* of King *Charles* the Second, when 3 Models were brought him to choofe one of, in order to make his Statue for the Court at *Windfor* ; he chofe the *Roman* Emperors Drefs, and caufed it alfo to be executed in that other erected for him in the *Old Exchange* in *London.* The like is of K. *J.* in *Whitehall,*

and

and at *Chelfey-College,* our *Invalides.* Now
I appeal to all Mankind, whether in reprefenting a living Prince now a-days thefe
naked Arms and Legs are decent, and
whether there is not a *barbarity* very dif-
pleafing in it. The Father of thefe two
Kings, *Charles* the Firft, was the Prince
of this Age of the beft Relifh, and of a
found Judgment, particularly in Painting,
Sculpture, Architecture by Sea and Land,
witnefs the vaft Sums of Money he be-
ftowed upon *Rubens* and his Difciple *Van-
dyke.* Alfo the great Efteem he had for
the incomparable *Inigo Jones,* who was the
firft *Englifhman* in this Age that underftood
Building. I heard M. *Auzout* fay, when
he had viewed the *Banquetting-Houfe* at
Whitehall, that it was preferable to all the
Buildings on this fide the *Alpes;* and I
ought to believe him, he having ftudied
Vitruvius more than 40 years together, and
much upon the place at *Rome.* Alfo the
Ship the *Sovereign,* which was truly the
nobleft floating Caftle that ever fwam the
Sea. Yet after all this, that King had a
Statua Equeftris of himfelf erected, now
at *Charingcrofs,* caft in the full Habit of
his own time, and which I think may com-
pare with the beft of that fort at *Paris.*

I fhould beg Leave in the next place
to vifit the Palaces and Men of Letters
and

and Converfation : but I muft take notice
firft of the vaft Expences that are here in
Iron Baluftrades, as in the *Place-Royal,*
which Square is compaffed about with one
of 10 foot high. Of this fort and better
there are infinite every where in *Paris;*
which gives indeed a full view of the
beauty of their Gardens and Courts.

Firft, therefore, I faw the *Palais Mazarin,*
in which are many good Pictures, but the
Low Gallery is furnifht with a great Collection of Ancient *Greek* and *Roman* Statues, and is what I moft took notice of.
They were moft brought from *Rome* by
the *Cardinal.* Thofe which are *Togatæ* and
Cloathed, are as they were found; but fuch
as were made *Nudæ* or naked, are miferably
difguifed by the fond Humour of the
Duke *de Mazarin,* who in a hot Fit of Devotion caufed them to be caftrated and
mangled, and then frocked them by a
fad Hand with I know not what Plaifter
of *Paris,* which makes them very ridicu-
lous. *Cicero* fomewhere tells us, that fome
of the ancient Wife Men thought there
was nothing naturally obfcene, but that
every thing might be called by its own
Name; but our *Celfus* is of another mind,
and begs Pardon, being a *Roman,* that he
writ of thofe things in his own Tongue.

P. *Maza-
rin.*

Tis

'Tis certain upon our Subject, the Duke
fhould not have furnifht his Cabinet and
Gallery with Naked Pictures, but with the
Togatæ only; or if it had once pleafed him
to do otherwife, he fhould not have Cloathed them; which was at beft but a vain
Oftentation of his Chaftity, and betrayed
his ignorance and diflike of good things;
that is, fpoils and hides the noble Art of
the Sculpture, for which only they are
valuable.

But why fhould Nudity be fo offenfive,
fince a very great part of the World yet
defies Cloaths, and ever did fo; and the
parts they do moft affect to cover, is from
a certain neceffity only.

'Tis plain by thefe and many other Elegant Statues I faw at *Verfailles,* moft of
which were taken out hence, that the
Roman Cloathing was the moft fimple thing
imaginable, and that a *Roman* was as foon
undreffed, as I can put off my Gloves and
Shoes. The Men and Women went dreft
much alike. As for the fafhion of the
Roman Habit, it is evident by thefe ancient
Statues, (which *Oct. Ferrarius* has well and
reafonably followed in explicating the feveral Garments of the Ancients) that the
Tunica or Shirt was without a Collar or
Sleeves, and girt high up under the Breafts;
alfo, that the *Toga* or *Gown* was a wide and
                                          long

long Garment open at both ends, and let down over the Head, and fupported by the Left Hand thruft under the Skirts of it, whilft the top of it refted upon the left Shoulder. The Right Hand and Arm was naked, and above the Gown, fo that the Gown was ungirt and always loofe. Now for the purpofe, when a *Roman* made himfelf naked for the Bath, (as he daily did juft before eating) he had nothing to do but to draw up his left Hand, and the Gown fell down at his Feet; and at the fame time to loofe the Girdle of the Tunica, and to draw up both his Arms from under the Tunica, and that alfo fell at his Feet.

In the firft Ages of the Commonwealth they wore a Toga or Gown only, afterwards they put on next the Skin a Tunica or Shirt, and never added more in the very Splendour and Luxury of the Empire ; all other Matters of Cloathing, of what nature foever, have been invented fince.

I much admired, that in the great numbers of ancient Statues to be feen in and about *Paris*, I could never meet any one but what was Cloathed with a *Toga pura*, and no reprefentation of a Bullated one.

This *Toga* and *Tunica* both were made of fine white Wooll or Flannel : They
D had

had not a Rag of Linnen about them. This Flannel, I fay, was very fine; for the folds are fmall, and it falls into them eafily; and feems to be very light, by the handling of it, to raife it by the Finger and Thumb only, as is the Air of fome of the Statues, and the whole Garment to be fufpended by the left Shoulder. Upon the leaft ftraining of it, the Breafts and Nipples are vifible through it; alfo the proportions of the Thighs.

This wearing all Woollen in a hot Country brought on the ufe and neceffity of frequent Bathing: otherwife they could never have kept themfelves fweet and clean; and the neceffity of Bathing kept them to this fort of loofe Garment; and much Bathing brought in Oils, and Oils Perfumes infufed in them.

But in my mind a fair Linnen Shirt every Day is as great a prefervative to Neatnefs and Cleannefs of the Skin and Health, as daily Bathing was to the *Romans.* 'Tis certain, had they not ufed either fimple Oils of Olives, fometimes unripe and old, for the aftringency, and fometimes ripe and perfumed, the warm Water muft have much decay'd Nature, and made the Skin intolerable tender and wrinkled. The Naked *Indians* and *Blacks* fecure their Skins by Oils at this Day

from

from all the injuries of the Weather, both from Heat and Cold.

But the beft Rule of Health and long Life is to do little to our felves. People are not aware what inconveniencies they bring upon themfelves by cuftom, how they will plead for things long ufed, and make that pleafant, which is very deftru-ctive to their Healths ; as in the Cafe of Cloathing, Tobacco, Strong Waters, Steel Remedies, the drinking Mineral Waters, Bathing, Tea, Coffee, Chocholate, &c.

One little Statue in this Collection I took more particular notice of, for the elegance of the Sculpture, and the humour of the Drefs; it ftood upon a Table; it was the Figure of a *Sybil.* The Face of the old Woman was cut very deep into the Stone, within the Quoifure, like a Hood pulled over the Forehead ; a very Emblem of an Oracle, which is hid, dark, and am-biguous, as the Woman her felf, who would have neither her Face feen, nor her Saying eafily underftood ; that is, fhe is as it were afhamed of her Cheat.

What was the fancy of the Men of the firft Ages to make *Old Women Prophetesses,* to utter Oracles, and to interpret the Will of the Gods by the eating of Animals ? To make them *Sagæ* and *Veneficæ* is rea-fonable enough ; for old Age makes all

People fpiteful, but more the weaker Sex. To Poifon and Bewitch are the fecret Revenges of Impotent People.

The *Jews* were impatient of the Company of Women in their Religious Rites, left they fhould contaminate and fpoil all their Devotion. The *Romans* on the contrary thought Religion became Women better than Men, for befides the general parts they had in common with the Men in Adoration of their Gods, they had alfo peculiar ones, where the Men were not concerned. *Tully* bids his Wife fupplicate the Gods for him; for he tells her, he thought they would be kinder to her than him. Upon fome fuch Principle, probably, their Prophetefles were in efteem.

M. *Vivi-ers.* I faw the Apartment of Monfieur *Viviers* in the Arfenal; it confifts in 7 or 8 Ground Rooms looking into the great Garden; Thefe Rooms are fmall, but moft curioufly furnifht, and have in them the greateft variety and beft forted *China* Ware I ever faw, befides *Pagods* and *China Pictures :* Alfo elegant and rich *Beureaus*, *Book-Cafes*, and fome Paintings of the beft Mafters.

That which pleafed me moft, amongft the Paintings, were the Pieces of *Rambrants*, that incomparable *Dutch* Painter.

A

A Girl with a Cage in one Hand, and looking up after the Bird that had got out, and was flying away over her Head: She had Fright, Amazement, and Sorrow in her Looks. The other is an unlucky Lad leaning upon a Table, and looking with Mifchief in his Eyes, or that he watcht to do fome unhappy turn. The third is a young Gentleman in a Fur Cap *en difhabille*, after his wonted manner. The two firft are the moft natural Thoughts and Drefs that can be; but nothing certainly ever came near his colouring for Flefh and Garments. This part he ftudied paffionately all his Life, and was ever trying Experiments about it; and with what fuccefs, thefe and many other Pieces fhew.

Thefe Three Pictures of *Rambrant* are all of young People, and are finifht with all the art and perfection of Colouring, as fmooth as any Limning; which makes the Judgment of *Philibien* of him appear not juft: for he fitted his Paint according to the Age and Nature of the Subjects he wrought. I had the pleafure of feeing them again and again.

Monfieur *le Noftre*'s Cabinet, or Rooms, _{M. *le No-*} wherein he keeps his fine things, the_{*ftre.*} Controller of the Kings Gardens, at the fide of the *Tuilleries*, was worth feeing.

He

He is a very ingenious old Gentleman, and the Ordinance and Defign of moft of the Royal and great Gardens in and about *Paris* are of his Invention, and he has lived to fee them in perfection. This Gentleman is 89 years old, and quick and lively. He Entertained me very Civilly. There were in the three Appartments, into which it is divided, (the uppermoft of which is an Octogon Room with a *Dome*) a great Collection of choice Pictures, Porcellans, fome of which were *Jars* of a moft extraordinary fize; fome old *Roman* Heads and Bufto's, and intire Statues; a great Collection of *Stamps* very richly bound up in Books; but he had lately made a Draught of his beft Pictures to the value of 50000 Crowns, and had prefented them to the King at *Verfailles*. There was not any thing of Natural Hiftory in all his Cabinet.

I was feveral times with him, and once he carried me into an upper Clofet, where he had a great Collection of Medals in four Cabinets, moft Modern; amongft them there were four large Drawers, three of which were the Medals of King *William*. The fourth Drawer was of King *William*'s Anceftors and Family near 300, as he told me in all; he had been 40 Years in making this Collection, and had purchafed

many

many of them at vaſt Rates. He has certainly the beſt Furniture for an *Hiſtoria Metallica*, that I ever ſaw. The *French* King has a particular Kindneſs for him, and has greatly inricht him, and no Man talks with more freedom to him ; he is much delighted with his Humour, and will ſit to ſee his Medals, and when he comes at any Medal, that makes againſt him, he will ſay, *Sire, voyla une, qu' eſt bien contre nous !* as though the Matter pleaſed him, and he was glad to find it to ſhew it the King. Monſieur *le Noſtre* ſpoke much of the good Humour of his Maſter ; he affirmed to me he was never ſeen in Paſſion, and gave me many Inſtances of Occaſions, that would have cauſed moſt Men to have raged ; which yet he put by with all the Temper imaginable.

In this Cabinet I ſaw many very rare old China Veſſels, and amongſt them a ſmall *Roman Glaſs Urn*, very thick made, and ponderous, of a blue Sea colour; the two Ears were Feet divided into four Claws, but the very bottom of this Veſſel was ſmooth, and very little umbilicate ; and for this reaſon I cannot tell whether it might not be *caſt*, and not *blown*.

The *Palace of Luxembourg* is the moſt *Luxem-* finiſht of all the Royal Buildings; it is *bourg H.* very

very magnificent, well defigned, were it not for the trifling Interfections or round and deep Jointings of the Columns, which looks like a Cheefemongers Shop, and which is below the grandeur of the Orders; fo hard a matter it is to have a true Relifh of the ancient Simplicity, and not to add impertinent Ornaments. And to fay the truth, there are not many things in *Paris* where this Chaftity is ftrictly preferved; amongft thofe, where little is to be blamed, are the South-Eaft Front of the *Louvre*, the Facade of *St. Gervais*, and the whole Building of *Val de Grace*. And this Wantonnefs in additional Ornaments may perhaps be one reafon, why the *Doric* is more practifed there at this day, the *Metopæ* naturally admitting greater variety, and according to the intended ufe of the Building.

In this Palace is that famous Gallery, where the Hiftory of *Maria* of *Medicis* is painted by *Rubens*. Though this was done 70 years ago, it is as frefh as at the firft; fo great a Mafter he was in Colouring. His Flefh is admirable, and his Scarlet, for which, if he had not a fecret, not now underftood, he had lefs Avarice, and more Honour, than moft of our Modern Painters. 'Tis certain the goodnefs of Colours was one of the great

Cares

Cares and Studies of the late famous Painters; and that which feems moft to have obliged them to it, was the neceffity they put themfelves upon, to paint all their own Defigns, and more particularly the prefent Dreffes. And though *Rubens* in his Hiftory is too much a Libertine in this refpect, yet there is in this very place, which we now defcribe, much truth in the habit of his principal Figures, as of King *Henry* the Fourth, the Queen, her Son, the three Daughters and the Cardinal; though indeed the Allegoric affiftants in all the Tableaux are very airy and fancifully fet out. His Scholar *St. Ant. Vankyke* did introduce this Novelty too much in *England*, where the Perfons would bear it; as the Female Sex were very willing to do, who feem in his Time to have been mighty fond of being painted in *difhabille*. 'Twas this that cut out of Bufinefs the beft *Englifh* Painter of his Time, *Cornelius Johnfon*, and fhortned his Life by Grief. It is certain with a little patience all Drefs becomes *difhabille*; but I appeal, whether it is not better and much more pleafing to fee the old Fafhion of a dead Friend, or Relation, or of a Man of Diftinction, painted as he was, than a foppifh Night-Gown, and odd Quoifure, which never belonged to the Perfon painted.   But

But that which led me into this Re-
flection was, that the Modern Painters
have thereby an opportunity to be idle
and to have others to work under them;
it is fufficient to finifh the Face, and to
fend it out to be dreft at the Block; whereas were they obliged in Honour to paint
the whole Dreffes, this would make them
accurate in Colouring, through the great
variety which would daily occur, and that
noble Art be in a far greater efteem.

A good Artift might eafily reduce it,
and command the Purfes of thofe he paints,
to pay well for his labour and time, for it
is the lot but of very few Men to excel
in this Noble Art.

In the Antichamber of the Queen's
Apartment there are other Paintings of
Rubens, as, in three diftinct Tableaux, at
the upper end of the Room the Ceremonies
of the Marriages of her three Daughters,
to *Savoy*, *Spain*, and *England*. Alfo in an
other Hiftorical Tableau, on the fide of
the fame Room, he has painted his own
Picture, in a very free and eafie Pofture,
next the Eye, up in the very Corner,
looking out, as unconcerned in his own
Tableau, upon the three Ladies. He has
done his Wife in fome of the Tableaus,
in the great Gallery; but in the laft, where
the Queen is mounting up to Heaven, fhe

is

is drawn up after her; but whether it be
her full and heavy Body, or her Mind,
fhe is painted in a very unwilling Pofture,
bending back. It feems her Husband
liked her Company too well to part with
her eafily, or fhe with him.

Several of the Rooms of this Apartment were Wainfcoted with Cedar, wrought
in Flowers, as her Dreffing-Room and O-
ratory; which is rare in *Paris*. The Floors
were made of fmall pieces of Wood put
together in Figures; the inward Knots
were inlaid with Threads of Silver, which
have a marvellous effect; but the firmnefs,
duration, and intirenefs of thefe Floors,
after fo long laying, I moft admired:
whereas with us in *London*, and elfewhere
in *Paris*, they prove fo noify to tread on,
and faulty, that they are in a few years
intolerable.

'Tis pity the King has fo great an aver- The
fion to the *Louvre*, which if finifht, (which *Louvre.*
he might eafily do in two or three years)
would be the moft Magnificent Palace,
perhaps, that ever was upon the Face of
the Earth; and, indeed, except that be
done, *Paris* will never arrive at its full
Beauty.

There are two Stones in the Fronton of
the South-Eaft Facade of the *Louvre*,
which

which are fhewed to all Strangers, covering the very top of it, as Slates do, and
meet in an angle. Thefe are very big,
viz. 54 foot long a-piece, 8 foot broad,
and but 14 inches thick. The raifing fo
high thefe two vaft and tender Stones was
lookt upon as a Mafter-piece of Art, e-
qualling any thing of the Ancients of
that Nature. They were taken out of
the Quarries of *Meudon*, where Monfeigneur the Dauphin dwells.

I faw in the Galleries of the *Louvre* fome
of the Battles of *Alexander* by *Le Brun*;
which are by the *French* the moft admired
Pieces of Painting, that have been (fay they)
done by any Man on this fide the *Alpes*;
and of which they are not a little proud.

Alfo a large Piece of *Paulo Verenefe*,
prefented by the Senate of *Venice* to the
King.

I cannot pafs by unmentioned the vaft
number of great Cafes in one of the Galleries, wherein are the *Play-things or Pup-
pets* of the Dauphin, when a Child:
They reprefent a Camp in all its parts,
and coft 50000 Crowns.

But, indeed, that which moft furprifed
me in the *Louvre* was the *Attellier* or
Work-houfe of Monfieur *Gerardon*; he
that made Cardinal *Richelieu's Tomb*, and
the *Statua Equeftris* defigned for the *Place*
de

de Vendofme ; he told me he had been almoft ten years in making the Model and
Moulding and other things, as I faid before,
with affiduity and daily application.

He hath in the *Louvre* alfo two Rooms,
in one of which are many ancient Marble
Statues, and in the other are Brafs Statues
and *Vafa*, and a hundred other things relating to Antiquity. There is nothing in
Paris deferves more to be feen.

In this laft, I faw a fort of *Egyptian
Janus*, with *Silenus* on one fide, and a
Bacchus on the other : With many other
Egyptian Figures well defigned ; all of them
with a *hole* in the Crown of the Head.

Alfo a *Lion of Ægypt* very large of
Brafs ; but the defign rude, and more like
an *Indian Pagod*. This alfo had a large
fquare hole in the Back, near the Neck.
The *Siamites*, that came in an Embaffy
to *Paris*, were well pleafed to fee this
Figure, and faid, it was not unlike one of
theirs ; and that that hole ferved to put
the Incenfe in, that the Smoak might
come out of the Body and Noftrils of the
Lion. I doubt not but that alfo was the
ufe of the open Crowns of the reft of
the *Ægyptian* Figures, which I had feen
elfewhere, as well as here; and their
Heads ferved for *Perfuming Pots* for themfelves : and hence alfo might arife, that
cther

other Ornament of *Radiated Heads* ; in imitation of a bright Flame kindled within , and cafting Rays out of and round the Head.

There was alfo a fmall Image of a Lean Man, caft *bent*, in a fitting Pofture, with a Roll of Parchment fpread open upon his Knees, and he looking down upon it, Reading it. This was of *Solid Brafs*, the Head and all : This was found inclofed in a *Mummy*. He feemed to have a thin Linnen Garment on, perhaps fuch as the *Æ-gyptian* Priefts ufe to wear.

Alfo he fhewed us the *Mummy of a Woman* intire. The fcent of the Hand was to me not unpleafant ; but I could not liken it to any Perfume now in ufe with us ; tho' I make no queftion, but *Naptha* was the great Ingredient ; which indeed is fo unufual a Smell, that the *Mineral Waters* of *Hogsden* near *London*, (wherein the true *Naptha* is fubftantially , and of which I have fome Ounces by me, gathered off of thofe Waters) have impofed upon the ignorant in Natural Hiftory ; who would make them come from a chance Turpentine Effufion , or the Mifcarriage of a Chymical Experiment.

Here were alfo great variety of *Urns* and *Funeral. Vafa* of all Materials and Fafhions.

Alfo

Alfo an an ancient *Writing-Pen* coil'd up, with two ends erected both alike, reprefenting the Head of a Snake.

The *Ancient Heads* and *Bufto's* in Brafs are numerous and of great value. This Gentleman is exceeding courteous to all Strangers, efpecially to fuch as have the leaft good Relifh of Things of this Nature, to whom he fhews them gladly. It cannot be otherwife, that a Man educated in that noble Art of Sculpture, who fhall daily ftudy fo great a variety of Originals of the beft Mafters, but muft far excel the reft of Mankind, who practife without good Example, and by fancy moftly.

I was to fee Monfieur *Baudelot*, whofe Friendfhip I highly value: I received great Civilities from him. He is well known by his Books about the *Utility of Voyages:* he has a very choice and large Collection of Books of Greek and Roman Learning. I made him feveral Vifits, and had the pleafure of perufing his Cabinet of Coins, and fmall Images of Copper, which are many and of good value; as *Egyptian, Phrygian, Grecian* and *Roman.* Monfieur *Baudelet.*

Amongft

Amongſt his *Egyptian*, the moſt curious was a *Deus Crepitus* of admirable Workmanſhip, with a radiated Crown : It was an *Etheopian*, and therefore beſpoke its great Antiquity; for they very uſually repreſented their Kings under the Figures of their Gods.

There was alſo the Skeleton of a Woman of ſolid Copper, found in the Body of a Mummy, in a ſitting Poſture; not unlike that other mention'd above in Monſieur *Girardon's* Cloſet.

An *Apis* or a *Heifer* in Copper.

A Phrygian *Priapus* of elegant Workmanſhip : The *Phrygian Cap* pointed and hanging down behind, as our Caps in *Diſhabille* are now worn.

Of all which, and many more, this learned Antiquary intends to write.

In his Cabinet of Medals I could not find one of *Palmyra*, for which I carefully enquired; for I was willing to add what could be found in *France* upon this Subject.

He has alſo many *Marbles from Greece*; moſt of which have been publiſh'd by *Spon*; ſave one, and that is the moſt Antient and moſt Curious of all; concerning which he is ready to publiſh a Diſſertation. 'Tis a Catalogue in three Columns, of the Names of the principal
Perſons

Perfons of *Erectheis*, one of the chiefeft Tribes of *Attica*, that were killed in one and the fame year in five feveral Places, where the *Athenians* fought under two Generals, as in *Cyprus*, in *Egypt*, in *Phænicia*, in *Ægina*, in *Halies*. *Here are* 177 *Names in the Three Columns. See* Table I. Fig. 3.

The *Mantis* clofes the Column, who dyed in *Egypt*, that is, the Phyfician. Magick and Phyfick went together in thofe Days : nay, the very Comedians and Poets, thofe neceffary Men of Wit, fought ; for none were exempt from being inroll'd that were born in the Kingdom or Republick of *Attica*.

The Antiquity of this Marble, befides the known Hiftory and Names which juftifie the time of thofe Men : The Figure of the Letters are an undoubted Argument : For there are no double Letters here ; no *n*, no *ω*, but all graved with e, o; alfo the Letters, L, P, Π, R, S, are very Roman. So that it is alfo an Evidence, that the Romans borrowed their Letters from the Antient Greek Alphabet.

The invention and borrowing of Letters was a great Happinefs to Mankind. The Embarras in which Writing is in *China*, is owing to the Misfortune of wanting an Alphabet; fo that the *Chinefes*

E   **are**

are forc'd to expreſs every Sentence and Thought by a different Character, which has multiplied their Writing to 120000 Characters; of which yet they have leſs need, than we in *Europe*, who perform all with twenty four Letters, (whereof five add Life to the other Nineteen, ſaith *Hippocrates*, which is an Argument of the Age he writ in : *The Knowledge of Grammar*, i. e. *Reading and Writing, depends upon ſeven Figures, de Dieta.* 1.) The *Chineſes* know much leſs than we; they have no other Morals, they have leſs Philoſophy, leſs Mathematicks, fewer Arts, and yet much narrower Knowledge of Natural Hiſtory, becauſe they can have the Knowledge only of that part of Nature which they have at home : In what therefore ſhould they employ this Multitude of Characters ! 'Tis, I ſay, their Misfortune not to have thought of an Alphabet : Their common Language is as eaſily learnt, and conſequently might as eaſily be writ as any in *Europe*.

But to return to Monſieur *Budelot's* Stores. In this Cabinet I alſo ſaw ſome *Baſſe-Relieves :* One of *Praxiteles* well deſigned ; one of *Muſos* the Comœdian : Amongſt the reſt of the Marbles there is a Baſſe-Relief, very extant, and finely finiſh'd, of a Cupid aſleep, leaning his
Head

Head upon his Left Arm : In his Hand
he holds two *Poppy Heads.* 'Tis probable
the Poppies were Emblimatique from the
Power they have in Love-Affairs. Indeed, moſt Poiſons affect thoſe Parts
chiefly, being the great Sluce of the Habit of the Body, or Circle of the Blood ;
and no People uſe Poppy more, and
ſtand more in need of it, than the Men
who delight in Polygamy, the *Mahome-
tans,* or underſtand it better ; as *Olearius*
teſtifies.

He had an antick *Buſto* of *Zenobia* in
Marble, with a thick radiated Crown ; of
which he very obligingly gave me a Copy, well deſigned from the Original : This
was brought out of *Aſia* by Monſieur
Thevenot.

He ſhewed me a *Diſſertation* he had written out fair for the Preſs, about a certain
ancient *Intaglia* of *Madames,* of *Ptolome-
us Auletes,* or the Player upon the Flute :
In this the thin *Mufler* is the moſt remarkable thing, which covers the Mouth and
Noſe. This Head is ingraved upon an A-
methyſt.

I enjoyed this Gentleman's Company
very often ; and had much Diſcourſe with
him about his Books of the *Utility of Voyages ;* and in one Converſation took the
freedom to diſſent from him about the In-
　　　E 2　　　terpretation

terpretation of that Coin in Monſieur *Se-guin*, which he calls *Britannick*.

Monſieur *Boudelot* reads it thus, *Jovi Victori Saturnalia Io !* or *Jovi Victoria Sat. Io !*

I had rather read it thus, *Io! Sat. Victoriæ Io !* upon the occaſion of his returning with the Soldiers, filling their Head-Pieces with the Shells they had gathered off of the Sea-ſhore; and the little uſe of his new invented Letter the *Digamma,*which he inſtituted or borrowed from the *Æolique* to expreſs V Conſonant.

The Shells were a Triumph much like this ſmall addition to the Alphabet; which laſted no longer than his time : that is, *Victory enough :* (for ſo ſtupid a Prince as *Claudius :*) Let's return with the Spoils of the Ocean, and adorn his new invented Letter with a Palm-Branch : the Reverſe of this Coin being a Lawrel-Crown : Both the Signs of Victory.

About the *Bouſtrophedon* way of Writing, mentioned by *Suidas* and *Pauſanias*, or turning again as the Ox Plows, or the Racers about the *Meta* in the *Cirque*, in my opinion it could be nothing elſe, but the Serpentine manner of Writing found in *Swedeland* in *Runique* Letters.

He ſhewed me alſo a *Stone*, taken lately out of the Body of a Horſe at *Paris*, which

which was his Death; and dying ſtrangely, they diſſected him, that is, certain ignorant People; in the lower part of the
Body, probably the Bladder) was found
this Stone: It weighs, as I gueſs, two
Pound; it is as round as a Cannon Ball;
it is laminated like an Onion; for the
firſt *Couche* was broken up in ſome Places,
of a dark Hair colour, and tranſparent;
or like ſome cloudy Agats which I have
ſeen: It was very ponderous. Such like
tranſparent Stones I had a Patient voided
often in *Yorkſhire.* I ſaw another tranſparent one, which was cut out of the
Buttock of an Alderman at *Doncaſter*;
he was twice cut in the ſame place, at
ſome years diſtance. Another I had in
ſome meaſure tranſparent, voided by a
Patient, which was of the very colour of
a Coffee-Berry when burnt; but of this
Horſe Stone Monſieur *Boudelot* writ me a
Letter before I left *Paris,* which I deſign to
publiſh.

I was by Invitation from Monſieur *Caſ-* ſ*bſerva-*
ſ*ini* at the *Obſervatoire Royal,* built on a *toire.*
riſing Ground juſt without the City Walls.
This Building is very fine, and great Art
is uſed in the vaulted cut Roofs and winding Stair-Cafes. The Stones are laid inſide outſide, with the moſt regularity I e-

ver

ver faw in any Modern Building. In all this Building is there neither Iron nor Wood, but all firmly covered with Stone, Vault upon Vault. The Platform a top is very fpacious, and gives a large and fair View of all *Paris*, and the Country about it ; it is paved with Black Flint in fmall Squares, which I make no doubt are fet in Cement or Tarras, that is, the *Pulvis Puteolanus.*

We were fhewed a Room well furnifht with Models of all forts of Machines ; and a very large *Burning-Glafs*, about three Foot diameter, which at that time of the year, *viz.* in the beginning of *February*, did fire Wood into a Flame, in the very moment it came into and paft through the *Focus.*

I was indifpofed, and fo could not accept of the Favour which was offered me of feeing the Moon in their Telefcopes ; and to go down into the Vault, which was contrived for feeing the Stars at Noontide, but without fuccefs. I was told by Monfieur *Roman* afterwards, that he faw there a Rock formed in the Cave by the dropping of a Spring of Petrifying Water ; of which Nature are all the Wells in *Paris.*

In the *Flore* of one of the Octogone Towers they have defigned with great accuratecuratenefs and neatnefs with Ink, an Univerfal Map in a vaft Circle. The North-Pole is in the Center. This is a Correction of other Maps upon the lateft and beft Obfervations.

His Nephew Monfieur *Moraldi* was with him; as for his *only Son*, he was in *London* at that time : I afterwards was with him at his Father's, a very hopeful young Gentleman, and well inftructed by his Father in the Mathematicks, and all other ufeful Learning.

The *Triumphal Arch* out of the Gate of St. *Antoine* is well worth feeing; for in this the *French* pretend not only to have imitated the Ancients, but to have out-done them. They have indeed ufed the greateft Blocks of Stone that could be got, and have laid them without Mortar, and the leaft fide outward, after the manner of the Ancients; but I am afraid their Materials are very fhort of the *Roman*, and their Stone is ill chofe, though vaftly great. *Triumphal Arch.*

Indeed the *Defign* is moft Magnificent; it is finifht in *Plaifter*, that is, the *Model* of it, in its full Beauty and Proportions.

I fuppofe it was intended for a Gate of Entrance into the City; for it fronts the great Street of the Suburbs, and has a vaft

E 4 Walk

Walk planted with Trees leading from it towards *Bois de Vincennes*.

There is nothing more built but the four Parts of the Foundation of the true Building, raifed only to the Foot of the Pedeftals : The foundation is laid twenty two Foot deep.

Amongft the vaft Blocks of Stone, which take up a great compafs before the Building, I found feveral forts, all brought from the Quarries not far from *Paris*; all of them are a kind of courfe Grit, which will not burn into Lime. They diftinguifh thefe Stones into four forts ; 1. *Pierre d'arcueil*, for the firft two or three Couches or Lays above the Foundation. This is the beft and hardeft of all. 2. That of *St. Clou*, which is good, and the next beft. I did not find by the Blocks defigned either for the Walls of the Building, or the Rounds of the Pillars, that the Beds of Stone of *St. Clou* are above two Foot thick, 3. That of *St. Lieu* ; this is but indifferent, but yet much better than that Stone, which is taken up out of the Stone Pits in and about *Paris*, which makes the fourth fort of Stone. If it be wrought up into Walls, as it is taken out of the Pits, it is very apt to be flawed by the Froft : but if it be laid in the Air, and kept under cover for two years, then it becomes dry and more durable.

I

I was often at the Hofpital *des Invalides*, becaufe it was near our Lodgings ; it did not anfwer my Expectation : The Galleries, and moft of the Offices were narrow, and too little for fo vaft a Croud of infirm People : Neither do I think the Situation of it, or the Avenues to it fo beautiful as ours at *Chelfey* ; which for the quantity of *Wards*, Air, and Cleanlinefs, not to fay Building , is infinitely beyond it. Indeed the Dome and Church, when finifhed, will be fomething extraordinary.

I faw but one Piece in *Paris* of the Ruines of an *Old Roman Building* ; it was in *La Rue de la Harpe*. The Vaults are very high and large. The manner of Building is near the fame I formerly caufed exactly to be figured and defcribed at *York*, and which is publifhed in the *Philofophic Tranfactions :* That is, the infide and outfide of the Walls are compofed of fix Rows of fmall fquare Stones, and then four Rows of flat, thin and broad *Roman Bricks*, and fo alternatively from the top to the bottom. Which makes it probable it was built after *Severus*'s time : For this was the *African* manner of Building, as *Vitruvius* tells us ; and therefore might well be, what Tradition here fays of it, *viz.*

An old Roman Building.

viz. part of *Julian* the Emperor's Palace, or *Thermæ.*

St. Inno-
cents.

St. Innocent's Church-yard, the publick Burying-place of the City of *Paris* for 1000 years, when intire (as I once faw it) and built round with double Galleries full of Skulls and Bones, was an awful and venerable fight : But now I found it in Ruines, and the greateft of the Galleries pulled down, and a Row of Houfes built in their room, and the Bones removed I know not whither : The reft of the Church-yard in the moft neglected and naftieft pickle I ever faw any Confecrated place. 'Tis all one, when Men, even the Roman Catholicks, have a mind, or 'tis their Intereft, to unhallow Things or Places, they can do it with a good Stomach ; and leave the Tombs of Chancellors and other great Men without Company or Care. What no body gets by, no body is concerned to repair : But 'tis ftrange amongft fo many Millions of dead Men, not one Wonder-working Saint fhould ftart up to preferve it felf and Neighbours from Contempt and Scandal. That fo much Holy Earth, brought, as 'tis faid, fo far off, fhould never produce one Saint, but rather fpue up all its Inhabitants, to be thus fhuffled and diffipated.   Amongft

Amongſt the many Cabinets of *Paris* **Buco.** there is nothing finer than the Collection of Monſieur *Buco, Garde-Rolles du Parlement.* You paſs through a long Gallery, the one ſide of which is a well furniſhed Library, and alſo well diſpoſed in Wired Caſes. This Gallery leads into two Rooms very finely adorned with Pictures, Vaſa's, Statues and Figures in Braſs, alſo with China, and the famous Ennamel Veſſels, formerly made in *Poitu,* which are not now to be had ; and a thouſand other curious things.

I very particularly examined his large quantity of *Shells,* conſiſting in near ſixty Drawers. There were indeed very many of a ſort, and but few but what I had ſeen before, and figured. He very obligingly lent me thoſe I had not ſeen, to have the Deſigns of them done. He had many very perfect and large ones of Land and Freſh-water *Buccina;* but yet a great number were wanting of thoſe very Tribes which I have publiſh'd in my *Synopſis Conchyliorum.*

Here were alſo two or three very fair ones of that ſort of compreſt Snail, which have their Tail on the ſame ſide with their Mouth : and the vulgar Name, by which thoſe *Men of Ca-*
binets

binets diftinguifh them, is not amifs, *viz.*
Des Lampes.

He fhewed me a Bivalve, which is not
uncommon (a large *Blood-red Spondile*)
for which the late Duke of *Orleans* gave
900 Livres, which is above 50 *l. Sterling*;
and he alfo affured me, that the fame Perfon offered a *Parifian* for 32 Shells 11000
Livres : Which Sum was refufed; but the
Duke replied, That he knew not who was
the greater Fool, he that bid the Price, or
the Man that refufed it.

I alfo faw in this Collection an *Hippocampus* about four Inches long, the Tail
fquare, thick Bellied and Breaft like a
Miller Thumb, winged not unlike a fort
of flying Fifh, but the Fins were fpoiled;
the Membranes being torn from the Bones
of the Wings, the Head long and fquare
like the Tail, with a fort of tufted Mufle.
This Fifh I took to be of the *Hippocampus* Kind; and (as he told me) it was given him by my Lady *Portfmouth*, poffibly
out of King *Charles's* Collection, who had
many curious Prefents made him : (as one
of Shells from the States of *Holland*, many of which I have feen in other Hands)
but he fuffered them all to be diffipated
and loft.

Here alfo was a *Vefpetum Canadenfe* of a
moft elegant Figure, and admirable Contrivance;

trivance ; of which I have a Drawing. This is intire in all its parts ; it is as big as a middle-fized Melon , Pear-fafhion, with an edge running round, where it is thickeft , from which edge it fuddenly declines and leffens into a point ; at the very end of the point, on one fide, is a little hole, with pulvinated or fmooth Edges inclined inward ; otherwife it is whole, and wrought upon the Twig of a Tree, of a very fmooth Sattin-like Skin. *Table* 1. *Figure* 1.

Alfo the Striated Skin of an *African* Afs, fupple and well cured, which I had never feen before. It is certainly a moft beautiful Animal ; and, I admire, after fo many Ages that it has been known to the People of *Europe*, it could never be tamed, and made of common ufe, as the reft of the 'Horfe Kind. This was only of two colours, *viz.* broad Lifts of White and Bay or Chefnut colour drawn from the Back down the Sides to the Belly, which was all White : The Lifts were parted at the Back by a very narrow Ridge of fhort Hair ; which Lifts alfo went round the Legs like Garters. The Hair coloured Stripes of the *African* Afs were, near the Back, three or four Fingers broad, alfo the Lift down the Back was very broad.

Ano-

Another Skin of a Cap-Afs I afterwards faw at Dr. *Tournefort's* ; and the Stripes were the fame, but much broader and darker coloured ; it may be from the different Ages. This fort of Striping feems to be peculiar to the Afs ; for the moft common to be feen with us have all a *Black Lift* down the Back ; and two more, that is, on each fide one, running down the Shoulders.

I faw Monfieur *Tournefort's* Collection of Shells, which are well chofen, and not above one or two of a fort; but very perfect and beautiful, and in good order, confifting of about twenty Drawers.

There was amongft them a very large *Land Shell*, the fame which I have figured from the *Mufeum* at *Oxford*, having its turn from the Right Hand to the Left. Alfo many very excellent and large Patterns of other *Land Snails* ; alfo a *Frefh-water Muffel* from *Brafil*, which I had never feen before ; a Pair of them he gave me ; and many Species of *Frefh-water Buccina* from the *Caribe* Iflands : Alfo an *Auris Marina Spiffe echinata*; which was new to me.

Amongft the Shells the *Thin Oyfter*, which fhines within like Mother of Pearl, and has in the uppermoft end of the flat Valve, near the Hinge, *a Hole*. Thefe he brought
with

with him, and took them up alive from the Rocks in *Spain* ; he faid they were very offenfively *bitter* to the tafte. Thefe being perfect, I had the opportunity of feeing that hole fhut with a peculiar and *third* Shell, of the fafhion of a Pouch or Shepherd's Purfe.

I fhall fay nothing of his vaft Collection of Seeds and Fruits, and dried Plants, which alone amount to 8000, and in this he equals, if not excels, all the moft curious Herbarifts in *Europe.* His Herbarifations about *Paris* he gave me to carry for *England*, juft then printed off : Alfo he fhewed me the Defigns of about 100 *Enropean Non Defcript Plants*, in 8*vo.* which he intends next to publifh.

He alfo fhewed me ten or twelve fingle Sheets of Vellum, on each of which were painted in Water Colours very lively, one fingle Plant, moftly in flower, by the beft Artift in *Paris*, at the King's Charge. Thofe are fent to *Verfailles*, when the Doctor has put the Names to them, and there kept : In this manner the King hath above 2000 rare Plants, and they work daily upon others. The Limner has two Louis's for every Plant he paints.

I faw there alfo the *Vefpetum Canadenfe Maximum*, about twelve Inches long, and fix in diameter ; of a Pear fafhion ; it hangs

by

by a long and broad Loop to the Twig of a Tree : The broad or lower end is a little pointed, and rifing in the middle : The outward Skin is as ſmooth as Vellum, and of a whitiſh Grey, next to the Pearl-colour. The Button at the bigger end in this being broken, and the outward Skin pilled off, I could ſee a hole of about half an Inch diameter in the very middle, into which the Waſps go in and out. The Cells are ſexangular, but of a very ſmall ſize, not much bigger than a Duck Quill, or very ſmall Gooſe Quill; and conſequently appear very thick ſet, and numerous. *See the Figure above, Table* I.

He ſhewed me alſo a very great *Julus* from *Braſil*, at leaſt ſix Inches long, and two about, round like a Cord, very ſmooth and ſhining, of a kind of Copper or Brazen colour : The Feet infinite, like a double Fringe on each ſide : This he had from *F. Plumier*, who afterwards gave me a Deſign of it drawn by the Life, and in its proper colours. *Table* V.

Dr. *Tournefort* ſhew'd me a Preſent which was made him by his Countryman of *Provence*, Monſieur *Boyeur d' Aguilles*, of a large Book in Folio of curious *Stamps*. This is only the firſt part of his Cabinet, all grav'd

at

at the Author's Charge; and he is faid to
be another *Peiresk*, which would be happy
for Mankind, and a great Honour to that
Country to have produced two*Mæcenas's* in
one Age.

I was to fee Monfieur *Verney* at his A- *Verney.*
partment at the upper-end of the Royal
Phyfick-Garden; but miffing my Vifit,
went up with a young Gentleman of
my Lord Ambaffador's Retinue, to fee
Mr. *Bennis*, who was in the Diffecting
Room, working by himfelf upon a dead
Body, with its Breaft open and Belly gut-
ted : There were very odd things to be
feen in the Room. My Companion, it being Morning, and his Senfes very quick and
vigorous, was ftrangely furprized and
offended; and retired down the Stairs
much fafter than he came up. And indeed, a private Anatomy Room is to one
not accuftomed to this kind of Manufa-
cture, very irkfome if not frightful :
Here a Basket of Diffecting Inftruments,
as Knives, Saws, *&c.* and there a Form
with a Thigh and Leg flayed, and the
Mufcles parted afunder : On another Form
an Arm ferved after the fame manner :
Here a Trey full of Bits of Flefh, for the
more minute difcovery of the Veins and
Nerves; and every where fuch difcouraging

F   Ob-

Objects. So, as if Reason and the Good of Mankind, did not put Men upon this Study, it could not be endured : for Instinct and Nature most certainly abhors the Employment.

I saw Monsieur *Merrie*, a most painful and accurate Anatomist, and free and communicative Person, at his House *Rue de la Princesse*. His Cabinet consisted of two Chambers : In the outward were great variety of Skeletons; also entire Preparations of the Nerves ; in two of which he shewed me the mistake of *Willis*, and from thence gathered, that he was not much used to dissect with his own Hand. The *Pia Mater* coating the spinal Nerves but half way down the Back, where it ends : The *Dura Mater* coating the lowermost twenty pair : Which *Willis* (as he said) has otherwise reported.

But that which much delighted my Curiosity, was the Demonstration of a blown and dried Heart of a *Fœtus*; also the Heart of a *Tortoise*.

In the Heart of a *Fœtus*, he shewed it quite open, and he would have it that there was no Valve to the *Foramen Ovale ;* which seemed equally open from the Left Ventricle to the Right , as the contrary : That its Diameter well near equall'd that

of

of the *Aorta* : That the two Arteries, which afcend up into the two Lobes of the Lungs (and are the Ramifications of the Pulmonick Artery, after it has parted with the *Canal of Communication*, which goes betwixt the Pulmonick Artery and the lower or defcending Branch of the *Aorta*) both put together, far exceed, if not double, the diameter of the *Aorta* it felf.

He therefore, not without good reafon, affirms, That of all the Blood which the *Vena Cava* pours into the Right Ventricle of the Heart, and is thence in a *Fœtus* forced. up into the Pulmonick Artery, a great part is carried by the Canal of Communication into the defcending Trunk of the *Aorta*, and is fo circulated about the Body, the Lungs (as to that part) being wholly flighted : Alfo that of the two remaining thirds of the Blood, which is carried about the Lungs, when it comes down the Pulmonick Vein , that which cannot be received by the *Aorta*, (and all cannot, becaufe the *Aorta* is much lefs than the two Branches of the Pulmonick Artery put together) is therefore *difcharged back* through the *Foramen Ovale* into the Right Ventricle of the Heart, and fo thrown up again with the reft of the Blood, coming from the *Vena Cava*. So that one

part

part of the two remaining parts of the Blood is daily carried about the Body, as in an adult Fœtus, and a third part only circulates in the Lungs, paffing by the Body or grand Circulation.

That all this is done to abbreviate and reduce the Circulation to a leffer compafs, is certain ; and fo for the fame Reafon and End that other leffer Circulation of the Liver is flighted by the Blood, which returns from the Placenta, by a Canal of Communication betwixt the *Porta* and the *Vena Cava.*

The Reafon he gives of this I cannot at all allow of, as being very ill grounded ; and therefore I fhall not trouble my felf to confute, or fo much as name it. *See his printed Paper in one of the monthly Memoirs of the* Academy des Sciences.

As for the *Heart of the Land Tortoife,* it was preferved in Spirit of Wine, and all the three Ventricles thereof flit and opened ; fo that I had not all the Satiffaction I could have wifh'd : but the Left Ventricle in this Animal had no Artery belonging to it, but did receive only the Blood which defcended from the Lungs, and convey it by the *Foramen Ovale* into the Right Ventricle : That the third or middle Ventricle was only an Appendix

to

to the Right, and had the Pulmonick Artery iffuing from it. So that the Blood in a *Tortoife* was in a manner circulated like that in a *Fœtus,* through the Body, the Lungs as it were, or in good part flighted.

This Thought of Monfieur *Merrie's* has made a great Breach betwixt Monfieur *Verney* and himfelf ; for which Reafon I had not that freedom of Converfation as I could have wifh'd with both of them ; but 'tis to be hoped there may come good from an honeft Emulation.

Two Englifh Gentlemen came to vifit me, Mr. *Bennis* and Mr. *Probie.* They were lodged near the Royal Garden, where Monfieur *Verney* dwells, and makes his Anatomies, who in three Months time fhewed all the Parts of the Body to them. He had for this purpofe at leaft twenty Human Bodies from the Gallows, the Chatelet, (where thofe are expofed who are found murthered in the Streets, which is a very common bufinefs at *Paris*) and from the Hofpitals.

They told me, Monfieur *Verney* pretended to fhew them a Valve, which did hinder Blood from falling back into the Right Ventricle by the *Foramen Ovale.* This Valve they faid he compared to the Papillæ in the Kidneys, Mufculous and

F 3   Flefhy :

Flefhy: That if Wind was blown into
the *Vena Palmonalis*, it did not pafs
through the *Foramen Ovale*, but ftop there,
by reafon of the Valve: That he did believe contrary to Mr. *Merrie*, that no Blood
did circulate through the Lungs in an
Embrio.

Again, in another Converfation with
Monfieur *Merrie*, he fhewed me the blown
Hearts of an Embrio, and that of a Girl
of feven Years old. I faw clearly, that the
Skin of the fuppofed Valve of the *Foramen Ovale*, was as it were fufpended with
two Ligaments , and that in the Girl's,
the two fides of the *Foramen Ovale* were
drawn one over the other, and fo clofed
the Hole ; but were eafily to be fepa-
rated again by a Briftle thruft betwixt
them.

Alfo it feemed to me, that this Membrane in an Embrio might cover the *Foramen Ovale*, like the *Membrana Nictans* in
a Birds Eye ; that is, be drawn over it,
and fo hinder the Ingrefs of the Blood
from the *Vena Cava*, as oft as the Right Auricle beats : But the dilating it felf might
give way to the defcending Blood of the
Vena Pulmonalis ; and poffibly the Embrio
living as it were the Life of an Infect, can
by this Artifice command the Heart.

I

I remember in Difcourfe that Day with him, he told me, That Monfieur *Verney* had an old *Cat*, and a young *Kitling* juft born, put into the Air Pump before the *Academie Royalle des Sciences :* That the *Cat* died after fixteen Pumps,but the *Kitling* furvived five hundred Pumps; which favours in fome meafure the command young Animals have of their Hearts.

At another Vifit Monfieur *Merrie* obligingly procured for me the Heart of a Human Embrio, with the Lungs intire. He tried before me the Experiment upon Blowing, and alfo fyringing Water into the *Aorta*, both which filled the Auricles and Ventricles, and freely came out at the *Vena Cava* only. Then he opened the Right Auricle and Ventricle, where the *Foramen Ovale* was open only at one corner, not the tenth part of its breadth; and a Membrane drawn over the reft; which Membrane was faftned to the fides quite round. Then he opened in the fame manner the Left Ventricle and Auricle, and there it was evident, that that Membrane which clofed the Hole, had two narrow Straps or Mufcles by which it was faftned to the oppofite fides, after the manner of fome of the Valves of the Heart.

I

I told him, that it muſt follow from
this, that the *Foramen Ovale* was ſhut and
opened more or leſs, at the pleaſure of
the Embrio, according to the Neceſſities
of Nature, and the quantity of Blood
that was to paſs: That it was probable,
that all Inſects had a command of their
Hearts, (of which I had given large Inſtances * elſewhere) by ſome ſuch Paſſage,
which they could ſhut altogether, or in
great part, as they had a mind, in Winter,
in Fear, or Faſting for want of Food:
That the ſhutting up of the Paſſage in
adult Animals was therefore done in an
inſtant, by drawing the Curtain fully,
which could never be again drawn back
and opened, becauſe of the great Torrent
of Blood, which now entred the Right
Auricle, and ſtopp'd it in that Poſture,
which in time would altogether ſtiffen
and loſe its Motion of Relaxation. As a
Hen, when ſhe ſleeps, draws over the
Membrana Nictans; and likewiſe when ſhe
dies, the ſame Membrane covers all the
Eye.

Mr. *Bennis* procured me the Heart of a
Human *Fœtus*; · which had but juſt
breath'd; the which I examin'd with
Monſieur *Litre* of *Caſtres* in *Languedoc*, a-
nother very underſtanding and dextrous
Anatomiſt, and who teaches Scholars
of

* Exercitat Anatomi- ca I.

of all Nations the practice of Anatomy.
The Experiments here were repeated as
formerly defcribed : Both Wind and
Water paffed the *Foramen Ovale* , both
from the *Vena Pulmonum*, and from the
Aorta. That which I obferved in this
Heart more particularly , was , that the
Membrane or Valve on the Left fide of
the *Foramen Ovale* was flat, and extended
almoft over the Hole, without any *Limbus*
round its Edges, becaufe it was nothing
but the very Subftance of the *Auricula
Siniftra* continued, or a Procefs thereof :
But on the Right fide the *Vena Cava* being
joined to the Auricle, it had a rifing
Edge round that part of it, whence it
proceeded ; that is, that the two Faces
had contrary Openings, and being drawn
as it were one over the other, they fhut
the Hole ; but not fo firmly, but the
Hole might be more or lefs open all a
Man's Life. For thofe two Oval Proceffes
fticking clofe together in a blown and
dried Heart, that is not to be much
heeded : for I have feen them dry with
the Hole open ; but it has been like as betwixt unglued Paper, or as the Urethers
defcend betwixt the Skins of the Bladder,
or as the fame happens to the *Ductus Bila-
ris* in its infertion into the Guts.

The

The fame Perfon brought me the Heart of a Man 40 Years old, in which the *Foramen Ovale* was as much open, as in a *Fœtus* new Born; and the Ligaments very confpicuous, which tack the fides of the Valve to the Auricle, and go over to the other fide of the Border.

Monfieur *du Pes* Surgeon *Interne* of the *Hôtel-dieu*, made me a Vifit, and brought along with him to fhew me, the Skull of a Man, who had been troubled moft grievoufly with the Head-ach for many Years, and died in that Hofpital: All the top of the Skull was grown up, and fpread all over with a fort of fungous Bodies, of the very fame fubftance and hardnefs with the Skull, alfo it was perforated with innumerable fmall holes, and fome fo big as to receive the top of my little Finger. A ftrange fort of *Spina Ventofa!* He hath lately fent me a printed Tract of this Cafe, and fome others.

Monfieur *Poupart* of the Academic-Royal did accompany him in this Vifit to my Lodgings, who very kindly invited me to his Houfe to fee his Diffections of Infects, particularly of the *Horfe-Leach* lately publifht, he was unwilling to hear that *Francifco Redi* had made the Diffection of that Animal at leaft 20 Years ago, and difcovered it to be *androgynous:* however he might not have
feen

feen the Book, which I was willing to ex-
cufe. I reckon it is one part of the Inftitution
of Philofophical Societies ftrictly to inquire
into what is New, in order to give every
Man his juft praife.

I was not better pleafed with any Vifit F. *Plum.*
I made, than with that of F. *Plumier,*
whom I found in his Cell in the Convent of the *Minimes.* He came home in the
Sieur *Ponti*'s Squadron, and brought with
him feveral *Books in Folio,* of Defigns and
Paintings of *Plants, Birds, Fifhes,* and
Infects of the *Weft-Indies;* all done by
himfelf very accurately. He is a very
underftanding Man in feveral parts of
Natural Hiftory, but efpecially in *Botanique.*
He had been formerly in *America,* at his
return Printed at the King's Charge a Book
of *American* Plants in Folio. This Book
was fo well approved of, that he was fent
again thither at the King's Charge, and
returned after feveral Years wandring a-
bout the Iflands with this Cargo. He was
more than once Shipwrackt, and loft his
Specimens of all things, but preferved his
Papers, as having fortunately lodged them
in other Veffels; fo that the things themfelves I did not fee. He had defigned and
diffected a Crocodile; one of the Sea Tortoifes; a Viper, and well defcribed the
Diffections.　　　　　　　　**His**

His Birds alfo were well underftood, and very well painted in their proper colours. I took notice of three forts of Owles, one with Horns, all diftinct Species from our *European*. Several of the Hawk Kind and Falcons of very beautiful Plumage; and one of thofe, which was Coal-black, as a Raven. Alfo (which I longed to fee) there was one Species of the Swallow Kind, very diftinct from the four Species we have in *Europe*.

Amongft the Fifh there were two new Species of *American* Trouts, well known by the Flefhy Fin near the Tail.

Amongft the Infects there was a *Scolopendra* of a foot and an half long, and proportionably broad *Tab.* 6. alfo the *Julus* very elegantly painted, which I had feen before in Dr.*Tournefort's* Collection. *Table* 5.

Alfo a very large Wood-Frog, with the extremity of the Toes webbed.

Alfo a Blood-red *Polypus*, with very long Legs, two of which I could difcern by the Draught were thick *acetabulated*. This, he told me, was fo venomous, that upon the leaft touch it would caufe an infupportable burning pain, which would laft feveral Hours.

There were alfo fome few Species of the Serpent and Lizard Kind.

There

There were but few *Shells*; but amongſt them there was a *Murex* (See *Table* 4.) which dies purple, with the Fiſh as it exerts it ſelf in the Sea. Alſo that Land *Buccinum* (ſee *Tab.* 3.) which I have figured, and which lay Eggs with hard Shells, and for bigneſs, and ſhape, and colour, ſcarce to be diſtinguiſht from the Sparrow Eggs. And becauſe the *Meurex* and this *Buccinum* was drawn with the Animals creeping out, I deſired a Copy of them, which he freely and in a moſt obliging manner granted me. He deſigned the *Buccinum Terreſtre* in the Iſland of St. *Domingo*, where he found it.

Amongſt the vaſt Collection of Plants, I obſerved the Torch Kind and Ferns were of all others the moſt numerous; of each of which there were an incredible number of Species. There were two or three Species of Goosberries and Currans; and ſome Species of Wild Grapes; all which F. *Plumier* told me were good to eat.

He told me theſe Drawings would make 10 Books, as big as that he had publiſht; and Two Books of Animals. He had been often at *Verſailles* to get them into the Kings *Imprimerie*; but as yet unſucceſsfully; but hoped e're long to begin the Printing of them. Note, That the Bookſellers at *Paris* are very unwilling,

or

or not able to print Natural Hiſtory; but all is done at the Kings Charge, and in his Preſſes.

I Viſited Monſieur *Dacier and his Lady,* two very obliging Perſons, and both of great Worth, and very Learned.

I think our Profeſſion is much beholden to him, for his late elegant Tranſlation of *Hippocrates* into *French,* with Learned Notes upon him. I wiſh he may live to finiſh what he hath ſo happily begun. I read over the Two Volumes he has printed with great delight.

He ſeems to favour the Opinion of thoſe, who think, the Circulation of the Blood was known to him; in which he errs undoubtedly. 'Tis manifeſt his Anatomy was rude, dark, and of little extent; but 'tis alſo as manifeſt, that he knew very well the effect of the Circulation. As for Example, 2. *de Diæta. c.* 12. *All the Body* (ſays he) *is purged by Reſpiration and Tranſpiration, and what Humour thickens, is ſubtilized and thrown out by the Skin, and is called Sweat.*

Again, 3. *de Diæta. c.* 5. ſpeaking of a ſort of foul and impure Bodies, he ſays, *More is by Labour melted out of the Fleſh, than the Circular Motion (of the Blood) hath purged off.* There are a great number of

of Inftances of this Nature. In Converfation I put this to him, which he avowed
was all he thought.

He told me he had two more Volumes
ready for the Prefs, and did intend not
to give it over, till he had gone through
all the Works of *Hippocrates.* In which
Volumes will be thefe Treatifes: *Of
Dreams: Of the Regimen in Acute Difeafes:
The Prognofticks : The Prorrhetiques: The
Aphorifms: The Coaques.*

On that *Aphorifm* he feemed to me to
have a very happy thought, *coƌa non,
fed cruda purganda funt* ; which makes it
of the fame fenfe with that other, *Si quid
movendum eft, move in principio.*

I muft needs fay this for *Madam Dacier,*
his Wife , though I knew her , by her
Writings, before I faw her, the Learnedft
Woman in *Europe,* and the true Daughter
and Difciple of *Tanaquil Faber;* yet her
great Learning did not alter her genteel
Air in Converfation, or in the leaft appear in her Difcourfe ; which was eafie,
modeft, and nothing affeƌed.

I vifited Monfieur *Morin,* one of the M. *Morin.*
Academie des Sciences, a Man very curious
in Minerals ; of which he fhewed me
fome from *Siam,* as Jafpers, Onyxes, Agats,
Loadftones, *&c.* He fhewed me alfo excellent Tin Oar from *Alface.* Alfo from
France

France a great Block of a fort of Amethyft of two or 300 weight. Some parts of it (for he had feveral Plates fawed and polifht) were very fine, and had large Spots and Veins of a deep coloured Violet. It was defigned for a Pavement in *Marchetterie*, of which he fhewed me a *Carton* drawn in the Natural Colours.

This puts me in mind of a vaft Amethyft I had feen at *London*, brought from *New-Spain*, and expofed to Sale; it weighed, as I remember, Eleven Pound odd Ounces; and was moft perfectly figured both point and fides, after the manner of a *Briftol* Diamond, or common Rock Cryftal; but this Block here was rude, and without any fhape.

I cannot fay much of the meeting of thefe Gentlemen of the *Acad. Royal. de Sciences*, there are but few of them, about 12 or 16 Members; all Penfioned by the King in fome manner or other.

L' Academies des Sciences.

They endeavoured in the War time to have printed *Monthly Tranfactions* or Memoires after the manner of ours in *London*; but could not carry them on above two Volumes or Years, for without great Correfpondence this can hardly be done. And ours is certainly one of the beft Regifters that ever was thought on, to preferve a vaft number of fcattered Obfervations

in

in natural Hiftory, which otherwife would run the hazard to be loft, befides the Account of Learning in printed Books.

I heard Mr. *Oldenburgh* fay, who began this Noble Regifter, that he held Correfpondence with feventy odd Perfons in all Parts of the World , and thofe be fure with others : I ask'd him what Method he ufed to anfwer fo great variety of Subjects, and fuch a quantity of Letters as he muft receive weekly ; for I knew he never failed , becaufe I had the Honour of his Correfpondence for ten or Twelve Years. He told me he made one Letter anfwer another, and that to be always frefh, he never read a Letter before he had Pen, Ink and Paper ready to anfwer it forthwith; fo that the multitude of his Letters cloy'd him not, or ever lay upon his Hands.

The monthly Regifter, or Philofophic Tranfactions is one of the beft Copies which hath been printed in this Age; it is now fold for 13 *l. Sterling*, and not many remaining to be had of them neither.

The *Abbot Bignon* is Prefident, Nephew to Monfieur *Pontchartrain*. I was informed by fome of them, that they have this great advantage to incourage them in the purfuit of Natural Philofophy, that if any of the Members fhall give in a Bill of Charges

G ges

ges of any Experiments which he fhall have made ; or fhall defire the Impreffion of any Book, and bring in the Charges of Graving required for fuch Book, the Prefident allowing it and figning it, the Money is forthwith reimburfed by the King. As it was done in Dr. *Tournefort's Elements de Botanique,* the Cuts of that Book coft the King 12000 Livres. And the Cuts intended, and now graving for another Book of new Plants found in his Voyages into *Portugal* and *Spain,* will coft 100 *l. Sterling.*

Alfo, if Monfieur *Merrie,* for Example, fhall require live Tortoifes for the making good the Experiments about the Heart, they fhall be brought him, as many as he pleafes, at the King's Charge.

Thefe, befides their Penfions, I fay, were fome of the Advantages they have injoy'd ; but the War, for this Reafon, has lain heavy upon the Philofophers too.

Mr. *Butterfield.*

Mr. *Butterfield* is a right hearty honeft *Englifhman,* who has refided in *France* thirty five Years, is a very excellent Artift in making all forts of Mathematinal Inftruments, and works for the King and all the Princes of the Blood, and his Work is fought after by all the Nations of *Europe* and *Afia.*

He

He more than once shewed me (which is his great Diversion) a mighty Collection of Loadstones, to the value of several hundred Pounds *Sterling*.

Some he had as hard almost as Steel, and others soft and friable; yet of these he had those which were of as great Virtue as any of the hard : That of the equally hard there were very great difference.

He had one which weighed naked not above a Drachm, and would naked take up a Drachm and an half; but shod would take up 144 Drachms of Iron, if rightly applied, that is, if the Iron to be taken up did firmly and in a plain touch alike both the Feet.

The best shod were these that follow.

1. A *Slate Loadstone*, which I noted not so much for its strength, but because of its peculiar make, being fairly and distinctly laminous throughout, weighing one Ounce and an half, draws up one Pound.

2. A Smooth Loadstone, weighing one Drachm, two Scruples, fourteen Grains, draws up eighteen Ounces, that is eighty two times its weight.

3. Another Smooth Loadstone, weighing sixty five Grains, draws up Fourteen Ounces, that is, one hundred and forty four times its weight.

It

It is furprizing to fee a Loadftone no bigger than a Hazel-nut, take up a huge Bunch of Keys.

We have a very large *Slate Loadftone* in the Repofitory at *Grefham-Colledge*, at leaft fix Inches over : This alfo is but weak : Whether the *Laminæ* do fpoil the Virtue, as though they were but fo many diftinct Stones pack'd together. And yet a Loadftone which takes up, *ex. gr.* 6 pound weight, cut by the Axis in two halves, and both halves fhod again, will take up eight pound.

It is plain, that Experiments are better made with a *Terrella*, or fpherical Loadftone, than a fquare one ; and his way of capping the *Terrella* is very well contrived.

A fquare Loadftone made into a *Terrella*, will near take up as much weight as it did before, though a great deal of the Stone is loft in the rounding, by virtue of the different Shooing.

He entertained us full two Hours with Experiments neatly contrived about the Effects of the Loadftone.

The Experiment of approaching a Loadftone to the Spring of a Watch is very fine ; it caufes the Balance to move very fwift, and brought yet nearer, to ftop quite and ceafe moving.

Ano-

Another Experiment was an Inch-broad Plate of Iron, turned into a Ring of about four inches diameter, which had evidently two North and two South Poles, which he faid he had feen in a Loadftone, and had contrived this in imitation of Nature. The working of them with filings of Steel, drigged upon a Plate, fet upon the Ring, did clearly manifeft the double Polarity.

Alfo the fufpending of a Needle in the Air, and a Ball of Steel upon the point of it, by a Thread, which a weight kept down, that it could not afcend higher, than fuch a diftance within the fphere of the activity of the Loadftone.

Again, the free working of the Needle in Water, through Brafs, Gold, Stone, Wood, or any thing but Iron. He told us he had a Stone, which would work through a Stone Wall of eighteen Inches.

Laftly, he demonftrated by many Experiments, how the *Effluvia* of the Loadftone work in a Circle, that is, what flows from the North Pole, comes round, and enters the South Pole; on the contrary, what flows from the South Pole, enters the North, and in its way puts in order all fuch Filings of Steel it meets with; that is, according to the difpofition of its own whirling, and the circular

Lines

Lines it keeps in its flying about the Load-ftone. Indeed, it is pleafant to fee, how the Steel Filings are difpofed ; and in their arangement one clearly fees a perfect Image of the Road, which the whirling invifible Matter takes in coming forth, and re-entring the Poles of the Load-ftone.

He fhewed us a Loadftone fawed off that piece of the Iron Bar, which held the Stones together at the very top of the Steeple of *Chartres*. This was a thick Cruft of Ruft, part of which was turned into a ftrong Loadftone, and had all the properties of a Stone dug out of the Mine. Monf. *de la Hire* has printed a Memoir of it ; alfo Monf. *de Vallemont* a Treatife. The very outward Ruft had no Magnetic Virtue, but the inward had a ftrong one, as to take up a third part more than its weight unfhod. This Iron had the very Grain of a folid Magnet, and the brittlenefs of Stone.

Thefe Gentlemen who have writ of this, have, in my Opinion, mifs'd their purpofe, when they enquire, how it comes to pafs to be thus turned ; for it is certain, all Iron will in time go back into its Mineral Nature again, notwithftanding the Artifice of Melting and Hammering. I have feen of thofe hammered *Spanifh* Cannon,

non which had lain many years buried in
the Ground, under the old Fort at *Hull* in
Yorkſhire, which were thoroughly turned
into brittle Iron Stone, or Mine again; and
would not own the Loadſtone, no more
than the reſt of our *Engliſh* Iron Mine, till
it was calcined, and then ſhewed it ſelf
to be good Iron again. Alſo I have ſeen,
and had by me, a piece of Wood taken
out of *Lough-Neah* in *Ireland*, which was
not only good Iron Mine, but a Loadſtone too; ſo that it is evident, Nature, in
this ſort of Mine, goes backwards and forwards, is generated and regenerated; and
therefore Monſ. *de la Hire* has well uſed
the Term of Vegetation in this Affair,
which I had done many Years before him
in my Book *De Fontibus Medicatis Angliæ*,
that is, out of Iron, Mine will grow; and
out of Mine, a Loadſtone; as in the petrified Wood.

I do not relate theſe things, as though
they were new Diſcoveries; the World
has long ſince known them by the great
Induſtry of our moſt learned Countryman *Gilbert* of *Colcheſter*, to whom little
has been added after near a hundred Years,
though very many Men have written of
this Subject, and formed divers Hypo-
theſes to ſolve theſe Phænomena. A
Dutchman, Mr. *Hartſoeker*, one of the

Academy des Sciences, has publifh'd a Treatife of the Principles of Natural Philofophy, and has accounted for thefe and many more Experiments of this Nature, which he had fhewn him by Mr. *Butterfield*, whom he mentions very honourably.

And yet after all, the nature of thefe *Effluvia* are little known, and what is faid by *Des Cartes* of Screw-fafhioned Particles, and the invifible Channels and Pores and Pipes of the Loadftone, are all meer Fancies without any Foundation in Nature. It is well called by fome a certain Magnetic Matter, but what Properties it hath, is little underftood.

It is very ftrange to me, that a little Loadftone, of that prodigious force, fhould have fo fhort a Sphere of Activity, and not fenfibly to affect Iron above an Inch or two; and the biggeft and ftrongeft not above a Foot or two. We fee the Vortices in Water, how wide they work round about them, vaftly increafing the Circles; and what little refiftance the Air can make to a Body of that fubtilty, as the *Effluvia* of the Loadftone, which can with eafe penetrate all Bodies whatfoever, Marle, Flints, Glafs, Copper, Gold, without any fenfible diminution of its Virtue. Again, we fee
the

the Flame of a Lamp in Oil, or Tallow, or Wax, how fhort it is ; and how long and tapering it is in Spirit of Wine. If therefore the Magnetick Matter was darted out of infinite fmall Pipes, and was of the nature of a more fubtile and invifible Flame, why does it not continue its courfe in a direct Line to a great length, but return fo fuddenly ? We fee the perfpiration of our Skins to rife into the Air, and continue to mount, which yet has but a weak impulfe from the Heart, being interrupted and broke off, when it comes out of the Road of the Blood into the *Ductus Excretorii.* But the Circle of the Magnetick Matter is without any impulfe, that we know of, from the Stone ; and moves in a double Circle, and with a double and contrary Stream in the fame Pipes, contrary to the Laws of the Circulation of the Blood in Animals ; which has naturally but one Current, and one Road round ; for the whole Mafs of Veffels, in which the Circulation of the Blood is concerned, is but one continued Pipe.

Until the Nature of the *Effluvia* is better known, no very fatisfactory Account can be given of the moft common Phœnomena of the Loadftone, *ex. gr.* why it does not draw to it all Bodies alike ?
why

why a great Loadſtone, though weak, extends its Virtue much farther than a ſmall one, though ſtrong ? Why a Load-ſtone communicates its Virtue to Iron as ſoon as it touches it, nay even at ſome di-ſtance, and gives it the Properties of a Loadſtone.

The Truth is, the Earth's being a great Magnet ſeems to me a meer Viſion and Fable ; for this reaſon, becauſe it is not Iron. 'Tis true, Iron Mine is the moſt common of all Minerals, and found al-moſt in all places ; but it holds not any proportion with the reſt of the Foſſils of the Earth ; and is not, at a gueſs, as a Million to other Foſſils. This ſeems evi-dent to any one, who has well conſide-red the chalky Mountains and Cliffs, the high Rag-ſtone Mountains and Lime-ſtone Cliffs, the ſeveral Quarries and Pits ſunk in-to the Bowels of the Earth for Coal and Lead, *&c.* how little Iron there is to be found in compariſon of other Matters. Add to this, that very little of that very Iron Mine, which is to be found any where, is Magnetick, or capable of Obedience to the Magnet, till it is calcined. Whence therefore ſhould all thoſe Magnetick *Efflu-via* ariſe, which are ſuppoſed every where plentifully to incompaſs the Earth ? And why ſhould they be ſuppoſed to be every where

where wandring in the Air, fince 'tis evident, they make hafte to return to the Stone, that emitted them, and are as afraid to leave it, as the Child the Mother, before it can go ?

Towards the difcovery of the Nature of the *Effluvia* of the Loadftone, fuch Particulars as thefe, in my Opinion, ought chiefly to be confidered, and profecuted with all Induftry. The Loadftone is very good, if not the beft Iron Mine. The fole Fufion of the Loadftone turns it into Iron. The Fire deftroys its very Virtue, and fo does Vitrification Iron. Fire will make Iron Mine own the Loadftone, and turn to a Magnet. Ruft, (into which all Iron will naturally turn) and the reduction of Iron again to its Mine, will take away all the Magnetick Capacity of Iron. A Loadftone cannot be made to alter its Poles, but Iron may ; nor be deftroyed, but by the Fire. A great and long Bar of Iron is naturally a Loadftone, if held up perpendicularly, and it changes its Poles at the pleafure of him that holds it : A ftrong Loadftone lofes much of its Virtue by touching Iron, but after a few Days recovers it again. A fmall and weak Loadftone cannot touch to give its Virtue to a great lump of Iron. A Loadftone expofed

posed to the Air is spoilt in time. The
deeper the Vein of Iron Mine is, where
Loadstone is found, the better the Stone,
and how far this holds true, is to be considered: For I do not doubt, but a very
hard Stone may be found near the Day, as
well as deeper. A Ruler or long Plate of
Steel is much better touched with the Virtue of the Loadstone, than a Plate of meer
Iron of the same Figure; but on the contrary a Plate of Iron sticks much faster to
the Loadstone than a Plate of Steel; so
as if a Loadstone draws up a Plate of Steel
of three Ounces, it will draw up a Plate of
Iron of four Ounces and more. Why Iron
fastned to the Poles of a Magnet does so
vastly improve its strength, as to be 150
times stronger than when naked.

Since therefore a Loadstone is nothing
else but good Iron Mine, and may be turned
into Iron; and Iron most easily and of
it self into Loadstone, the way to find
out the Nature of those *Magnetick Effluvia,*
seems to be to enquire strictly into the Nature of Iron Mine, and Iron it self; and not
to run giddily into Hypotheses, before we
are well stocked with the natural History of
the Loadstone, and a larger quantity of
Experiments and Observations relating to
Iron and its Mine, with all the Differences
and Species of them; which I think has hitherto

therto been little heeded : For Nature will be its own Interpreter, in this, as well as in all other Matters of natural Philofophy.

Mr. *Butterfield* in another Converfation told me, he had obferved Loadftones, which were ftrong without arming ; and being armed, had not that great advantage by it, as one could have expected : And that on the contrary, there were others, which had a more incredible Virtue when armed, than they did promife.

That it feldom happens, that a Loadftone hath as much Virtue in one of its Poles, as in the other ; and that a bit of Iron is touch'd equally well at either of the Poles of one and the fame Loadftone.

That there are Loadftones which take up much, and which notwithftanding are incapable of well touching Iron : fo that a Stone armed, which takes up feven Pound, yet cannot communicate to a Ruler of Iron the Virtue of taking up a very fmall Needle.

That a Loadftone of ten Ounces, being reduced to the weight of fix Ounces, or thereabouts, did almoft the fame Effect as before, &c.

I

I caufed Mr. *Butterfield* to make the *Slate Loadftone* into a *Terrella*, and when fhod it was indeed but of little force ; but I obferved its Poles to lie level with the *Laminæ*, of which it was was compofed.

N. B. A ftrong Loadftone ought to have large Irons, and a weak one but thin Irons ; fo that a Stone may be over-fhod.

I waited upon the Abbot *Droine* to vifit Monfieur *Guanieres*, at his Lodgings in the *Hoftel de Guife.* This Gentleman is Courtefie it felf, and one of the moft Curious and Induftrious Perfons in *Paris.* His Memoirs, Manufcripts, Paintings, and Stamps are infinite, but the Method in which he difpofes them, is very particular and ufeful. He fhewed his *Portefuilles* in Folio, of Red Spanifh Leather finely adorned. In one, for Example, he had the general Maps of *England*; then the particular Maps of the Counties : then the Maps of *London*, and Views about it : Then the Stamps of all the particular Places and Buildings of Note about it ; and fo of all the Cities in *England*, and Places and Houfes of Note of the Counties.

In other Book-Cafes, he has the Stamps of the States-Men of *England*, Nobility of both Sexes, Soldiers, Lawyers, Divines, Phyficians, and Men of Diftinction.

And

M. Guanieres.

And in this Method he hath all *Europe* by themſelves.

His Rooms are filled with the Heads of a vaſt number of Men of Note in Oil Paintings, and Miniatures or Water-Colours. Amongſt the reſt, an Original of King *John*, who was Priſoner in *England*, which he greatly values.

He ſhewed us the Habits in Limning from the Originals, done by the beſt Maſters, of all the Kings and Queens and Princes of *France*, for many Ages backwards. Alſo the Turnaments and Juſtings at large ; and a thouſand ſuch things of Monuments.

He was ſo Curious, that he told me, he ſeldom went into the Country without an *Amanuenſis*, and a couple of Men well skilled in Deſigning and Painting.

He ſhewed us amongſt other curious Manuſcripts, a Capitularie of *Charles* V. alſo the Goſpel of St. *Matthew* writ in Golden Letters upon Purple Vellum. This ſeemed to me to be later than that Manuſcript I ſaw at the Abby of *St. Germans*; that is, the Letters leſs and more crooked, tho' indeed, the Letters of the Title Page are exactly ſquare.

One Toy I took notice of, which was a Collection of Playing Cards for 300 Years. The oldeſt were three times bigger, than

than what are now ufed, extreamly well limned and illuminated with gilt Borders, and the Paftboard thick and firm; but there was not a compleat Set of them.

Amongft the Perfons of Diftinction Madame *de Scudery.* and Fame, I was defirous to fee *Madamoifelle de Scuderie*, now 91 years of Age. Her Mind is yet vigorous, tho' her Body is in Ruins. I confefs, this Vifit was a perfect Mortification, to fee the fad Decays of Nature in a Woman once fo famous. To hear her Talk, with her Lips hanging about a Toothlefs Mouth, and not to be able to Command her Words from flying abroad at Random, puts me in mind of the *Sibyl's* uttering Oracles. Old Women were employed on this Errand, and the Infant-World thought nothing fo Wife, as Decayed Nature, or Nature quite out of Order; and preferred Dreams before reafonable and waking Thoughts.

She fhewed me the Skeletons of two *Chameleons*, which fhe had kept near four years alive. In Winter fhe lodged them in Cotton; and in the fierceft Weather fhe put them under a Ball of Copper, full of hot Water.

In her Clofet fhe fhewed me an Original of *Madame Maintenon*, her old Friend and Acquaintance, which fhe affirmed was

very

very like her: and, indeed, fhe was then very beautiful.

The Marquis *d' Hopital*, one of the *Aca-* Marquis *d' Hopital.* *demie des Sciences*, whom I found not at home, returned my Vifit very obligingly. I had a long Converfation with him about Philofophy and Learning; and I perceived the Wars had made them altogether Strangers to what had been doing in *England.* Nothing was more pleafing to him, than to hear Mr. *Ifaac Newton's* Preferment, and that there were hopes, that they might expect fomething more from him : he expreffed a great defire to have the whole Sett of the *Philofophic Tranfactions* brought over, and many other Books, which he named, but had not yet feen. He told me, it was not poffible for them to continue the Monthly Memoirs, as they had done for two years only, becaufe they were but very few in number of that Society, and had very little Correfpondence. Indeed, I did inquire once of fome of that Body, why they did not take in more, fince there were very many deferving Men in the City, as I inftanc'd in *F. Plumier.* They owned he would be an Honour to the Body; but they avoided to make a Prefedent for the Admiffion of any Regulars whatfoever.

H   I

I repaid the Marquis his Vifit: He lives in a fine Houfe, well furnifht: the Garden pretty, with neat Trelliage, wrought with Arches and other Ornaments.

He expreffed a great Defire to fee *England*, and Converfe with our Mathematicians, whofe Works he coveted above all things, and had ordered all to be brought him over.

His Lady alfo is very well Studied in the Mathematicks, and makes one of the Learned Ladies in *Paris*; of which number are Mad. *Dacier*, the Dutchefs of *Main*, Mad. *Scuderie*, Mad. *de Vicubourg*, Mad. *d' Efpernon* the Daughter, Mad. *Pref. de Ferrand*, and others, whofe Names I have forgot.

Pezron. I bought the Works of *Pere Pezaron*, a *Bernardin*, now *Abbot de Charmoyfe* near *Rheims*. This is a very Learned and very difinterefted Author, and by his free way of Writing has got him Enemies amongft the Regular Clergy. The Books I bought were his *Antiquities, or Account of Time*; *The Defence of it againft Two Monks*; *An Effay or Commentary upon the Prophets*; *The Hiftory of the Gofpel*.

He is now upon giving us the *Origin of Nations*, where he will fhew, that *Greek* and *Latin* too came from the *Celtique* or *Bas-breton*; of which Country he is. He told

told me he had 800 *Greek* Words perfect
Celtique. I fettled a Correfpondence betwixt him and Mr. *Ed. Floid* ; which he
moft readily granted, and which he faid
he had long coveted.

Monfieur *Spanheim*, now Envoy Extra- Monfieur
ordinary from the Duke of *Brandenbourgh Spanheim.*
at *Paris*, told me, that the King of *France's*
Colleƈtion of Medals is far the beft in
Europe, or that ever was made. Having
the opportunity of Difcourfing him often,
his fick Lady being my Patient, I inquired more particularly of him , what he
had feen of *Palmyra*, of *Zenobia, Oedenatus, Vabalathus.* He defired a Memoir of
me, which I gave him, of what I would
have him fearch for in the King's Cabinet,
and promifed me all the Satisfaƈtion he
could give me in that Affair.

I told him I had met with nothing yet,
but a fair Bufto in White Marble of *Zenobia*, in the Cabinet of M. *Baudelot ;* which
was part of Monf. *Thevenot's* Colleƈtion of
Marbles from the *Eaft.*

I was to wait on Monf. *Vaillant* at his Monfieur
Appartment in the Arfenal. I found only *Vaillant.*
his Son at home, who very civilly Entertained me ; and fhewed me a Book in
Quarto of his Father's of *Greek* Medals,
near Printed off ; but without Cutts.

The Title was *Nummi Græci Imperatorum*; he goes down no lower than to *Claudius Gothicus*. He hath added a large *Appendix*, with References to all the moſt Remarkable Heads about the Cities and the People.

I left a Memoir with his Son; and in a ſecond Viſit, I found the old Gentleman at home, very buſie in his Flower Garden; of which I ſhall ſpeak hereafter.

He told me, as to the Memoir I had left, he had never ſeen any Coins of *Oedenatus*; yet he had very lately parted with one of *Zenobia* to the Duke of *Maine*. As for *Vabalathus*, he had ſeen ſome of him in Braſs; and one he had in Silver, which he very obligingly made me a Preſent of; and that this was the only Silver Coin he had ever met with of him.

This is his Reading of it.

VABALATHUS. V. G.R. IMP. R.

Vices gerens Imperii Romani.

Les autres y liſent mal. YCRIMOR.

He gave me alſo the Stamps of the Heads of *Zenobia* and *Vabalathus*, done from the King's Medals. *See Tab.* 2. Theſe were deſigned for a ſhort Hiſtory of all

the

the Emperors and Empreſſes, which he has
by him written in *French*, but not publiſht. Nothing could be more Civil and
Franc than this Gentleman, whom I believe to be the beſt Medaliſt in *Europe :*
He told me he had made 12 Voyages all
over *Europe* and *Aſia Minor* on purpoſe :
That he had ſeen and deſcribed the Contents of more Cabinets, than any Man
ever did before him ; and it is evident by
his Works, that he has made good uſe of
them.

I had a Viſit from Mr. *Cunningham*,
Tutor to my Lord *Lorne*, a very Learned
and Curious Man in Books. I askt him
(knowing him to have been lately at *Rome*)
very particularly about the Papers of Monſieur *d' Azout*. He told me, that he ſaw
him not above half a year before he died,
and was very intimately acquainted with
him, and ſaw him for a Twelvemonth very
often. That he told him, that he had a-
bout 80 difficult Paſſages in *Vitruvius*,
which he had Commented and Explained ;
and the Correction of a great number of
Errata in the Text. Alſo that upon *Julius
Frontinus* (though that was a much leſs
Book) he had much more to ſay, than
he had upon *Vitruvius*. What is become
of his Papers I could not learn from him,
nor any in *Paris*.

H 3

Monſieur

Monfieur *d' Azout* was very Curious and Underftanding in Architecture; for which purpofe he was 17 years in *Italy* by times; I do remember, when he was in *England* about 14 years ago, he fhewed me the Defign of feveral of our Buildings drawn by himfelf; but of that of the *Banquetting-Houfe* at *Whitehall*, he expreffed himfelf in very extraordinary Terms, telling me, it was the moft Regular and moft Finifht Piece of Modern Workmanfhip he had feen on this fide the *Alpes*, that he could not enough praife it: That *Inigo Jones*, the Architect, had a true relifh of what was Noble in that Art.

It is time now to leave the Private Houfes, and to Vifit the *Publick Libraries*; and with them fuch Perfons, as are more particularly concerned in the Hiftory of Learning.

M. l' Abbe Drouine. Monfieur *l' Abbe Drouine* came to vifit me at my Lodgings. I returned the Vifit the next day at his Appartment in the College *de Boncourt*. He had four or five little Rooms well furnifht with Books; in the biggeft he had a Collection of Catalogues of Books, and of all fuch, who had writ the Accounts of Authors; above 3000 in all Languages. He told me, he had ftudied the Hiftory of Books with the utmoft utmoſt application 18 years, and had brought his *Memoirs* into a good Method; That he had thoughts of Printing the firſt Tome this year, which would be of the moſt ancient Authors, *Greek* and *Latin*; That he intended to continue them throughout all the ſucceeding Ages down to our Times; which he ſaid he had performed in good part.

He ſhewed me the Catalogue of Authors in four very thick *Folio's*; alphabetically diſpoſed by *Family Names*, under ſome ſuch Title as this: *Index alphabeticus omnium Scriptorum, cujuſcunque facultatis, temporis & linguæ.* Thoſe came to about 150000.

He alſo ſhewed me his Alphabetick Memoirs in Sheets of the Authors and Books they had writ, and in great forwardneſs. And laſtly, the Chronological Catalogue, in which form he intends to print the whole.

He is a very Civil and well Tempered Perſon, very Learned and Curious, and of a middle Age, fit to continue and finiſh ſuch a Laborious Work. I was infinitely obliged to him for his frequent Viſits.

I was to wait on Monſieur *Gurnier*, one of the Heirs of Monſieur *Thevenot*, to ſee the Remains of that Famous Man's Library.

Thevenot's Library.

H 4

ry. There are a great number of *Oriental* MSS. yet unfold.

He fhewed me the MS. of *Abulfeda*, with its *Latin* Verfion, done by Monfieur *Thevenot* ; and the *Matrices and Forms of Arabick Letters*, which he had, at his own Charge, caufed to be cut for the printing of certain proper Names in it.

He went or defigned to go into *England* and *Holland* to get it printed, but was called back by Monfieur *Louvois*'s Order, to print it in *France* at the King's Charge ; but the late Wars coming on, it was fet afide, and is like to be fo ; for he was turned out of his place of Library-Keeper to the King, and died in Difgrace.

Thofe great number of Oriental Books he had moft from his Nephew, whom he fent abroad for that purpofe, and who died in his Travels.

This Man was, as it were, the Founder of the *Academie des Sciences*, and was in his own Nature very Liberal, and gave Penfions to many Scholars.

Amongft other things I faw there a large Dictionary or Grammar of the *Algonquin Tongue*, one of the Nations of the *Weft-Indies*. The Fugitive Jefuit, who writ it, dwelt amongft them 20 years.

Here I alfo faw a Hiftory, with large and accurate Defcriptions of the *Quadru-peds*

peds of that part of the *Weſt-Indies* by the
ſame Author.

As for the Papers of *Swammerdam,* which
indeed were the things I moſt coveted to
ſee, they were much beneath my Expectation, not anſwering the Printed Catalogue
of *Thevenot, p.* 239. There were indeed
ſome Corrections of the Figures of his general Hiſtory of Inſects, and ſome Additions, as though he intended another Edition of that Book.

Alſo towards a particular Hiſtory, there
were ſome ſmall Treatiſes, or rather ſome
Figures only of the *Tadpole.* Again, Figures relating to the Natural Hiſtory of
a certain *Day Butterfly*; Of the *Aſilus*; Of
the *Scuttle Fiſh* ; Of the *Scarabæus Naſicor-
nis*; and ſome conſiderable number of
Snails, as well naked, as fluviatil, and Sea
diſſected; at leaſt figured with their Bodies exerted, and ſome of their Bowels ex-
tracted ; and which ſeemed to me to be
well underſtood and delineated. There
were two or three Sticht Books in *Dutch*
of four or five Sheets a-piece, belonging
to thoſe Plates or Figures. But the Gentleman would not part with any of them ;
becauſe, he ſaid, they had been ſecured by
the *Abbot Bignon,* for the King's uſe. However, all theſe I judge well worth Printing, when it ſhall pleaſe that *Society* to
do it.   Laſtly,

Laftly, I faw in his Cuftody a fair MS. of *Michael Servetus,* with a Treatife at the end of it, which, as he faid, was never publifht; being a Comparifon of the Jewifh and Chriftian Law, its Juftice and Charity.

King's Li-
brary. Monf. *l' Abbe de Brillac,* Almoner to the Prince of *Conti,* very oblingly offered to carry me to the *Kings Library;* but I civilly declined it, for I had been told, it was better to make Vifits by ones felf: for no Stranger but was very welcome at all times; not only on the days it was publickly open, as it is upon *Tuefdays* and *Fridays.*

Monfieur *Clement,* the Deputy Library-Keeper, made us welcome, and invited us to come again, and fpend a whole day with him. He made me in particular a very great Compliment, as a confiderable Benefactor to that place, fhewing me moft of the Books, and the Names of the reft, I had publifht in *Latin;* and fhewed a great fatisfaction, that he had got the *Synopfis Conchyliorum,* which he had caufed to be bound very elegantly. I told him, that I was very forry to fee it there, and wondered how he came by it; for it was, I affured him, but a very imperfect trial of the Plates, which I had difpofed of to fome few Friends only, till I fhould be

be able to clofe and finifh the Defign;
which I now had done to my power,
and would redeem that Book with a better Copy at my return into *England:*
The fame Promife I renewed to the *Abbe
Louvois,* the Library-Keeper, at his own
Inftance, when I had the Honour to Dine
with him. The Reader will pardon me
the Vanity, if I tell him, that this Book
was no inconfiderable Prefent, even for
fo great a Prince, as the King of *France*;
for that befides the time that it took me
up (Ten Years at leaft) at leafure hours,
to difpofe, methodife, and figure this part
of Natural Hiftory, it could not have been
performed by any Perfon elfe for lefs than
2000 *l. Sterling*; of which Sum yet a great
fhare it ftood me in, out of my Private
Purfe. This young Gentleman is Brother
to Monfieur *Barbefieux,* Intendant of the
Affairs of War; he takes great care to ap-
ply himfelf to his Studies, and for that
purpofe has two of the Sorbone conftantly with him to inftruct him. He lives
great, and has a Houfe, which joins upon the King's Library, of which he is
Keeper. We were Entertained by him
with all the Civility imaginable, and freedom of Converfation.

This

This Library is now placed in a Private House, and taken out of the *Louvre*, but it is intended to be removed to the *Place de Vendofme*, where one fide of that Magnificent Square is defigned for it. In the mean time it is here moft commodioufly difpofed into 22 Rooms; 14 above Stairs, and 8 below and above. Thofe below are Philofophy and Phyfick, and the Shelves are Wired, to fecure them. Above are the Books of Philofophy and Human Learning; and it is in thofe Rooms only the promifcuous Crowd are admitted twice a Week. In the middle Rooms, which makes the great Body of the Library, are, for Example, Catalogues of Books; Hiftories in one of *England* and *Holland*; in another the Hiftories of *France* and *Germany*; in another the Hiftories of *Italy*, *Spain*, *&c.* in another Bibles of all forts; and the Interpretations; in another *Greek* MSS. in another *Latin* MSS. in another the Civil and Municipal Laws of all Nations; in another the Original Papers of State; in another *Stamps*, where, by the by, the King had the Collection of Monf. *Marolles* to divert him, in one of his Sickneffes, bought in at a vaft Sum. The Catalogue alone of thefe Stamps, no bigger than two fmall Almanacks, coft me 14 Livres; fo much Strangers are impofed

poſed upon by the Crafty Bookſellers of
Rue St. Jaques; but 'tis not in *France* a-
lone, where People are made to pay for
their Humour.

They have two Indexes of this Library ;
one relating to the Matter and Contents
of Books ; and another Index of Authors,
wherein are all the Works they have of
them, and the Titles of all likewiſe that
they know of, that are wanting, with an
Aſteriſm to ſuch in the Margent ; which
is well done, that they may know what
they have to buy in. It is indeed a vaſt
Collection, and worthy ſo great a Prince.
This Library conſiſts at leaſt of 50000
Volumes of Printed Books ; and 15000
MSS. in all Languages.

They work daily and hard at the Catalogue, which they intend to Print ; I ſaw
10 thick Folio's of it, fairly tranſcrib'd
for the Preſs. It is diſpoſed according to
the Subject Matter of the Books, as the
Bibles and Expoſitors, Hiſtorians, Philo-
ſophers, *&c.* They purpoſe to put it into
the Preſs this year, and to finiſh it within
a Twelvemonth.

In the King's Library I was ſhewn an
Ancient *Greek* MS. of *Dioſcorides*, writ in
a ſort of thin or narrow Capitals, with
the Plants painted in Water-colours ; but
the firſt Book was wholly wanting, and
there-

therefore the *Animals* not there, which yet was what I moft defired to fee; for there are fome things relating to them, which we are at this day in great doubt of; and it would have been fome fatisfaction to have feen by the Pictures, what the middle Ages, at leaft, had thought of them.

In the fame Room alfo we were fhewn the Epiftles; which was one part of the fame MS. which we have at *Cambridge*, which is the Gofpels only. *Beza* was poffeffed of ours, from whom we had it. It is written in *fquare Capitals*, and very fhort Lines, and much worn out in many places. This comes much fhort of the *Alexandrian* MS. at *St. James's* for Beauty and Antiquity.

There was another MS. *of the Gofpel of St. Matthew*, which was but of late difcovered; a very fair Volume in a large Folio. This was cut to pieces in the back, and had been fhuffled and bound up again; and another Book overwritten in a fmall Modern *Greek* Hand, about 150 years ago. The firft Writing was turned fo pale, that they took no pains to rub it out. One of the Library-keepers obferving this, hath reduced it again by paging it a-new; and with a little heeding 'tis yet very legible. The Letter is as

fair

fair a fquare Capital as any I have feen.
There are fome Interpolations very noto-
rious, as about the Defcent of the fick
Man into the Pool of *Bethefda*, which I
fuppofe will be accounted for by the Induftrious and Learned Collator.

I obferved the *China* Manufcripts which
Father *Beauvais* brought this year as a
Prefent to the King.   They are about 44
Packs of fmall Books, of a long Quarto
fafhion, put up in loofe Covers of a Pur-
ple Sattin glued on Paftboard; of Natural
Hiftory, of Dictionaries relating to the
Expofition of their Characters, &c.

The King hath a Sett much of the fame
before in White Sattin, with their Titles.

Here alfo I fee the third Decad of *Livy*,
a large Quarto in Vellum, without Diftinction of Words in fair large Capitals.
It is fuppofed by Monfieur *Baluze* to be
1100 years old.

Yet the Manufcript of *Prudentius Hym-
nes*, which was alfo fhewed us, is a much
fairer Letter, and therefore thought to
be older by one Century at leaft.

Here alfo I faw a famous *Latin Roll* or
Volume, written on Ægyptian Paper, In-
tituled, *Charta Plenariæ Securitatis*, taken
the 38th. year of *Juftinian*; it is fairly
Ingraved and Interpreted Letter by Letter
upon Copper by Monfieur *Thevenot*. I
faw

faw the Print thereof : It is writ long-
ways the Roll and not crofs; in three
Columns : The Column in the middle is
three times as long as the two end Columns. The Roll is not above a foot broad.

They fhewed us alfo in this Houfe,
the Apartment of Monfieur *Huygens,* which
was very Noble, and well for Air, upon
the Garden : But here he fell Melancholy,
and died of it in *Holland.* He fhewed the
firft Token of it by playing with a Tame
Sparrow, and neglecting his Mathematick
Schemes. 'Tis certain, Life and Health
of Body and Mind are not to be preferved,
but by the Relaxation and unbending the
Mind by Innocent Diverfions. For Sleep
is nothing elfe that I know of, but the
giving up the Reins, and leting Nature to
act alone, and to put her in full poffeffion
of the Body. We have a convincing Inftance of this, in being a-Bed awake. No
Man (if never fo little indifpofed) can
lie ftill fcarce three Minutes without turning; and if it come not prefently upon
us, we muft turn again and again; and
at length we become fo intolerably weary,
that our Bed is a very wrack to us.
Whereas, if we chance to fall afleep,
though we lie in one and the fame pofture feven hours, we fhall wake frefh
and without pain, as tho' the Body did not
weigh

weigh at all upon it felf in Sleep. 'Tis certain, the Nerves and Mufcles are in little or no Tenfion in Sleep; but when we are awake, are always ftretched and com-preffed, whence wearinefs : which, if up-on our Feet, or fitting, we are not fenfible of, becaufe we remove quick and with eafe, and of courfe; but laid, we foon find our felves very uneafie, till we change the Pofture.

But this is not all in the King's Library : There are other things to be feen, *viz.* a confiderable number of ancient Roman and Egyptian Antiquities; as, *Lamps*, *Pateras*, and other Veffels belonging to the Sacrifices : A *Siftrum* or Egyptian Rattle with three loofe and running Wires crofs it.

Amongft the great variety of *Egyptian Idols*, there was one betwivt two and three Foot long of Black Touchftone, with Hie-roglyphicks ingraven down before. I took particular notice of the Grain of this Stone; and at my return, having had the Honour of a Paper from Mr. *Molyneux* from *Dublin*, giving an account of thefe vaft and ftupendious *Natural Pillars* to be feen in *Ireland*, fome of them of fifty Foot high, and thick in proportion, and that the Stones or Joints, which conftitute thefe Pillars, are of the *Lapis Lydius*, or *Ba-*

I   *faltes*

faltes Kind, having feen one of the Joints
at *Grefham-Colledge* , I eafily agree with
him ; but much admire, that the *Peble
Kind* fhould produce fuch regular Figures ; which is certainly the very hardeft
Stone to be found in *Europe*, and which no
Tool of ours will cut.

This alfo is another Inftance (the carved Obelisks being one) of the different
make and goodnefs of the *Egyptian* Chif-
fels ; of which, and of the retrieving the
ancient Temper of Steel, I have publifh'd
a Difcourfe in the *Ph. Tranfactions* fome
years ago.

I fhould have had more fatisfaction in
this Kind, had I met with what I ear-
neftly fought for , the *Egyptian* Tombs,
which were a long time in the Garden of
Monfieur *Valentine* at *Paris* ; but were un-
luckily fent away to his Houfe at *Tours*,
not long before our coming to *Paris*.
One of thefe Tombs is faid to be of Black
Touchftone, to have been brought out of
the higher *Egypt*, and to be full of *Hiero-
glyphicks*. Of this in particular *Kircher* has
written.

There is in this Collection a large Piece
of *Tin Oar* from *England*, very curious ;
it has on one fide of it a great number of
fair and large Opaque Cryftals of Tin, fhining like polifh'd Steel. The *Plaines* of thofe
Cry-

Cryftals I could not eafily reckon; but fure I am, having with care examined all the Stone Cryftals I could meet with, both precious and more common, and alfo the Cryftals of all Foffil Salts, I never before obferved that Figure in any of them, but believe them of a peculiar Nature, proper to Tin Oar. I call them Cryftals, tho' Opaque, becaufe angular and of one conftant Figure.

I was at the College of *Clermont* with *Pere* P. *Har-Hardouin*: he fhewed me the Library with *douin*. great Civility; it confifts of two long Galleries; The Galleries are well furnifht with Books, having Lights only on one fide, and the Windows are not over large; with Tables under each Light, very commodioufly placed for Writing and Reading. Alfo cretain Clofets for Manufcripts, and others for forbidden Books. In this he fhewed me a great Collection of *Janfenius's* Original Letters. In the other a *Greek* Manufcript of the Prophets, of *Eufebius's* own Hand-Writing; it was in Capitals, but of a different Character from any I had feen: The Letters very erect, but fomething thinner, and not fo fquare.

Alfo a vulgar *Latin* in Capitals, very ancient.

I told him I was well pleafed with his *Pliny in ufum Delphini*; and that it was to

I 2   the

the Honour of the *French* Nation to have laboured more particularly upon that Author ; *Dalechampius* firſt, then *Salmaſius's Exercitationes Plinianæ* ; and laſtly, this his moſt elegant Edition.

The Books are well diſpoſed under gilt Titles, as, *Medici in Folio,* and over-againſt them, where the Windows will permit, the *Medici in Quarto :* In the other Gallery runs a Baluſtrade, within which are plac'd the *Octavo's* and *Twelves.*

At one end of the upper Gallery is a very large Tableau, an Original of *Nicolo,* of the Maſſacre of *Agamemnon ;* in it there is this commendable, That in ſuch a horrid Fury and ſuch variety of Murders in half-naked Figures, no one indecent Poſture is to be ſeen.

Pere Hardouin ſeemed to doubt of the *Inſcription of Palmyra* put out by M. *Spon ;* That the *Greek* was faulty, and the *Syriac* very queſtionable. I told him we had had it lately copied, carefully and truly by one at *Rome ;* which took away his Objection of the multiplicity of Letters.

Both he and *Vallant* agreed, that they had never ſeen any Medal of *Oedenatus.* He very obligingly anſwered my Memoir about *Palmyra, Zenobia,* and *Vabalathus,* with a tranſcript of all the Coins he had ſeen, and had in his poſſeſſion : which follows.

Num-

Nummi Zenobiæ.

CEΠTIMIA ZHNOBIA CEB. ℞. *Spes. eſt apud Seguinum,* p. 62.

Oedenati nullum vidi, niſi apud Occonem, nullum Palmyrenum.

Vabalathi apud Com. Foucault,*rei ærariæ ac judiciariæ Præfeftum in Neuſtria inferiore.*

A.K. Λ. ΔOM.ΑΥPHΛIANOC. CEB.*capite laureato. Sub ipſum Aureliani mentum litera* L.*abſque anni numero.*

℞. ΑΥΤ. EPMIAC OΥABΑΛΑ⊙OC A⊙HNOΥ. *capite radiato.*

AVT. K. Λ. Δ. ΑΥPHΛIANOC CEB. *capite laureato.* L. A.

℞. AVT. EPMIAC. OΥABΑΛΑ⊙OC. A⊙H. *capiie diademate.* L. Δ.

AVT.K. Λ. Δ. ΑΥPHΛIANOC CEB. *capite laureato.* L. B.

℞. AVΓ.EPMIAC. OΥABΑΛΑ⊙OC. A⊙H. NOΥ *capite diademate.* L. E.

IMP. C. AVRELIANVS AVG. *capite radiato.*

℞. VABALATHVS VCRIMPR. *alii male* VCRIMOR. *ſic olim interpretatus ſum.* Vice Cæſaris, *reftor imperii Romani.*

IMP. C. VHABALATHVS AVG. *capite rediato.*

℞. VICTORIA AVG. *viftoria geſtat palmam & coronam.*

The

The Library of the *Grand Jesuits*, near
the Gate *St. Antoine*, is a very fair Gallery of great length and breadth, and well
furnish'd with Books, on the very top of
the House. They find, that Books keep
much drier and sweeter there, than in lower Rooms, besides the advantage of a clear
Sky-light.

P. Daniel is Library-Keeper , and was
very civil to me ; he shewed me a Letter,
which he had just then received from
Monsieur *Huetius*, the learned Bishop of
d' Auranches near *Mont St. Michael's* in *Nor-*
mandy ; wherein he told him, that having lately received the Catalogues of
Books printed in *Holland* and *England*,
during the War , he found that Learning was much alike at a kind of stand in
Holland and *France* ; but, that it had yet
Life and Vigour in *England*, which he re-
joiced at.

And, indeed, I had had the same
thought from more of the French before.
Even the Jesuits themselves will be little
considered, if Learning fall into neglect
and disgrace. Oratory ceased with the
Commonwealth of *Rome* ; and so will all
sorts of Learning without Emulation and
Rewards.

He

He shewed me *P. de la Chaise's* Cabinet of Medals.

Also a *Vestal* of Copper found at *Dee*, in the Country of *le Forest*.

Also a very intire *Loaf* or *Roman* ten Pound weight of Red Copper, on which was inscribed *Deæ. Sec P. X.*

Also a square Stone Urn, or small Tomb, well carved and inscribed.

D. M.

S V L P I C I O.

N O T O.　A D E S T E

S V P E R I.

I saw the Quire of the Abbey of *St. Germains,* and the Altar near the lower end of it; in which Position also I remember to have seen an Altar in the Quire of *St. John's* Church at *Lions*; both plain Tables. Monsf. *l'Abbe de Villiers,* who has an Apartment in the Convent, a learned Man, went with me, and to the Library also; which is two large Galleries well furnish'd; at the end of one of them is a large Closet of Manuscripts; also another *Armoir* in

L' Abbaie de St. Germains.

I 4　　　　the

the great Library, where the moſt ancient
Manuſcripts are kept, yet with more care.
In this I ſaw the *Pſalter*, as it is believed,
of *St. Germain*, who lived in the ſixth Century ; it is certainly very ancient ; being a
large Quarto of fine Purple Vellum, and
on it are writ the *Pſalms* in large Capital
Letters, with Comma's or Points.   The
Letters ſeem to have been of Silver ; and
the great initial Capitals of Gold.

They ſhewed alſo a *Pſalter* in the ſhort
Notes of *Tyro*, *Tullius's Libertus* ; with a
Diſcourſe concerning the uſe of ſuch Short-
Hand in the beginning of the Manuſcript ;
it was writ very fair on Vellum, with Red
Ink, as I remember.

The Codicils or waxen Table-Books of
the Ancients, which were thin Cedar
Boards about fourteen Inches long, and five
broad, ſix or eight of them glued together
by Shreds of Parchment : The Rims were
a little raiſed, with a flat and broad Border, the better to preſerve the black Wax,
which was ſpread over them.   I ſaw
more of theſe afterwards in the King's
Library ; and by the Letter it is manifeſt,
they were in uſe much later, than I could
have imagined.   This here was in *Latin*,
and I could read here and there a Word,
for the Ground was much torn up, as *Pro
duobus Falconibus, &c.*   The Style, or Steel
Pen

Pen had cut through in many places : fo that with a good Eye-glafs I could fee the Board bare. I take this Paft to be nothing elfe but what the *Etchers* in Copper ufe at this Day to cover their Plates with, to defend from the *Aqua fortis* ; which is a Compofition of Bitumen and Bees Wax.

Here alfo I faw a Manufcript of three or four Leaves written upon true *Egyptian* Paper, in which with an Eye-glafs 'twas eafie to difcern, how the Flags were difpofed, length-ways and a-crofs, one over another. The Letters which remained, which were but few, were large and fair fquare Capitals. This Fragment I take to be the moft ancient Writing they have.

I vifited in this Convent, at his Chamber, *Pere Mabillon*, who has fo well deferved of the Commonwealth of Learning by his Writings, and particularly that Excellent Book *De re Diplomatica* ; he feemed to me to be a very good natured and Free hearted Man ; and was very well pleafed to hear, that our Catalogue of *Englifh* Manufcripts was fo forward in the Prefs at *Oxford*. He thankfully owned the favour of the *Cotton* Library ; and was very forry to hear of Dr. *Bernard's* Death, of whom he

P. Mabillon.

fpoke

fpoke very kindly; but he expreffed a wonderful Efteem for Dr. *Gale,* the Dean of *York.*

In another Converfation I had with *P. Mabillon,* (for he was my Neighbour, and I was often with him) telling him the Account we had brought us of *Palmyra,* and the Tracts that were written of it, and that more was intended to be publifh'd about it: he was much concerned, that thofe Accounts, which were pure Matters of Learning in general, were written in *Englifh;* and he told me, he was afraid it might be with us, as it was with them, fince they cultivated their own Language fo much, they began to neglect the ancient Tongues, the *Greek* and *Latin.*

He fhewed me certain Figures not ill ta-ken with Red Chalk, of fome very ancient Monuments obferved by fome of the Fa-thers of their Order; one of which was prefent in the Chamber, upon the Moun-tain of *Framond* near *Salme,* which lies in the middle of that Tract of the Mountain, called *La Vauge,* betwixt *Alface* and *Lorrain.* There were great Remains of an ancient City. Thefe Figures, which the Fathers fhewed me, were about twelve in all; but five or fix of them were of *Mercury;* a Cock at his Foot; a *Chlamys* knotted upon the Right Shoulder, hanging at his Back; his

his Hair laid in Curles about his Face, and
tied with a Ribban, whofe two ends might
be feen on the top of his Head, like Horns;
a *Caduceus* in his Hand, which was very
differently reprefented in all the Figures of
him; fometimes held up, other times the
Point refting at his Feet; fometimes the
Snakes were twifted about a Stick; and
again in others without one, or the De-
figner had taken no notice of it; fometimes
the Tail of the Serpent fpread and flying
about; and again in others clofe twifted
with many Braids; a Girdle came round
the bottom of his Belly, and which had
in the middle of it two Rings, one faftned
to the other, and hanging betwixt his
Legs. Thefe many Statues of *Mercury* in
a *French* Country are a Confirmation of
what *Cæfar* fays of the Religion of the
Gauls, in his fixth Book, *Deum maxime
Mercurium colunt : hujus funt plurima fimu-
lacra, &c.*

There were fome few *Roman* Letters on
fome of them, which were fo imperfect,
that I could make nothing of them.

The *Library of St. Genevieue* is a very
large and fair Gallery, upon the very top
of the Houfe, well ftored with Books on
both fides up to the top, and kept in Cafes
wired with Brafs; which is a good fecu-
rity,

rity, and hinders not the Books from being feen.

Alſo it is adorned with fair *Buſto's* of the ancient Men of Learning.

The *Muſeum* is a little Cloſet on the ſide of this Gallery; of which there is a Book lately publiſh'd; I ſaw in it very little of Natural Hiſtory, that was remarkable. They keep half a dozen Joints of a large *Cornu Ammonis*, which they ſhew as a Rarity. But it is well ſtored with ancient *Idols* and Sacrificing *Veſſels, Lacrymatoirs*, *Pateras, Strigils*; alſo ancient *Weights and Meaſures; Coins*, and particularly the *As*, and its firſt and latter Diviſions.

There we ſaw an ancient *As*, with *Etruſcan Letters* of a kind of Red Copper; The Letters ſeem to be a-kin to the old *Greek* Characters. Theſe are the Capital Letters about the Coin going round, and bringing every Letter before you. *See Table* 1. *Fig.* 2.

As quaſi Æs: This is very reaſonable; for before the *Greeks* had invented double Letters, the *Romans* were ſkilled in their Writing. So *Vitruvius* * tells us *Ærugo* was in the *Hetruſcan* Tongue called *Eruca*. Whence undoubtedly by Tranſlation the common Caterpillar had its Name, from its *blueneſs;* which alſo is an evidence, that the *Tuſcan* Writing was in the old *Greek* Character.

* *De archi-tect.* l. 7. c. 2. Ed. *Barbari.*

But

But nothing pleafed me more than to have feen the Remains of the Cabinet of the *Noble Piere/c.* the greateft and heartieft *Mecœnas*, to his power, of learned Men of any of this Age.

Amongft the firft and very old Brafs *Roman* Coins there was a *Sextans* with a *Caduceus of Mercury* on one fide, and a *Scallop Shell* on the other; probably, becaufe they might have at firft had the ufe of *Shell Money*, as fome parts of both the *Indies* and *Africa* have at this day, till *Mercury*, whofe Emblem that Staff is, taught them the ufe of Metallic Money.

Alfo in this Cabinet are wet Meafures, as the ancient *Congius*, of which they have an old one, and an exact Copy of that of the *Capitol*; alfo a *Sextarius*, and a *Quartarius*. Now the *Congius* containing 120 Ounces; the *Sextarius* twenty Ounces; the *Hemina* ten Ounces; the *Quartarius* five Ounces. I doubt not, but the *Cyathus*, by reafon of the aforefaid Divifion, held two Ounces and an half; which is the Meafure fo frequently to be met with in old Phyfick Authors, and of fo great concern in *Dofes*.

In that *Hetrufcan As* before-mentioned, one Cap coifs or covers the double Head of *Janus*. I faw an ancient Statue of *Mercury* in the Garden belonging to the King's Library

in

in *Paris,* where *Mercury* has upon his Head
a long Cap doubled, or laid double upon
his Head, as though there were some affini-
ty betwixt those two Inventors of Trade,
Arts and Learning.

Here also we saw the *Steel Dyes of the
Paduan Brothers,* by which they stamp'd
and falsified the best ancient Medals so well,
that they are not to be distinguish'd but by
putting them into those Molds; which
makes them very valuable, there being
100 and more of them, and are prized at
10000 Crowns. They stampt upon old
Medals, whereby the Cheat was the greater; for by this means they were of the ancient Metal, had the green Coat, and the
same ragged Edges.

I saw a Picture here of about six Inches
over, finely painted in *Mosaic,* the very
little Squares were scarce visible to the naked Eye, but the whole appeared like the
finest Hatchings in *Stamps;* yet by the application of a good Eye-glass, I could readily distinguish the Squares of all Colours,
as in other *Mosaiques.* This sort of Painting had a very admirable effect, besides
the duration.

Here was also the *Leg of a Mummi* well
preserv'd, the Toes only bare, black and
shining as Pitch: The Bandage was very curious, and was disposed in Oblique Circles,
De-

Decuffated ; but the Filleting very narrow.
I told the Father, that this was ftill Flefh ;
and that Mummy therefore in *Venice-Treacle* did break *Lent,* if given at that time :
He anfwered, he did not believe it : I told
him how he fhould be covinced, *viz.* if that
Leg was kept a good while in a damp Cellar, it would yield and ftink like very Carrion, tho' it was at leaft 3000 years old ;
which thing happened to one in *London,* fo
carelefly laid by.

There was one thing very curious, and
that was an ancient *Writing Inftrument* of
thick and ftrong Silver-Wire, wound up
like a hollow Bottom or Screw; with both
the ends pointing one way, and at a diftance; fo that a Man might eafily put his
Fore-finger betwixt the two Points, and the
Screw fills the Ball of his Hand. One of
the Points was the Point of a Bodkin, which
was to write on Waxed Tables : The other
Point was made very artificially, like the
Head and upper Beak of a Cock, and the
Point divided in two, juft like our *Steel
Pens ;* from whence undoubtedly the Moderns had their Patterns ; which are now
made alfo of fine Silver and Gold, or Prin-
ces-Metal ; all which yet want a Spring,
and are therefore not fo ufeful as of Steel,
or a Quill : But a Quill foon fpoils. Steel is
undoubtedly the beft, and if you ufe *China*
Ink,

Ink, the moſt laſting of all Inks, it never ruſts the Pen, but rather preſerves it with a kind of Varniſh, which dries upon it, tho' you take no care in wiping it.

M.Colberts
Library. I ſaw the Library of the late Monſieur *Colbert*, that great Patron of Learning. The Gallery, wherein the printed Books are kept, is a Ground-Room, with Windows on one ſide only, along a fine Garden. It is the neateſt Library in *Paris*, very large, and exceedingly well furniſh'd. At the upper-end is a fair Room, wherein the Papers of State are kept ; particularly thoſe of the Adminiſtration of Cardinal *Mazarine*, and his own Accounts, when he was in Employment. Theſe make up many hundred Folio's, finely bound in Red Maroquin and Gilt.

The Manuſcript Library is above-ſtairs, in three Rooms, and is the choiceſt of that kind in *Paris :* It contains 6610 Volumes. The Catalogue of them Monſieur *Baluze* ſhewed me ; which he ſaid was deſigned ſhortly for the Preſs.

He ſhewed me many rare Books, *Carolus Calvus's* Bible, a vaſt Folio in Vellum, and his Prayer-Book or Hours, all writ in Gold Letters.

Alſo

Alſo the *Miſſa Beati Rhenani*, whereof all the Copies were burnt but four. The Original Deed of the Agreement of the Greek and Roman Church at *Florence*, The *Regalia* agreed upon at *Lyons*, and many others, which I have forgot.

I ſaw neither *Greek* nor *Latin* Manuſcript, but what had the Marks of the Goths upon them : that is, the Letters maimed, and conſequently not very ancient.

He ſhewed us *Servieto's* Book, for which he was burnt at *Geneva* ; which coſt Monſieur *Colbert* at an Auction in *England*, 25 Crowns. The Title is, *De Trinitatis Erroribus Libri* 7. *per Michaelem Serveto alias Reves ab Aragonia Hiſpanum* 1531. I had forgot the particular place where the Circulation of the Blood through the Lungs is mentioned : but he told me very civilly, I ſhould have it Tranſcribed at any time.

We told him, we came to ſee him as well as the Library : He replied, it was his hap to have more Reputation than Merit. He was a little old Man, but very chearful, and of a quick Wit.

He complained much of the Refuſal of the Emperor's People concerning the Manuſcripts of *Vienna*, in order to the publication of the *Capitulaires :* For he ſaid, Let-

K

ters were never at War : That for his part
he had moſt willingly given leave for at
leaſt Twenty four Manuſcripts to be col-
lated for Dr. *Mill's* Edition of the New
Teſtament.

*Library of
the* Sor-
bonne. The *Library of the Sorbonne* is a very
long and large Gallery, reaſonable well
ſtored with Books; no Catalogue printed.

Amongſt the Manuſcripts, they ſhew,
Titus Livy in French, upon Vellum, in a
very large Folio , bound in two Books:
The firſt is almoſt throughout illuminated
with very fine Miniatures. The Book is
dedicated to King *John* , by *Peter Berchorius:* And in the Title Page is a very curious Deſign of that King receiving the Preſent from the Author of the Tranſlation.

Amongſt the Illuminations and Ornamental Pictures in the Margin , I could
not but take notice of a *Braſs Cannon* fired,
well painted , with two large Arms or
Gudgeons , one on each ſide near the
Touch-hole ; which evinces Cannon to
have been in uſe at that time.

This Manuſcript confirms the loſs of
Titus Livy, and that it was deficient in
that Age, as to what is now wanting,
there being nothing more in this than
what is in the Printed Copy. This was
the

the Gift of Cardinal *Richlieu* to the Library; who in a manner rebuilt the whole College, and beautified it as it is. His Tomb is in the middle of the Quire, before the great Altar, in White Marble; and is for plainnefs and exquifite Performance, the beft thing of that kind I ever faw.

I faw the *Library of St. Victor :* This *Library of* moft Antient Convent is the beft feated *St. Victor.* of any in *Paris;* has very large Gardens, with fhady Walks, well kept. The Library is a fair and large Gallery : It is open three days a week, and has a range of double Desks quite through the middle of it, with Seats and Conveniencies of Writing for 40 or 50 People.

The Catalogue was not finifht, nor intended to be printed; which yet I think is always neceffary in all Corporations, for check of lofs of Books, for the ufe of Strangers, for Benefactions.

In a part of it, at the upper end, are kept the Manufcripts; they are faid to be 3000; which though not very ancient, have yet been found very ufeful for the moft correct Editions of many Authors. This is one of the pleafanteft Rooms that can be feen, for the Beauty of its Profpect, and the Quiet and Freedom from Noife in the middle of fo great a City.

In

In this Convent is very prettily lodged in an outward Court, Monſieur *Morin,* another Phyſician of that Name. In his Apartment, he hath a large and excellent Collection of Phyſick Books and Natural Hiſtory. He ſaluted me with the greateſt Kindneſs imaginable ; and at firſt word, ask'd me, if there was any more of Sir *Francis Willoughby's* Works printed beſides his Hiſtory of Fiſhes, and that other of Birds ; both which he had. He had in another Room a well ſtored Muſæum of Natural Hiſtory, of all ſorts, and of comparative Anatomies : A Cabinet of Shells, another of Seeds, among which were ſome from *China :* Variety of Skeletons, *&c.*

Celeſtins. I ſaw the *Celeſtins.* The Library is an Upper-Gallery, very pleaſant and plentifully furniſh'd with Books. This is a very fine Convent ; with the nobleſt *Dortoire,* having open Galleries round : Alſo, very large Gardens, with Alleys and ſhady Groves ; and divers Kitchen-Gardens well cultivated. Alſo a Vineyard of White-Wine Grapes, well kept ; which is the only thing of that kind within the Walls of *Paris.*

Here

Here I alfo faw the Clofet or Cell of
P. Hochereau ; who had a very choice
Colle&ion of Original Paintings of very
many of the beft Mafters : Amongft the
reft, I took notice of the Originals of
Rambrant, excellent Pieces, St. *Peter and
the Cock : The Nativity of our Saviour :* And,
The Maſſacre of the Innocents. His Colouring is not to be imitated ; his Invention
great and natural, and the Defign moft
corre&.

I was to vifit *Piere Mallebranche* of the
Fathers of the Oratory : They live very
neatly together in a kind of Community,
but under no Rule : He was very hand-
fomly lodged, in a Room well furnifh'd :
He is a very tall lean Man, of a ready Wit
and chearful Converfation.

After an Hours Difcourfe, he carried me
into the *Publick Library* of the Houfe : A
fair Gallery well lighted, and well furnifh'd with Books ; with an Apartment at
the upper-end for Manufcripts , where
were many Greek and Hebrew. Amongft
the reft , the Library-Keeper fhewed us
the *Samaritan Pentateuch*, of which *Morin*
made ufe. It feemed to me to be much
later than that of Sir *John Cotton's* Library with us, becaufe it was of a much
fmaller Letter, and more broken in the

*Les Peres
de l'Ora-
toire.
P. Malle-
branch.*

K 3 Writing,

Writing, which was all I am capable to judge by.

They were bufie in reforming the Difpofition of the Library ; and making a good Catalogue, according to the Method of the late Archbifhop of *Rheims* ; and which I liked well of, they had drawn out fome hundreds of Books, and expofed them in the middle of the Library, upon a long Table, for Sale, as being Duplicates ; and from the Sale of them to furnifh themfelves with what they wanted.

The Books which were written by Proteftants, I obferved, they were lock'd up in wired Cafes, not to be come at without particular leave.

The Freedom and Nature of this Order puts me in mind of what I heard of a certain rich and learned Man, Monfieur *Pinet*, of the Law, who put himfelf at length into Religion, as they fay, amongft thefe Fathers, but firft perfuaded his Cook to do fo too; for he was refolved not to quit his good Soupes, and fuch Difhes as he liked, whatever became of his Penance and Retirement. This Compliment the elegant and learned Monfieur *Peletier*, in Monfieur *Colbert's* place, Comptroller General of the *Finances*, made his Guefts at his Country Houfe near *Choify*, having voluntarily quitted all his Employments

at

at Court : He faid, he referved his Cook, tho' he retrench'd the reft of his Retinue ; they might therefore expect a flender Philofopher's Dinner, tho' well drefs'd.

It is wonderful to confider how moft of the reft of the Orders *abufe* themfelves for *God's Sake*, as they call it. Hunger and ill Diet not only deftroys a Man's Health, but maugre all his Devotion , puts him out of Humour, and makes him repine and envy the reft of Mankind ; and well if it do not make him alfo curfe in his Heart his Maker ; *Job* is not every Man's Roll to act. The Original and Rife of Natural Philofophy and Phyfick, was to invent a more wholfom and better Food, than the Beafts have, and to eat Bread and Flefh inftead of Herbs and Corn , to drink Wine inftead of Water : Thofe, and a thoufand other things, were the Bleffings of Phyfick, and ftill the good management of thefe things, both in Health and Sicknefs, are under the Directions of the Phyficians. Now for a fort of *Melancholy* and *Wilful Men*, to renounce thefe Comforts, and deftroy their Healths, and all this upon a pretended Principle of Religion and Devotion, feems to me, I confefs, great Ingratitude to God the Author of it.

K 4

Indeed, I heartily pitied *F. P.* an industrious honeſt Man, after his return from the *Indies,* who was nothing but Skin and Bone; and yet by the Rules of his Order he could not eat any thing that was wholſom and proper for his Cure; nothing but a little ſlimy naſty Fiſh and Herbs : And though he took, as he told me, *Hypocochoana* five times, it had no effect upon him. 'Tis true, I never heard him complain : But what will not blind Prejudice do againſt all the Reaſon of Mankind!

I know ſome of theſe Men have been uſeful to Mankind by their Studies; but the very ſame Men would have been much more, had they ſtay'd with their Neighbours, and taught the World by their Converſation and Example : Wiſdom, and Juſtice, and Innocence, and Temperance, which they highly pretend to, are not things to be hid in Corners, but to be brought forth to inſtruct and adorn the Age we live in : To abandon the World, and all the Conveniences of Life and Health, is (let them ſay what they pleaſe) the height of Chagrin, and not Religion.

There were ſome other publick Libraries I ſaw, as that of the *Grands Auguſtins,* Colledge *Mazarin,* Colledge *Navarre,* and

great

great many more I did not fee for want of
an opportunity; but there is nothing particular I remember about them.

There is fuch a Paffion of fetting up for
Libraries, that Books are come to moft un-
reafonable Rates.

I paid to *Aniffon* thirty fix Livres for *Nizolius* , twenty Livres for the two fmall
Quarto's of the Memoirs of the *Academie
de Sciences*, that is, as I may fay, for two
Years Philfophick Tranfactions; for they
began thofe monthly Memoirs in imitation of ours, out of the Regifters of the
Academy, but did not think fit to continue
them above two Years.

As to *Stamps*, I had a mind to have
bought a compleat Set of *Melans*, that incomparable Mafter; but I was ask'd two
hundred Livres, and twelve excepted,
which might amount to as much more: For
fome of his Gravings in *Octavo* done at
Rome, they ask'd me a Piftol a-piece ; and
for the Head of *Juftinianus* a Louis ; which
yet is his Mafter-piece.

I was at an Auction of Books in the
Ruè St. Jaques, where were about forty or
fifty People, moft Abbots and Monks. The
Books were fold with a great deal of tri-
fling and delay as with us, and very dear :
For *Hifpania illuftrata Aud. Sciotti*, of the
Francfort Edition, from twenty Livres, at
which

which it was set, they bid up by little and little to thirty six Livres ; at which it was sold. The next was a *Catalogue of French Books* in a thin Folio in an old Parchment Cover by *De la Croix de Maine*, eight Livres. And so I left them to shift it amongst themselves.

I had it from some of the best Stationers in *Paris*, that the dearness of Paper and Books, proceeded not only from the Taxes, but from the few Workmen that were left, and the decay of the Mills ; and that whereas in *Zaintogue* alone, they were us'd to make before the War yearly 120000 Reams of Paper, there was not now 15000 there made. And this Reason holds in a great many other their Manufactures.

After having said so much of the *Publick Libraries*, I cannnot but congratulate their Happiness, to have them so well secured from Fire ; it being one of the Perfections of this City to be so built and furnish'd, as not to have suffered by it these many Ages ; and, indeed, I cannot see how Malice it self could destroy them, for the Houses here are all built of Stone, Wall, Floors, Stair-cases and all, some few Rooms excepted ; no Wainscot, Woollen or Silk Hangings, which cannot be fired without giving notice by the intolerable

lerable ftench, and the fupply of much Fuel.
'Tis well for us in *London*,that there are very
few publick Libraries, and thofe fmall and
inconfiderable, and that the great number
of Books are diftributed into a thoufand.
Hands, (no Country in *Europe* can com-
pare to us for private Libraries) for if they
were together in fuch vaft quantities as in
Paris, Learning would run the hazard of
daily fuffering. Here with us, methinks,
every Man that goes to Bed, when afleep,
lies like a dead *Roman* upon a Funeral Pile,
dreading fome unexpected *Apotheofis*; for
all is combuftible about him, and the
Paint of the Deal Boards may ferve for
Incenfe, the quicker to burn him to
Afhes.

In the next place I will account for
what I faw, that feemed to me fingular and
new in the Improvement of Arts, or wanting in our Country.

I faw the *Potterie of St.Clou*, with which I *Potterie* of
was marvelloufly well pleafed : for I confefs *St. Clou.*
I could not diftinguifh betwixt the Pots
made there, and the fineft *China Ware* I
ever faw. It will, I know, be eafily granted
me, that the *Paintings* may be better defigned and finifh'd (as indeed it was) becaufe our Men are far better Mafters in that
Art than the *Chinefes* ; but the *Glazing*
came

came not in the leaft behind theirs, not for whitenefs, nor the fmoothnefs of running without Bubles : Again, the *inward Subftance* and Matter of the Pots, was, to me, the very fame, hard and firm as Marble, and the felf fame Grain, *on this fide Vitrification.* Farther, the *Tranfparency* of the Pots the very fame.

I faw them alfo in the Mold undried, and before the Painting and Glazing was applied, they were as white as Chalk, and melted upon the Tongue like raw Tobacco-Pipe Clay, and felt betwixt the Teeth foft like that, and very little gritty; fo that I doubt not but they are made of that very Clay.

As to the Temper of the Clay, the Man freely owned to me, it was three or four times well beaten and wet, before it was put to work on the Wheel; but I believe it muft firft be melted in fair Water, and carefully drawn off, that the heavieft part may firft fink; which alfo may be proper for Courfer Works.

That it required two, and fometimes three or four Fires to bake it, to that height we faw it in the moft finifh'd Potts : Nay, fome of them had had eleven Fires.

I did not expect to have found it in this Perfection, but imagined this might have arrived at the *Gomron Ware*; which is, indeed,

deed, little elfe but a total Vitrification; but I found it far otherwife, and very furprifing, and which I account part of the Felicity of the Age to equal, if not furpafs the *Chinefes* in their fineft Art.

As for the *Red Ware* of *China*, that has been, and is done in *England*, to a far greater Perfection than in *China*, we having as good Materials, *viz.* the *Soft Hæmatites*, and far better Artifts in Pottery. But in this particular we are beholding to two *Dutchmen* Brothers, who wrought in *Staffordfhire* (as I have been told) and were not long fince at *Hammerfmith*.

They fold thefe Pots at *St. Clou* at exceffive Rates; and for their ordinary Chocolate Cups ask'd Crowns a-piece. They had arrived at the burning on Gold in neat Chequer Works. He had fold fome Furnitures of Tea Tables at 400 Livres a Sett.

There was no Molding or Model of *China Ware*, which they had not imitated; and had added many Fancies of their own, which had their good Effects, and appeared very beautiful.

Monf. *Morin* in Converfation told me, that they kept their Sand as a Secret to themfelves; but this could not be for other purpofes than colouring: Alfo he faid they ufed Salt of *Kelp* in the Compofition, and made

made a thing not unlike *Frit* for Glafs to be wrought up with White Clay; neither could this be, for I did not tafte it in the Raw Pots.

The ingenuous Mafter told me, he had been twenty five years about the Experiment, but had not attained it fully, till within thefe three Years. I, and other Gentlemen brought over of thefe Pots with us.

Glafferie. The *Glafs-Houfe* out of the Gate of *St. Antoine* well deferves feeing; but I did lament the Fondery was no longer there, but removed to *Cherborne* in *Normandy* for cheapnefs of Fuel. 'Tis certainly a moft confiderable addition to the Glafs-making; for I faw here one Looking-Glafs foiled and finifh'd, eighty eight Inches long, and forty eight Inches broad; and yet but one quarter of an Inch thick. This, I think, could never be effected by the Blaft of any Man; but I fuppofe to be run or caft upon Sand, as Lead is; which yet, I confefs, the toughnefs of Glafs Metal makes very much againft.

There they are polifhed; which imploys daily fix hundred Men, and they hope in a little time to employ a thoufand in feveral Galleries. In the lower they grind the courfe Glafs with a Sand-Stone, the very

fame

fame they pave the Streets in *Paris*; of which broken they have great heaps in the Courts of the Work-houfes : This Stone is beat to Powder, and fifted through a fine Tamis. In the upper Gallery, where they pollifh and give the laft Hand, they work in three Rows, and two Men at a Plate, with Ruddle or powdered Hæmatites in Water.

The Glaffes are fet faft in White Puttie, upon flat Tables of Stone, fawed thin for that purpofe. The grinding the Edges and Borders is very troublefome, and odious for the horrid grating noife it makes, and which cannot be endured to one that is not ufed to it ; and yet by long Cuftom thefe Fellows are fo eafie with it, that they difcourfe together as nothing were. This is done below, and out of the way of the reft.

'Tis very diverting to fee the joint Labour of fo many Men upon one Subject. This has made Glafs for Coaches very cheap and common; fo that even many of the *Fiacres* or Hackneys, and all the *Remifes* have one large Glafs before.

Amongft the *Bioux* made at *Paris*, a *Artificial* great quantity of *Artificial Pearl* is to be *Pearl.* had of divers forts; but the beft are thofe which are made with Scales of *Bleaks.* Thefe

Thefe *Bleaks* they fifh in the River *Seine* at *Paris*, and fell them to the Pearl-makers for that purpofe.

Monf. *Favi*, at the *Pearle d' Angleterre*, told me, that he paid for the Fifh only of the little River *Tier of Ville Neuve St. George*, four Leagues off of *Paris* by the year a hundred and ten Piftols. This Fifh in *French* is called *De la Bellette :* Sometimes in Winter he has had thirty Hampers of the Fifh brought him, for the Scales only, which he ufes in Pearl-making. He fells fome Strings for a Piftol : and they have formerly been fold much dearer. This fort is very neat and lafting.

Enquiring of a Goldfmith, a great Dealer in Pearl, about thofe which were made of the Scales of Fifhes, he told me, that it was fo : That the Scales were beat to Powder, and that made into a Liquid Pafte with Izing-glafs, and caft into the hollow Glafs Beads, and fo gave the colour by way of foil from the infide.

I ask'd him, if he had any Frefh-water and *Mufcle Pearl* ; and he forthwith fhewed me one of twenty three Grains, of a bluifh Colour or faint Carnation, perfectly globular ; he told me he valued it at 400 *l.* for that it would mix or match better with the Oriental *Sea Pearl*, than the bluifh ones. Further, he affured me he had

had feen Pearl of fixty odd Grains of Frefh-
water Mufcles; and fome Pear fafhion-
ed. That in *Lorrain*, and at *Sedan*, they
fifh'd many Pearls in the Rivers therea-
bout.

The formerly fo famous a Workhoufe, The *Gobe-*
the *Gobelins* is miferably fallen to decay; *lins.*
perhaps, becaufe the King having furnifh'd
all his Palaces, has little more to do for
them.

Here I faw the making *Marble Tables* inlaid with all forts of coloured Stones.

Alfo the *Atteliers* or Work-houfes of
two of the famous Sculptures *Tuby*; in
which was a *Lacoon* copied in White Marble admirably; alfo that other of *Quoifivox*,
in which was, amongft other rare Pieces,
Caftor and Pollux, in White Marble, exceeding beautiful and large; a Copy alfo after
the Antique.

At *Hubins the Eye-maker*, I faw Drawers *Hubins.*
full of all forts of Eyes, admirable for the
contrivance, to match with great exactnefs
any *Iris* whatfoever: This being a Cafe,
where mif-matching is intolerable.

He himfelf alfo formerly wrought in
falfe Pearl, and affirmed, that the Glafs
Pearls were painted within with a Pafte
made of the Scales of the *Bleak* only;

　　　　　　L　　　　　　which

which he faid was a good Trade here to the Fifhermen, who fold the Scales for fo much the Ounce. Thefe Necklaces were formerly fold at great Prices, two or three Piftols a-piece.

I faw the *Platrerie*, or *Plafter Quarries near Montmartre*, and the manner of burning of it. 'Tis burnt with open Fire, fet up againft it : The hardeft Stone is burnt enough in two or three hours time.

The top *Band or Bed* is very hard like a Freeftone, they diftinguifh the Beds by feveral Names, *i. e.* 1. *Mutton,* 2. *Lane,* 3. *Bufier,* 4. *Cliker,* 5. *Grosban,* 6. *Pillier noir, &c.*

That which they call *Lane* is like *Talke* or *Selenites* tranfparent, and fplits in thin Flakes ; but there is but little of it, and the Beds are fmall : This feems to be but a *Fluor* to the greater Beds of Grey Stone. This Rock is covered with a kind of Grey Sand to a great depth ; which is not of the nature of Plafter.

Though this Plafter burnt is never ufed (that I could learn) to fertilize either Corn-Ground, or Pafture, as our Lime-ftone is ; yet I fee no reafon, why it may not, it being full of Nitre, if it has lain long in damp Caves.

This

This is not peculiar to *Paris* only ; for I have seen Quarries of it near *Clifford-Moore* in *Yorkshire* ; where it is call'd *Hall-Plaster*.

The Plaster here gives them great readiness in Building, for it works with ease ＆ They make Balls or Lumps of it, and lay them one upon another, and so run up in a trice, an intire Chimney, or Walls for Example, of many Fathom high : But this is very apt to crack, and not easily to be mended afterwards. It sets and dries so very quick, that it seems it cannot be compounded with Sand or Laire to make it tough.

I cannot omit the *Mill-stones*, which they grind their Wheat with at *Paris*, as upon the River of the *Gobelins* out of the Gate St.. *Bernard*, where it falls into the *Seine*, and all throughout *Picardy* down to *Calais*, where I have seen great numbers of them. *Mill-stones.*

These Mill-stones are very useful, and so sweet, that not the least grit is ever found in their Bread : They are mostly made up of pieces, two, three, or more set together by a Cement, and hooped round with Iron to keep the pieces faster together. They are made of a kind of *Honeycomb-Stone*, wrought by the Petrification

L 2　　　　　　　　of

of Water, or *Stalactites*. The very felf-fame Stone I have feen Rocks of on the River Banks at *Knaresborough*, at the dropping Well in *Jorkfhire* : therefore I advife my Countrymen to put thefe excellent Stones in practice; for certainly no place ftands in more need of it; for the Bread in the North of *England* is intolerable gritty, by reafon of thofe *Sand* or *Moore Stones*, with which they grind their Corn.

Thefe Stones are fold at 500 Livres a pair; whence they come I forgot to be informed.

In the next place we will fee how the *Parifians* Eat, Drink, and Divert themfelves.

Of the Food of the Parifians.

Bread.   The Diet of the *Parifians* confifts chiefly of *Bread* and *Herbs*; it is here, as with us, finer and courfer. But the common Bread or *Pain de Goneffe*, which is brought twice a Week into *Paris* from a Village fo called, is purely white, and firm, and light, and made altogether with Leaven; moftly in three Pound Loaves, and 3 *d.* a Pound. That which is bak'd in *Paris* is courfer and much worfe.

As

As for the *fine Manchet*, or *French* Bread, as we call it, I cannot much commend it; it is of late, fince the quantity of Beer that is brewed in *Paris*, often fo bitter, that it is not to be eaten, and we far exceed them now in this particular in *London.*

The *Grey Salt* of *France* (which there at Table, is altogether in every thing made ufe of) is incomparably better and more wholfom than our White Salt. This I the rather mention, becaufe it feems not yet to enter fully into the confideration and knowledge of our People; who are nice in this particular to a fault. But I muft take leave to tell them, that our Salt caufes Thirft, and fpoils every thing that is pretended to be preferved by it, be it Fifh or Flefh. For whether boiled from the inland Salt-Pits, or the Sea-Water, it is little lefs than Quicklime, and burns and reefes all it touches; fo that 'tis pity to fee fo much good Fifh as is caught upon the Northern Line of Coaft, particularly the Cod. and Ling, and Herring, now of little value, which were formerly the moft efteemed Commodities of *England.* 'Tis certain, there is no making good Salt by fierce and vehement boiling, as is ufed; but it muft be kerned either by the heat of the Sun, as in *France*; or by a full

and

and over-weighty Brine, as at *Milthrope* in the *Wafhes* of *Lancafhire* ; for in no other place in *England* I ever faw it right made; but yet that is not there underftood to purpofe ; for they alfo boil the Brine, which poffibly by fome flight Artifice might be brought to give its Salt without ftrefs of Fire.

I have heard the old Fifhermen at *Scarborough*, *Robin Hood's Bay*, and *Whitby* fadly complain of it ; but they could not help it : For now the Merchants bring them no other, the *Shields* being fo near them. An Inftance alfo to confirm this is, that the People in *Cornwal* were up in a very great Riot, becaufe it pleafed the Parliament at the beginning of the War, to deftroy what ever *French Salt* was taken as Prize : Thofe Men knew how neceffary it was to cure their Pilchards with. Laftly, the Parliament themfelves were, at the inftance of the Victuallers of the Navy, convinced, in fome meafure, of the Goodnefs of it by paffing an Act, in the hight of the War, to fave two Prize Ships of *French Salt*, for the ufe of the King's Slaughter-houfe.

White Kidney Beans mdLentils. In *Lent* the common People feed much on White *Kidney Beans*, and White or Pale *Lentils*, of which there are great Provifions made in all the Markets, and to be had

had ready boiled. I was well pleafed with this *Lentil* ; which is a fort of Pulfe we have none of in *England.* There are two forts of White *Lentils* fold here ; one fmall one from *Burgundy,* by the Cut of *Briare* ; and another bigger, as broad a-gain from *Chartres* : A third alfo much larger, is fometimes to be had from *Languedoc.* Thofe excepted our Seed Shops far exceed theirs, and confequently our Gardens, in the Pulfe-kind for variety ; both Pea and Bean.

The *Roots* differ much from ours. There are here no round Turneps, but all *long ones,* and fmall ; but excellently well tafted, and are of a much greater ufe, being proper for Soupes alfo ; for which pur-pofe ours are too ftrong : We have, indeed, of late got them into *England* ; but our Gardners underftand not the mana-ging of them. They fow them here late after *Midfummer* ; and at *Martinmas* or fooner, before the Froft begin, they dig them up, cut off the tops, and put them into Sand in their Cellars, where they will keep good till after *Eafter* ; nay, till *Whitfuntide.* Whereas if the Froft take them they are quite fpoilt ; and that piece of ill Husbandry makes them to be defpifed here ; having loft their tafte,

Long Turneps.

L 4 and

and they foon grow fticky in the Ground. The Sandy Plains of *Vaugerard* near *Paris* are famous for this fort of moft excellent Root. After the fame manner they keep their Carrots.

After we had been two or three Days Journey in *France*, we found no other Turneps, but the *Navet*; and ftill the nearer *Paris* the better. Thefe, as I faid, are fmall long Turneps, not bigger than a Knife-haft. and moft excellent in Soupes, and with boiled and ftewed Mutton. I think it very ftrange, that the Seed fhould fo much improve in *England*, as to produce Roots of the fame kind fix or ten tims as big as there; for I make no queftion but the long Turneps, of late only in our Markets are the fame.

Potato's.   The *Potato* are fcarce to be found in their Markets, which are fo great a relief to the People of *England*, and very nourifhing and wholfome Roots; but there are *Jerufalem Artichokes.* ftore of *Jerufalem Artichokes.*

Cabbage.   They delight not fo much in Cabbage, as I expected, at leaft at the Seafon, while we were there, from *December* to *Mid-fummer.* I never faw in all the Markets once *Sprouts*, that is, the tender Shoots of Cabbages; nor in their publick Gardens, any

any referves of old Stalks. The Red Cabbage is efteemed here, and the Savoy.

But to make amends for this, they a-
bound in vaft quantities of large *Red Oni-
ons* and *Garlick*. And the long and fweet
white *Onion* of *Languedoc* are to be had
alfo here. Alfo Leeks, *Rockamboy*, and
Shallots are here in great ufe.

It has been obferved, that the Northern
People of *Europe* much delight in Cabbage,
as the *Ruſſes, Poles, Germans, &c.* 'Tis certain, the Cabbage thrives beft in cold Coun-
treys, and is naturally a Northern Plant,
and the Keel is to be found wild upon the
Maritime Rocks, as I have feen it at *Whitby*,
and the Cold ripens it, and makes it more
tender and palatable.

The Southern People are pleafed with
the Onion Kind, for the fame Reafon, for
that the great Heats meliorate them, but
give a ranknefs to the Cabbage. The *Leeks*
are here much fmaller, than with us;
but to recompence this, they are blancht
here with more care and art, and are three
times as long in the white part, which is
by finking them early fo deep in mellow
Earth. There is no Plant of the Onion
Kind fo hardy as this, and fo proper for
the cold Mountains, witnefs the ufe the
Welſh have made of them from all Ages;
and

and indeed it is excellent againſt Spitting of Blood, and all Diſeaſes of the Throat and Lungs.

Lettice.   Though the Lettice be the great and univerſal Sallet, yet I did not find they came near our People, for the largeneſs and hardneſs of them; indeed, about a Week, before we left *Paris,* the long Roman Lettice filled their Markets, which was incomparable, and I think beyond our *Sileſian.*

White Beets.   *April* and *May* the Markets were ſerved with vaſt quantities of white *Beets,* an Herb rarely uſed with us, and never that I know of, in that manner for Soups. The Leaves grow long and large, and are tied up, as we do our Sileſian or Roman Lettice to blanch, and then cut by the Root. The Stalks are very broad and tender, and they only are uſed, ſtript of the green Leaves. They Cook thoſe Stalks in different manners.

Aſparagus.   The *Aſparagus* here are in great plenty, but for the firſt Month they were very bitter and unpleaſant; from whence that proceeded, I cannot gueſs; afterwards I did not much perceive it.

They

They are fo great Lovers of *Sorrel,* *Sorrel.*
that I have feen whole Acres of it planted
in the Fields; and they are to be com-
mended for it; for nothing is more whole-
fome, and it is good to fupply the place of
Lemons, againft the Scurvy, or any ill
habit of the Body.

But after all, the French delight in no- *Mufhroomes*
thing fo much as *Mufhroomes;* of which
they have daily, and all the Winter
long, ftore of frefh and new gathered in
the Markets. This furprifed me; nor
could I guefs, where they had them, till
I found they raifed them on hot Beds in
their Gardens.

Of *Forc'd Mufhroomes* they have many
Crops in a Year; but for the Months of
Auguft, September, October, when they naturally grow in the Fields, they prepare
no Artificial Beds.

They make in the Fields and Gardens
out of the Bar of *Vaugerard* (which I
faw) long narrow Trenches, and fill thofe
Trenches with Horfe Dung two or three
foot thick, on which they throw up the
common Earth of the place, and cover the
Dung with it, like the ridge of a Houfe,
high pitched; and over all they put long
Straw or long Horfe Litter. Out of this
Earth

Earth fprings the *Champignons*, after Rain; and if Rain comes not, they water the Beds every Day, even in Winter.

They are fix days after their fpringing, or firft appearance, before they pull them up for the Market.

On fome Beds they have plenty, on others but few, which demonftrate they come of Seed in the Ground; for all the Beds are alike.

A Gardner told me, he had the other Year near an Acre of Ground ordered in this manner, but he loft 100 Crowns by it; but moftly they turn to as good profit, as any thing they can plant.

They deftroy their old Beds in Summer, and dung their Grounds with them.

They prepare their new Beds the latter end of *Auguft*, and have plentiful Crops of *Mufhroomes* towards *Chriftmas*, and all the Spring, till after *March*.

I faw in the Markets the beginning of
Moriglio's. *April*, frefh gathered *Moriglio's*, the firft of that kind of *Mufhroom*, that I remember ever to have feen; though formerly I had been very curious and inquifitive
about

about this kind of Plant, and had di-
ftinguiſht and deſcribed 30 Species of them
growing in *England*; yet I do not remember ever to have found this Species with
us; it is blackiſh, and becomes much
blacker, when boiled, whence probably it
had its Name; but there are ſome few of
them, that are yellow. They are always
of a round Pyramidal Figure, upon a ſhort
thick Foot-ſtalk. The Foot-ſtalk is ſmooth,
but the outſide of the *Muſhroom* is all deep-
ly pleated and wrinkled like the inſide of
a Beaſts Maw. The Moriglio ſplit in two
from top to bottom is all hollow and
ſmooth, Foot, Stalk, and all. In this hol-
lowneſs is ſometimes contained dangerous
Inſects. The taſte raw, is not ungrateful,
and very tender. This *Muſhroom* ſeems to
me to be produced of the Tree kind.

This ſort of *Muſhroom* is much eſteemed
in *France*, and is moſtly gathered in Woods
at the foot of the *Oaks*. There were ſome
of them as big as Turky Eggs. They are
found in great quantities in the Woods in
Champagne, about *Reims*, and *Noſtre de
Dame de Lieſſe*.

They ſtring them, and dry them; and
they ſeem to me to have a far better reliſh
than the *Champignons*.

The

The *French* fay, there are no bad *Moriglio's*; but there are bad *Mufhrooms*. At firft I was very fhie of eating them; but by degrees, and that there was fcarce any Ragouts without them, I became pleafed with them, and found them very innocent. I am perfuaded the harm that comes from eating them, is from the noxious Infects and Vermin that feed upon them, and creep into them. I have often found them full of fuch Animals. Poffibly the Garden for forc'd *Mufhrooms*, being that is done in Winter, and in the Spring, may be much freer of this mifchief, at what time Infects are dead, or not much ftirring, than the wild *Mufhrooms* of *Auguft*. However fome of our People at our firft coming were very fick with Crayfifh and Mufcle Soupes, and particularly with *Ragoufts* of *Mufhrooms*, which gave them a fudden fhortnefs of breath, and fometimes Vomitings, or went off in a *Diarrhæa* or *Dyfentery*.

Fifh.

This City is well ferved with *Carp*, of which there is an incredible quantity fpent in the *Lent*. They are not large, and I think are the better for it, but they are very clean of Mud, and well tafted.

They have a particular way of bringing frefh Oyfters to Town, which I never faw with us; to put them up in *Straw Baskets* of a Peck, fuppofe, cut from the Shell, and

and without the Liquor. They are thus
very good for Stewing, and all other manner of Dreffing.

There is fuch plenty of *Macreufe*, a
fort of Sea Ducks, in the Markets all
Lent, that I admire, where they got fo
many; but thefe are reckoned and efteemed as Fifh, and therefore they take them
with great Induftry. They have a rank
fifhy tafte, yet for want of other Flefh
were very welcome. I remember we had
at our Treat at the King's Charge at *Verfailles* a *Macreufe Pye* near two foot diameter, for it was in *Lent*; which being
high feafoned, did go down very well
with rare Burgundy. There is a better
Argument in *Leewenhoeke* for Birds partici-
pating fomething of the nature of Fifh,
though their Blood is hot, than any the
Council of Trent could think of, and that
is, that the *Globuli* of the Blood of Birds
are Oval, as thofe of Fifhes are; but this
will take in all the Bird kind; which alfo
in time thofe Gentlemen may think fit to
grant.

As for their Flefh, Mutton and Beef if *Flefh.*
they are good in their Kind, they come
little fhort of ours, I cannot fay, they exceed them. But their Veal is not to be
compared with ours, being red and courfe;

and

and I believe no Country in *Europe* underftands the Management of that fort of Food like the *Englifh*. This was once proper to *Eßex* ; but now it is well known, that nothing contributes more to the whitenefs and tendernefs of the Flefh of Calves, than *often Bleeding* them, and giving them much Food of Milk and Meal , befides fucking the Dam. By much Bleeding the red Cake of the Blood is exhaufted, and becomes all *White Serum* or Chyle. The fame effect Cramming hath upon Poultry, fo as the Blood is well near all Chyle ; and the Livers of Geefe, fo fed by force, will become, for the fame reafon, vaftly great, and white and delicious.

I cannot but take notice here of a great prejudice the *French* lie under, in relation to our Flefh. 'Tis generally faid amongft them, that our Meat in *England* will not make fo ftrong Broth, as the *French*, by a third part. If they fay, not fo falt and favoury, and ftrong tafted, I agree with them ; and yet the *French* Meat is never the better. For firft their Meat is moftly leaner and more dry, and (which is all in all in this matter of Soups) is long kept, before it be fpent, which gives it a higher and falter tafte ; for as Meat rots, it becomes more urinous and falt. Now our People by cuftom, covet the frefheft Meat,

Meat, and cannot indure the leaft tendency to putrefaction; and we have good reafon to do fo, becaufe our Air is twice as moift as theirs, which does often caufe in the keeping of Meat a Muftinefs, which is intolerable to all Mankind. Whereas the Air of *France* being fo much drier, keeping of Meat, not only makes it tender, but improves the tafte. So that could we fecure our Meat, in keeping it from that unfavoury quality, it would far outdo the *French* Meat, becaufe much more juicy.

I don't remember I eat of above two forts of Flefh, but what we have as good or better in *England*, and that was of the Wild Pigs, and the Red-legg'd Partridge, Of thefe laft I eat at St. *Clou*, taken thereabouts; as to bignefs, they are much degenerated from thofe in *Languedoc*, and lefs; but far excel the grey Partridge in tafte.

As for their Fruits, our Journey was in the worft time of the Year, from *December* to *Midfummer*, fo that we had little fave Winter Fruits; fome few *Bon Chritiens* we tafted, not much better than ours, but fomething freer of ftones. The *Virguleus* Pears were admirable, but to our forrow, they did not laft long after our arrival.　　　M　　　The

Fruits.

The *Kentifh Pippin*, as we call it, was here excellent; but two other forts of Apples ftock the Markets. The Winter *Calvil* or *Queening*, which though a tender and foft Apple, yet continued good till after *Eafter*. Alfo the *Pome d' Apis*, which is ferved here for fhew, more than ufe; being a fmall flat Apple, very beautiful, very red on one fide, and pale or white on the other, and may ferve the *French* Ladies at their Toilets for a Pattern to Paint by. However this tender Apple was not contemptible after *Whitfontide*; and, which is its property, it never fmells ill, though the Ladies keep it (as fometimes they do) about them.

I never met with any thing peculiar in their Sweet Meats, but a Marmalade of *Orange Flowers*; which indeed was admirable. 'Twas made with thofe Flowers, the Juice of Lemons, and fine Sugar.

The Wines *follow, and* Water *to Drink.*

Wines. The Wines about *Paris* are very fmall, yet good in their kind; thofe *de Surene* are excellent fome Years; but in all the Taverns they have a way to make them into the fafhion of a *Champagne* and *Burgundy*

The Tax upon Wines is now fo great, that whereas before the War they drank
them

them at Retail at 5 *d.* the Quart, they now fell them at 15 *d.* the Quart, and dearer, which has enhanfed the Rates of all Commodities, and Workmens Wages; and alfo has caufed many thoufand private Families to lay in Wines in their Cellars at the cheapeft hand, which ufed to have none before.

The Wines of *Burgundy* and *Champagne* are moft valued; and indeed, not without reafon; for they are light and eafie upon the Stomach, and give little difturbance to the Brain, if drawn from the Hogfhead, or loofe bottled after their fafhion.

The moft efteemed are *Vin de Bonne* of *Burgundy*, a *red Wine*; which is *Dolce Piquante* in fome meafure, to me it feemed the very beft of Wine I met with.

Volne, a pale Champagne, but exceeding brisk upon the Palate. This is faid to grow upon the very borders of *Burgundy*, and to participate of the Excellency of both Counties.

There is another fort of Wine, called *Vin de Rheims,* this is alfo a pale or grey Wine; it is harfh, as all *Champagne* Wines are.

The White Wines of value are thofe of *Mafcon* in *Burgundy.*

Mulfo in *Champagne*, a fmall and not unpleafant White Wine.

Chaëri is a quick and fharp White Wine, well efteemed.   M 2   In

In *March* I tafted the White Wines called *Condrieu,* and *d' Arbois,* but found them both in the Muft, thick and white as our Wines ufe to be, when they firft come from the *Canaries* ; very fweet, and yet not without a grateful flavour ; they clear towards Summer, and abate much of the flavour and fweet tafte. Thofe Wines thus in the Muft are called in the Prints *Vin des Liqueurs.*

There is a preparation or rather ftifling of the White Wine in the Muft, ufed in *Burgundy* and elfewhere, which they call *Vin Bouru* ; it a gives fweet tafte, and it is foul to the Eye ; thofe alfo are called *Vin des Liqueurs.* This is only drunk a Glafs in a morning, as an equivalent to Brandy.

Vin de Turene en Anjou of two years old, was one of the beft White Wines I drank in *Paris.*

Gannetin from *Dauphiné :* This is a very pale and thin White Wine, very like the *Verdé* of *Florence,* fweet, and of a very pleafant flavour, efpecially while it is *Des Liqueurs.*

The Red Wines of *Burgundy, Des quatres feuilles,* as they fay, or of four years old, are rare ; but they are efteemed much more wholefom, and are permitted to the Sick, in fome cafes, to drink of ; they are fine, and have a rough, but found tafte ;

not

not prickt, as I expected. This Term *Des quatres feuilles* is ufed alfo to *Volné*, or any other fort of Wine, which is kept any time.

There are alfo in efteem ftronger Wines at *Paris*, as *Camp de Perdris*.

Cofte Bruflee, both Red Wines from *Dauphine*, of very good tafte, and hot upon the Stomach.

De l' Hermitage upon the *Rofne*.

But the moft excellent Wines for ftrength and flavour are the *Red and White St. Laurence*, a Town betwixt *Toulon* and *Nice* in *Provence*. This is a moft delicious *Mufcat*. Thefe are of thofe forts of Wines, which the *Romans* called *Vinum paffum*, that were made of half Sun-dried Grapes: for the Grapes (efpecially the White Mufcadine Grapes) being ufually fooner ripe, than the common Grapes of the Country, called *Efperan*, *viz.* the latter end of *Auguft*, (as I have feen them in the Vintage at *Vic*, *Mirabel*, and *Frontiniac*, three Towns near the Sea in *Languedoc*, where this fort of Wine is made) they twift the Bunches of Grapes, fo breaking the Stalks of them, that they receive no longer any nourifh-ment from the Vine, but hang down and dry in the then violent hot Sun, and are in few days almoft turned into Raifins of the Sun; hence, from this infolation, the flavour of the Grape is exceedingly height-

M 3 ned,

ned, and the ftrength and Oilinefs, and
thick Body of the Wine is mightily improved. I think the *Red St. Lauren* was
the moft delicious Wine I ever tafted in
my life.

Befides thefe, here are alfo the White
Wines of *Orleans, Bourdeaux* Claret, and
thofe Excellent Wines from *Cahors:* alfo
Cabreton, White and Red, from about
Bayone, ftrong and delicious Wines: and
all forts of *Spanifh* Wines, as Sack, Palme,
Mountaine Malaga, Red and White, She-
ries, and indeed the *French* are, of late, very
defirous to drink of the ftrongeft Wines.

Ratafia.

Befides Wines, there is no Feafting without the drinking at the defert all forts
of Strong Waters, particularly *Ratafia's*;
which is a fort of Cherry-Brandy made
with Peach and Apricock Stones, highly
piquant, and of a moft agreeable flavour.

The pungent and acrimonious quality
of thefe and fuch like Kernels was not
unknown to the Ancients, and very poi-
fonous to fome Animals. *Diofcorides* tells
us, a Pafte made of the Kernels of *Bitter
Almonds* will throw Hens into Convulfions,
and immediately kill them. Birds have
but little Brain, and fo are the ftronglier
affected with this Volatil Venom. Not
unlike effects 'tis poffible Ratafia may
have

have in some tender and more delicate
Conftitution, and weak and feeble Brains,
and may be one caule of so many fudden Deaths, as have been obferved of
late.

Vattee is a fort of perfumed Strong-water
from *Provence*, made (as it is pretended) of
Muícat Wine diftilled with Citron Pills and
Orange Flowers.

Fenoulliet de l' Ifle de Ree, is valued much,
'tis much like our Annifeed Watcr.

I muft not forget the plain *Eau de vie*,
or *Nants Brandy* ; which was formerly the
Mornings Draught of (*Crocheteurs*) Por-
ters only ; but is now valued very much,
as one of the beft Spirits of Wine in *Europe* , and yet it is made of a poor, thin,
and half-ripe fowrifh White-wine of *Bri-
tany.* 'Tis worth enquiry, what the reafon of this fhould be, that so lean and
fowre a Wine, fhould yield so palatable a
Liquor, far beyond any the moft ripe and
oily Wines of *Languedoc*, *Spain*, or *Italy.*
I take it to be the due mixture of an Acid
and Oil ; which Acid is much wanting in
the ripe Wines. This therefore is a fort of
Natural Punch. And for the fame reafon,
I make no doubt, but our Grapes of the
growth of *England*, as unripe as moft of
them are, if preffed and fermented in a-

ny quantity would in like manner yield excellent Brandy.

These and many more forts of Strong-waters and ftrong Wines, both of *France*, and *Italy*, and *Spain*, are wont to be brought in, at the latter end of the *Defert* in all great Feafts, and they drink freely of them : Which Cuftom is new ; when I was formerly in *France* I remember nothing of it. But it is the long War that has introduced them ; the Nobility and Gentry fuffering much in thofe tedious Campagnes, applied themfelves to thefe Liquors to fupport the Difficulties and Fatigues of Weather and Watchings ; and at their return to *Paris*, introduced them to their Tables. Sure I am, the *Parifians*, both Men and Women, are ftrangely altered in their Conftitutions and Habit of Body ; from lean and flender, they are become fat and corpulent, the Women efpecially : Which, in my Opinion, can proceed from nothing fo much as the daily drinking ftrong Liquors.

Coffee, Tea, Chocolate. Add to thefe Drinks the daily ufe of Coffee with Sugar, Tea and Chocolate, which now is as much in ufe in private Houfes in *Paris*, as with us in *London :* And thefe fugar'd Liquors alfo add confiderably to their Corpulency.

I

I muſt not forget, that amongſt the Drinks that are in uſe in *Paris, Sider* from *Normandy* is one. The beſt I drank of that kind, was of the colour of Claret, reddiſh or brown: The Apple, that it was made of, was called *Frequins*, which is round and yellow, but ſo bitter, that it is not to be eaten; and yet the Sider that is made of it, is as ſweet as any new Wine. It keeps many years good, and mends of its colour and taſte. I drank it often at a private Houſe of a *Norman* Gentleman, of whoſe Growth it was; otherwiſe, if I had not been aſſured to the contrary, I could not have believed but that it had been mixt with Sugar.

There are alſo very many publick *Coffee-Houſes*, where Tea alſo and Choco-late may be had, and all the Strong-wa-ters and Wine above-mentioned; and innumerable *Ale-houſes*. I wonder at the great change of this ſober Nation in this particular; but Luxury, like a Whirlpool, draws into it the Extravagancies of other People.

'Twas Neceſſity from the badneſs of Water, and the want of Wine, either na-turally, as in a great part of *Perſia* and the *Indies*; or from their Religion, as

in

in *Turkey*,) that put Men upon the Invention of thofe Liquors of Coffee and Tea : Chocolate, indeed , was found out by the poor ftarv'd *Indians*, as Ale was with us. But what elfe but a wanton Luxury could difpofe thefe People, who abound in excellent Wines, the moft cordial and generous of all Drinks, to ape the neceffity of others?

Mighty things indeed are faid of thefe Drinks, according to the Humour and Fancy of the Drinkers. I rather believe they are permitted by God's Providence for the leffening the number of Mankind by fhortning Life, as a fort of filent Plague. Thofe that plead for Chocolate, fay, it gives them a good Stomach, if taken two hours before Dinner. Right; who doubts it? You fay, you are much more hungry, having drunk Chocolate, than you had been if you had drunk none ; that is, your Stomach is faint, craving, and feels hollow and empty, and you cannot ftay long for your Dinner. Things that pafs thus foon out of the Stomach, I fufpect, are little welcome there, and Nature makes hafte to get fhut of them. There are many things of this fort, which impofe upon us by procuring a falfe hunger.

The

The wild *Indians*, and some of our People, no doubt digest it; but our pampered Bodies can make little of it; and it proves to most tender Constitutions perfect Physick, at least to the Stomach, by cleansing that into the Guts; but that wears it out, and decays Nature.

It is very remarkable with what greediness the *Spaniards* drink it, and how often in a Day, five times, says † *Gage*, at least. The Women drank it in the Churches, and the disorder could scarce be remedied. This shews how little it nourishes.

The old *Romans* did better with their Luxury; they took their Tea and Chocolate after a full Meal, and every Man was his own Cook in that case. *Cæsar* resolved to be free, and eat and drink heartily; that is, to excess, with *Tully*; and for this purpose *Cicero* tells his Friend *Atticus*, that before he lay down to Table, *Emeticen agebat*, which I construe, he prepared for himself his Chocolate and Tea; something to make a quick riddance of what they eat and drank, some way or other.

There are two sorts of *Water* which they drink at *Paris*; Water of the *River Seine*, which runs through the Town; and the Water brought in by the *Aqueduct of Arcueil*; which, by the bye, is one of the

most

moſt Magnificent Buildings in and about *Paris*, and worth going to ſee. This noble Canal of hewn Stone conveys the Water fifteen Miles to *Paris*.

The River Water is very pernicious to all Strangers, not the *French* excepted, that come from any diſtance, but not to the Natives of *Paris*, cauſing Looſeneſs, and ſometimes Dyſenteries. I am apt to think the many Ponds and Lakes that are let into it to ſupply the Sluces upon the Canal *De Briare*, are in part the cauſe of it. But thoſe who are careful of themſelves purifie it by filling their Ciſterns with Sand, and letting it ſink through it; which way clears it, and makes it very cool and pa-latable.

Monſieur *Geofrys* hath this caution about the Waters of the River *Seine* (having as a Mark of the Magiſtracy he bore, a Pipe laid into his Court) that he drinks them drained through a great Body of Sand; that is three Foot at leaſt of fine Sand in a large Ciſtern: And it is by this means that they drink clear and cool, and no doubt are much more wholſom. The Ci-ſterns at *Venice* are made after this man-ner; which Sir *George Wheeler* in his Travels hath very particularly well de-ſcribed.

As

As for the Spring Water from the *Maifon des Eaux*, it is wholfom in this refpect, and keeps the Body firm ; but it is very apt to give the Stone, which the People of this Town are infinitely fubject to. An inftance of this I had by chance, when coming from feeing the *Aqueduct of Arcueil*, in the very Road, near the Wall of the *Aqueduct*, a great number of earthen Pipes, which had ferved to convey that Water to fome Houfe, were caft to mend the High-ways. I obferved, that of four Inches Diameter the hollow of the Pipes were all ftopt up to the breadth of a Shilling, with a firm Stone petrified ; fo that they were forc'd to break up the Pipes, being altogether ufelefs. Now what petrifies in the Water-Pipes is apt in fome weak Conftitutions to petrifie alfo in the *Kidneys* and *Bladder.* I think I have put this beyond difpute in my Treatife *De Calculo Humano,* and elfewhere.

In the next place we will fee how the *Parifians* divert themfelves ; which confifts chiefly in Plays, Gaming, Walking, or Coaching.

The Plays here are divided into two Houfes : One for the *Opera's,* and the other for the *Comedies.*

I

I did not fee many Opera's not being fo good a Frenchman, as to underſtand them when Sung. The Opera, called *l'Europe Gallante*, I was at feveral times, and it is look'd upon, as one of the very beſt. It is extreamly fine, and the Muſick and Singing admirable : The Stage large and magnificent, and well filled with Actors: The Scenes well fuited to the thing, and as quick in the removal of them as can be thought : The Dancing exquiſite, as being performed by the beſt Maſters of that Profeſſion in Town : The Cloathing rich, proper, and with great variety.

It is to be won lered, that thefe Opera's are fo frequented. There are great numbers of the Nobility that come daily to them, and fome that can fing them all. And it was one thing, that was troublefome to us Strangers, to diſturb the Box by thefe voluntary Songs of fome parts of the Opera or other : That the Spectators may be faid to be here as much Actors, as thofe employed upon the very Stage.

The *Comedies* have another Houfe in another part of the Town; for the Opera's are under the Roof of Monfieur, and it is part of the *Palais Royal.*

The

The Difpofition of the Theatre is much the fame, but fomething lefs. And here the Stage it felf is to be lett; where for *Strangers*, the Places are moft commodious, to hear and fee.

I heard many *Tragedies*, but without guft, for want of Language: But after them, the *Little Plays* were very diverting to me, paticularly thofe of *Moliere*, *Vendange de Surefme*, *Pourcegnac*, *Crifpin Medicin*, *le Medicin malgre luy*, *le Malade Imaginaire*, *&c.*

In this all agree, that though *Moliere's* Plays have *lefs of Intrigue in them*, yet his *Charaƈters of Perfons* are incomparable, fo true and juft, that nothing can be more. And for this Reafon, fo many of them are only of two or three Aƈts; for without an Intrigue well laid, the Charaƈters would have failed him, in which was his Excellency. However, this is now fo much become a Cuftom on the French Stage, that you ever have one of thefe little Pieces tack'd to the Tragedy, that you may pleafe your felf according to your Appetite.

'Tis faid *Moliere* died fuddenly in aƈting the *Malade Imaginaire:* which is a good inftance of his well perfonating the Play he made, and how he could really put himfelf into any Paffion he had in his Head.

Head. Alfo of the great danger ftrong
and vehement Paffions may caufe in weak
Conftitutions, fuch as Joy and Fear;
which Hiftory tells us, have killed many very fuddenly. He is reported to have
faid, going off the Stage, *Meffieurs*, *J
ay joue le Malade Imaginaire* ; *Mais je
fuis veritablement fort Malade* ; and he died within two hours after. This Account
of *Moliere* is not in his Life by *Perault*,
but it is true : And he yet has blamed
him for his Folly, in perfecuting the Art
of Phyfick, not the Men, in divers of his
Plays.

Moliere fent for Dr. *M*———, a Phyfician in *Paris* of great Efteem and Worth,
and now in *London*, a Refugé. Dr. *M*——
fent him word, he would come to him,
upon two Conditions; the one, that he
fhould anfwer him only to fuch Queftions
as he fhould ask him, and not otherwife
Difcourfe him ; the other, that he fhould
oblige liimfelf to take the Medicines he
fhould prefcribe for him. But *Moliere*
finding the Doctor too hard for him ,
and not eafily to be *Dupt*, refus'd them.
His Bufinefs, it feems, was to make a
Comical Scene in expofing one of the
learnedft Men of the Profeffion, as he
had done the Quacks. If this was his
Intention, as in all probability it was,

Molier e

Moliere had as much Malice, as Wit; which is only to be ufed to correct the Vicioufnefs and Folly of Men pretending to Knowledge, and not the Arts themfelves.

This I muft needs fay, that Obfcenity and Immorality are not at all upon the *French* Stage, no more than in the civil Converfation of People of Fafhion and good Breeding.

We may add to thefe the great *Balls* at Court and elfewhere. My Lord Ambaffador was at a *Ball* at Monfieur *de Montargis mardy Gras* ; the Masks were infinite and very furprifing, at leaft fix hundred Ladies ; and the Streets fo full of Coaches, that the Ambaffadors Coach could not ftir till feven in the Morning, and he forc'd to foot it, by virtue of a *Swifs* Guard, a long way before he could have a Convenience to carry him off. Amongft the Masks were the Duke *d'Elbeufe*, my Lady *Portfmouth*, &c. in *Capucins* Habit of Crimfon Velvet.

One Afternoon in *Lent*, I was to hear *Preaching.* a *Sermon* at *La Charite*, preached by an *Abbot*, a very young Man. His Text was about the Angels Defcent into the Pool of *Bethefda*, and troubling the Waters. I am not fo good a Frenchman as to

N　　under-

underſtand all he ſaid, but he had many good Arguments about the neceſſity of Grace, and the means to attain it. I was ſtrangely ſurprized at the vehemency of his Action, which to me appeared altogether Comical, and like the Actors upon the Stage, which I had ſeen a few Days before: Beſides, his Expreſſions ſeemed to be in too familiar a Style. I always took a Sermon to the People to require a grave and ornate kind of Eloquence, and not *Verba Quotidiana*, with a certain Dignity of Action; but 'tis poſſible this way here beſt ſuits with the Cuſtoms and Manners of the People, who are all Motion, even when they ſay the eaſieſt and moſt intelligible things.

I cannot ſay that our being Proteſtants gave us any great trouble in Converſation; and even in meeting the Hoſt, which we frequently did, whether a foot, or in Coaches, we had no Affront put upon us that I know of. Yet in the main, as to Religion, I could obſerve there was a great difference in the Tempers of the *French* Nation, from what they were ſome Years ago. Indeed, in the Nobility and Men of Learning I did not much take notice of it; for their genteel Manners hid it: but in moſt of the inferiour People it was moſt manifeſt: I mean, a certain Air of fierce-

neſs

nefs towards all Proteftants, and a fcorn
and contempt of us. If this Humour of
Bigotry continue, which undoubtedly
ows its beginning from the late Perfecution which they have made of their Bre-
thren and Neighbours, and Trade not be
opened, to take off, by Converfation, this
growing Evil, they will foon diftinguifh
themfelves by a new and odious Chara-
ter, and become the common Scandal
of *Europe*, as they were once the darling
People and School of good breeding.

　Gaming is a perpetual Diverfion here, if *Gaming.*
not one of the Debauches of the Town :
But Games of meer *Hazard* are ftrictly
forbid upon fever Fines to the Mafter of
the Houfe, as well private as publick,
where fuch Playing fhall be difcovered.
This was done upon the account of the Officers of the Army ; who, during the Winter
ufed to lofe the Money which was given
them to make their Recruits, and renew their
Equipages in the Spring. And indeed, fuch
quick Games, as *Baffet, Hazard,* &c. where
Fortune in a manner is all in all, are great
Temptations to Ruin, by the fudden Paffions they are apt to raife in the Players.
Whereas Games, where Skill, and Cunning,
and much Thought are employ'd, as well as
Luck, give a Man time to cool, and recover
his Wits, if at any time great Lofs fhall have

dif-

difmounted his Reafon: for he muft quickly come to himfelf again, or forfeit his Skill and Reputation in conducting the Game, as well as husbanding his Money.

Not long after our firft coming to *Paris*, the beginning of *January* we had the diverfion of a fplendidid *Fire-work*, given by the Cardinal of *Furftenbourgh:* His Apartment which he built in the Abby of *St. Germains* was wonderfully illuminated; but the Fire-work it felf was played off a Scaffold, built near the top of the two fquare Towers on the Weft-end of the Abby-Church; which made it the fafer, and gave a full and noble Profpect, not only to the City of *Paris*, but to *St. Clou* and *Meadon*, and the Country round. This Perfon is faid to have given the firft occafion or pretence of the War betwixt the Emperor and the King of *France*, for he clofed the publick Rejoicings for the conclufion of the Peace with the laft *Feu d' Artifice.*

Fair of St. Germains. We were in *Paris* at the time of the *Fair of St. Germain.* It lafts fix weeks at leaft: The Place where it is kept, well befpeaks its Antiquity; for it is a very Pit or Hole, in the middle of the *Fauxbourg*, and belongs to the Great Abbey of that Name. You defcend into it on all fides, and in fome places above 12 Steps; fo that the City is raifed above it fix or eight Foot. The

The Building is a very Barn, or Frame
of Wood, tiled over; confifting of many
long Allies, cro.Ting one another, the Floor
of the Allies unpaved, and of Earth, and
as uneven as may be: which makes it
very unealie to walk in, were it not the
valt croud of People which keep you up.
But all this befpeaks its Antiquity, and the
rudenefs of the firit Ages of *Paris*, which is
a foil to its Politenefs in all things elfe now.

The Fair confifts moft of Toy-fhops,
and *Bartholomew*-Fair Ware; alfo Fiance
and Pictures, Joiners Work, Linnen and
Woollen Manufactures; many of the great
Ribban Shops remove out of the Palais
hither: No Books: Many Shops of Con-
fectioners, where the Ladies are commodioufly treated.

The Toys or *Bijou* here are very prittily
invented and well finifht: and, indeed,
their Heads are always at work either to
add to the Old, or to invent New: but
they are extravantly dear. Some few
Shops there were in this Place and in the
Palais, which fold upon Honour, and to
all People whatfoever, Strangers and Natives alike; the explicite Prifes being writ
at length upon every thing in the Shop.
This was a very quick and eafie way of
buying, if you could have Faith enough to
believe them a penniworth.

The

The great Rendezvous is at night, after the Play and Opera are done ; and Raffling for all Things vendible is the great Diverſion ; no Shop wanting two or three Raffling-Boards. Monſieur, the Dauphin, and other Princes of the Blood come, at leaſt once in the Fair-time, to Grace it.

Here are alſo Coffee-Shops, where that and all ſorts of ſtrong Liquors above-mentioned are to be Sold.

Knavery here is in perfection as with us ; as dextrous Cut-Purſes and Pick-Pockets. A Pick-Pocket came into the Fair at Night, extreamly well Clad, with four Lacqueys with good Liveries attending him : He was caught in the Fact, and more Swords were drawn in his Defence than againſt him ; but yet he was taken, and delivered into the Hands of Juſtice, which is here ſudden and no jeſt.

I was ſurpriſed at the Impudence of a Booth, which put out the Pictures of ſome Indian Beaſts with hard Names ; and of four that were Painted, I found but two, and thoſe very ordinary ones, *viz.* a Leopard, and a Racoun. I ask'd the Fellow, why he deceived the People, and whether he did not fear Cudgelling in the end : He anſwered with a ſingular Confidence, that it was the Painter's fault ;

that

that he had given the Racoun to Paint
to two Mafters, but both had miftaken
the Beaft; but however, (he faid) tho'
the Pictures were not well defign'd, they
did neverthelefs ferve to Grace the Booth
and bring him Cuftom.

I faw here a Female *Elephant* betwixt Elephant.
8 and 9 foot high, very lean and ill kept.
Nothing could be more Docil, than this
poor Creature. I obferved, fhe bent the
Joints of her Legs very nimbly in making
her Salutes to the Company: Alfo that
the Nails of her Fore Toes, were large,
and almoft five Inches long. This was
from the Continent, having the Ears
entire. I had feen one about 13 Years a-
go in *London* much lefs, from the Ifland
of *Ceylon*, of another Species with *Scallop Ears*, and the Tail with two rows of
large, thick, and ftiff black Hairs.

Coaching in Vifits is the great and daily Coaching.
Bufinefs of People of Quality: But in
the Evenings, the *Cours de la Reyne* is
much frequented, and a great Rendezvous
of People of the beft Fafhion. The Place
indeed is very commodious and pleafant,
being three Alleys fet with high Trees of
a great length, all along the Bank of the
River *Seine*, inclofed at each end with

noble

noble Gates; and in the middle a very
large Circle to turn in. The middle Alley
holds four lines of Coaches at leaſt, and
each ſide Alley two a-piece : Theſe eight
lines of Coaches may, when full, ſuppoſing
them to contain near 80 Coaches a-piece,
amount to about 6 or 700. On the Field
ſide, joyning cloſe to the Allies of the
Coaches, there are ſeveral Acres of Mea-
dow planted with Trees, well grown, into narrow Allies in *Quincunx* Order, to
walk in the Graſs, if any have a mind to
light; and this muſt needs be very agreeable in the Heats of Summer, which we
ſtaid not to enjoy.

One thing this *Cours* is ſhort of ours in
Hide-Park, for if full, you cannot in an
hour ſee the Company twice you have a
mind to ſee, and you are confined to your
line; and oftentimes, the Princes of the
Blood coming in, and driving at Pleaſure,
make a ſtrange ſtop and embarras.

Beſides, if the Weather has been Rainy,
there is no driving in it, it is ſo Miry and
ill Gravelled.

Thoſe, who have a mind to drive further
out of Town for the Air, have Woods,
one to the Weſt, and another to the Eaſt,
moſt convenient. I mean, the *Bois de
Bologne, and the Bois de Vincennes;* this
laſt

laft is very opaque and pleafant. There are fome Ancient Roman Statues in the firft Court of this Houfe.

But for the Caftle in the *Bois de Bologne*, called *Madrid*, it was built by *Francis the Firft*, and it is altogether *Morefque*, in imitation of one in *Spain:* with at leaft two rows of covered Galleries running quite round, on the out-fide the four faces of the Houfe ; which fure in a very hot Country, are greatly refrefhing and delightful : And this is faid to be built on purpofe for a defence againft a much hotter Climate, than where it ftands ; which that King had no mind to vifit a fecond time.

But let us return to *Paris.* Towards 8 *Walking.* or 9 a Clock in *June* moft of them return from the *Cours*, and land at the Garden Gate of the *Tuilleries*, where they *Walk* in the cool of the Evening. This Garden is of the beft Ordonnance, and now in its full beauty, fo that Monfieur *Le Noftre* has feen it in its Infancy, for it is all of his Invention, and he enjoys his Labours in perfection. Certainly the *Moving Furniture* of it at this time of the Evening, is one of the Nobleft Sights, that can be feen. The Night I came away from *Paris*, a Lady of Quality, Madam *M* —— when I took my Leave of her, askt me, What I
had

had feen in *Paris*, that moft pleafed me;
I anfwered her civilly, as I ought to do;
but fhe would not take my Compliment,
but urged me for a further Anfwer: I told
her, (fince fhe would have it fo) that I
juft then came from feeing what pleafed
me beft; that was, the *Middle Walk* of the
Tuilleries in *June*, betwixt 8 and 9 at
Night. I did not think that there was in
the World a more agreeable place, than
that Alley at that hour, and that time of
the Year.

And now we are got into the *Gardens* of
Paris, I fhall give you a fhort tafte of all
of them of Note, at leaft of fuch as I faw.

Tuilleries. This of the *Tuilleries* is vaftly great,
has fhaded Tarraffes on two fides, one a-
long the River *Seine*, planted with Trees,
very diverting, with great Parterrs in the
middle, and large Fountains of Water,
which conftantly *Play*; one end is the
Front of that Magnificent Palace the *Louvre*; the other is low, and for Profpects,
open to the Fields. The reft is difpofed
into Alleys, and Grafs-Plots, and Copfes
of Wood; with a *great number of Seats*
upon Down in all parts, for the Accom-
modation of the Weary.

In

In the *Tuilleries* there is one thing, which I much liked, and that was an Amphitheatre of cut Hedges, with the Stage, Pits, and Seats, and the Scenes leading into the Stage very pretty; from all fides clofe Alleys leading into it.

Nothing can be more pleafant, than this Garden, where in the Groves of Wood the latter end of *March, Black-Birds* and *Throftles,* and *Nightingales* fing moft fweetly all the Morning, and that as it were within the City; for no Birding is fuffered here near this City, and the Fields round the Town, are all, every where, full of Partridges, and Hares, and other Game.

The *Garden* of the *Palace of Luxenbourg* is alfo vaftly great, and has fomething of Champatre in it, like St. *James's-Park* ; it is alfo filled with People daily of good Quality; but becaufe the hard Winters have deftroyed many of the Walks, by killing the Pole-Hedges, it is not fo frequented, as formerly; yet it hath its Fountains and Parterres, and fome well fhaded Alleys; and for Air, I prefer it before the *Tuilleries,* becaufe it is feated upon a high Ground next the Fields, in the *Fauxbourg* of St. *Germains.*

Luxenbourg *Garden.*

As

As to the King's *Phyſick Garden*, it is a very great piece of Ground, well furniſht with Plants, and open alſo to Walk in, to all People of Note. There is great variety of Ground in it, as Woods, Ponds, Meadows, Mounts, beſides a vaſt Level, by which it is fitted for the Reception and Growth of moſt ſorts of Plants.

I firſt ſaw it in *March* with Dr. *Turnefort*, and Mr. *Breman*, a very Underſtanding and Painful Gardner. The Green Houſes well ſtored with tender *Exoticks*, and the Parterrs with *Simples*; though but few of them then to be ſeen; yet by the Trees and Shrubs, and ſome Plants, which did not loſe their Heads, I could well judge of the Furniture.

Dr. *Turnefort* told me, that he ſhewed 100 Plants every Leſſon, and he had in the Summer 30 Leſſons, which made 3000 Plants; beſides the very early and late Plants, which he reckoned could not be leſs than 1000 more.

I took particular notice of theſe Plants in the Green Houſes at that time.

Jaſminum Aſoricum flore albo viridarii Regis Luſitanici.

Marum Cortuſii, which had been Potted 30 years.

Caryo-

Caryophyllus Creticus arborescens.
Smilax fructu nigro.
Iris bulbosa flore luteo.
Symphytum minus Boraginis flore.
Fraxinus Americana florida.
Stæchas folio serrato Bauhini.

This Garden is endowed by the King and Duke of *Orleans*, and has 2000 *l.* a Year *Sterling* Rents belonging to it, whereof 500 *l.* is given to the chief Physician who over-looks all, and the rest to the Botanic Reader, Dr. *Turnefort*, and under-Gardeners, with Lodgings for all.

Mr. *Breman* told me, he had in the beginning of *April* made an end of Sowing his Hot Beds, and had put into the Ground 2000 Species of Seed.

From the Mount in the King's Garden, on the other side the River, upon the declivity of a high ridge of Hills, I had a fair view of the Palace or Country-House of *Father la Chaise*, the King's Confessor; it is very finely seated against the South Sun, and well Wooded on both sides. A fit Seat for a Contemplative Person.

The Garden of the *Palais-Royal*, considering it is in the middle of the Town, is

Garden of the Palais-Royal.

is very large, has two or three great Bafins with their *jet d'Eau*, but not well kept; nor hath any thing elegant in it, but the good order and difpofition of its fhady Walks and Parterrs. It is ever full of good Company.

Garden of the Arfe-nal. The *Garden of the Arfenal* is much larger, and finer kept; has the profpects of the Fields, and lies open to the Ram-parts. It is alfo much frequented for the beauty of its Walks.

There are alfo divers Convents, which have fpacious and well kept Gardens, which are always open and publick to People of any Note; as the *Carthufians,* which is vaft and Champeftre. The *Ce-leftins,* very fine and large; That of St. *Genevieve,* which is great and very well kept; and the *Tarraffe* for length and breadth is incomparable, extreamly well planted with *Horfe-chefnuts;* having alfo on the South-fide upon the *Tarraffe,* three or four fquare Copfes of the fame Trees; which have a marvellous effect for Shade in Summer.

Thefe Private Gardens *I faw in* Paris.

D'Aumont. Its *Green Houfe* opened into the Dining-Room: The Orange-Trees feemed

feemed to have fuffered, and had their Leaves withered; for the Room was too broad by half.

The *Treillage*, at the upper end of the Garden , was very well adorned with Gilding, and had in the middle a Pavillon, in which was an old *Roman* Statue of a young Man, very well preferved. The fafhion of the *Toga* here was fo evident, that it might well pafs for a conviction to thofe, who have thought it to be a Plade, or a Garment open before like a Cloak.

This Treillage is performed with that variety of Ornaments, that it refembles Filegreen Work, and is large. The Painting of thefe Works in green is not well performed in all places alike; it is either too yellow, or of a fad dirty green, or Sea-green; few have hit the right Grafs-green colour. To do it well, it is to be primed in yellow, and then to be covered with *Vert de Montagne* or *Lapis Armeniacus*; of which laft colour we have plenty in *England* about *Maulham* in *Craven* in *York-fhire*.

This is the great benefit of Treillage in Cities, that befides the beauty of it to the Eye, it takes away and hides the ill profpect of the Neighbouring Houfes.

Here

Here were very many *Fig-Trees* well
grown in fquare Boxes ; and Parterrs well
ftockt with Flowers ; each fort by themfelves ; as *Tulips* a-part ; *Junkills* a-part;
Anemonies a-part ; *Ranunculus's* a-part ;
Daffadills a-part.

Puiffart. This Garden is very neat, and
open at the end to the *Tuilleries.* The
Treillage-Walk or Arbor at the upper end
is very fine, 70 Paces long, and 8 broad,
hath three Pavillons, all open at the top.
It is all of Iron, painted green, and coft
15000 Livres.

The Gardner was an Artift, and had fome
Plants in Cafes in good order, not to be
feen elfewhere, as large Rofemary Bufhes,
Jacobæa Maritima, Marum Syriacum, &c.

The Walls were well covered with Fruit-
Trees ; he had not cut his Peaches ; when
I askt him the reafon, he told me, it was
his way, not to cut them, till after flowring,
which he found by Experience to improve
the Fruit ; whereas he faid, the early cutting Stockt them, and impaired the Fruit.

The *Orangery* here was the moft beautiful Room, for the bignefs, I had feen, paved
with Marble, and neatly Wainfcoted with
Oak, from the top to the bottom, after
our *Englifh* manner. I make no doubt it
ferved to eat in in Summer, when cleared
of Trees.   *Bou-*

Bouvillier. I found not any thing more remarkable here, than the Treillage at the end.

Cormartin. The Treillage in this Garden was moſt admirable in the faſhion of a Triumphal Arch; half of it was an *Aviary*, with a Fountain in it, well ſtored with Birds.

Here were large Iron *Vaſa's* upon Pedeſtals, the firſt I had ſeen of the kind, painted over of a Copper colour.

Les Diguieres. This is the only Houſe in *Paris*, I ſaw kept, in all the parts of it, with the moſt exact cleanlineſs and neatneſs, Gardens and all.

In the Garden there were ſeveral pieces of Treillage; that at the upper-end was very noble, and coſt 10000 Livres; another piece of it coſt 6000. And I ſaw a ſmall one all of Iron-leaves painted green, the only one of the kind. Here alſo were *great Vaſa's of Treillage* upon Pedeſtals.

The Fountains in this Garden were very curious, tho' ſmall, with proper Ornaments, which had a marvellous Effect, when the Spouts plaid off.

O   The

The firſt Court was ſet about with Caſes of extraordinary large *Laurus Tinus*, and in the Gardens there were ſome cut into ſquare Pyramids.

A Perſon of Quality came into the Garden to me, who with great Civility conducted me up to the Apartments.

In the Apartment of the Dutcheſs, which was all of her own Contrivance, and had an Air of State and agreeableneſs beyond any thing I had ſeen, I obſerved, hanging down in the middle of the Bedchamber, the fineſt Cryſtal Candleſtick in *France :* The Pieces were all bought ſingle by her, and the contrivance and ſetting them together was her own ; it coſt 12000 Crowns.

But before I left the Garden, in an obſcure Parterre I ſaw the Tomb of a Cat, *viz.* a Black Cat Couchant upon a White Marble Cuſhion, fringed with Gold, and Gold Taſſels hanging at the Corners upon a ſquare Black Marble Pedeſtal. On one of the ſides of that Marble is writ in Letters of Gold.

Cy giſt Menine la plus amiable & la
Plus aimee de toutes les chattes.

On

On the other fide.

Cy gist une chatte jolie :
Sa maistresse, qui n' aimoit rien,
L' aime jusques à la folie
Pour quoy dire ! on le voit bien.

This is not the firft inftance of this kind of Folly : I have feen fomething of it in *England*; and have read much more in Hiftory.

If you blame me for tranfcribing this Epitaph, I will fubmit ; but I could never have forgiven my felf, if I had tranfcribed the many fine Infcriptions I met with at *Paris*, though in moft elegant and truly *Roman* Words; others in pure Court *French*. You may read them in the *Defcription of Paris*.

De Lorge. We had the good Fortune here to find the Marfhal himfelf walking in his Garden ; who entertained us with great Civility, *viz.* the Dean of *Winchefter* and my felf. This Garden was not finifh'd, and the Houfe it felf was but building; but it is one of the fineft in *Paris*, and has the advantage of a moft free and extended Profpect of the Fields and *Montmartre :* At the end of the Gar-

　　　　O 2　　　　　　den

den rifes a Terrafs equal with the Rampart.

That which was in this Houfe and Garden very commodious and noble was, that betwixt the two Courts the Coaches drive through a ftately Hall upon Pillars, and might land on either fide, up a ftep or two, which leads to the Staircafes and other Apartments; and then in the furtheft Court, which is only divided from the Garden by high Palifadoes of Iron, they turn, and take up the Company again; fo that no Weather offends them: Which is much wanting here; and more with us at *London*, where we moft need it.

This Hall is open upon Arches to the Garden, and the Staircafe it felf is fo contrived, that you enjoy a full Profpect of the Garden and *Montmartre* in defcending.

The Marfhal very obligingly fhewed us his own Apartment; for all the reft of the Houfe was full of Workmen; and in his Bedchamber his little *red Damask Field-Bed*, which he lay in now, and which alfo ferved him when he commanded upon the *Rhine*.

He fhewed us his great *Safh-Windows*, how eafily they might be lifted up and down, and ftood at any height; which Con-

Contrivance of Pullies, he faid, he had out of *England*, by a fmall Model, brought on purpofe from thence : There being nothing of this *Poife* in Windows in *France* before.

He alfo had us into a Sett of fmall Clofets or Rooms, after the *Englifh* fafhion, very prettily furnifhed, neatly kept, and retired, with his *Englifh* Keys to them, as he told us : And from thence we defcended a back Pair of Stairs. We did all we could to hinder him from feeing us take Coach : He fent his Page after us, to invite us fome day to eat with him.

Hoftel Pelletier. The Garden here was very neat, with a Treillage at the end, after the manner of a Triumphal Arch, but not very high, nor well painted; yet its Beauty and Finifhings differ much from any I had feen before. In the two Niches were plac'd great Iron Vafa's, or Flower-Pots, right before the middle of a Bafin of Water, which was fet a playing for our Entertainment, which is a Compliment the French are willing to oblige Strangers with.

In the *Orangerie* were very large Trees, and two pair of Mirtles in Cafes, cut Globewife, the beft and biggeft I had feen : Large Bufhes in Pots of *Marum Syriacum.* Great

O 3   ftore

ftore of Tulips, Anemonies, Ranunculus,
and other Flowers in Beds, in the Parterre,
each by themfelves.

Alfo Anemonies and Ranunculus's in
little earthen Pots, as with us ; but in very light Mold. Great and very fair *Laurus Tinus's* in Cafes. And which was fingular, a long one of the Garden Walls
were planted *Abel Trees*, whofe tops were
difpofed and fpread by an Iron Treillage into Arches at equal diftances, which had a
very good effect.

Hoftel-ful-　　The Garden of the *Hoftel-fullie* had no-
lie.　　thing remarkable in it.

Louvois.　　The beft Piece of Treillage of Iron Bars
and Wood intermixt, is that in the *Garden
of feu Mons Louvois*. And this is one of
the neateft Gardens in *Paris*. The whole
upper-end is adorned with a noble Treillage after the manner of a Triumphal
Arch ; it coft a great Sum of Money :
There are four Statues difpofed on Pedeftals under it, which have a good Effect ;
thefe are Antique, rarely good. One of
the firft Empreffes, a *Diana*, an *Apollo, &c.*
Here the Walks are hard Gravel, but not
rolled. On one fide of the Treillage is a
large *Aviary* well ftored with Birds.

The

The Walls of the Green-Houſe are *mat-*
ted; and large *Pans of Iron* hang down in
the middle of the Houſe, at equal diſtances, to every Window one : They have
Pullies to let them down, or run them up
to what height they pleaſe. This way may
very well correct the moiſtneſs of the Air,
which the *breath of the Plants* cauſe, and
ſufficiently warm them. Hot Beds puff
up Plants; yet a warm Air over their
Heads may be as uſeful to refreſh and nou-
riſh them in Winter.

The laſt private Garden I ſaw was that *Furnier.*
of Mr. *Furnier*, a few days before we left
the Town, nothing could be prettier. At
the upper-end a noble *Treillage*, two great
Vaſa's of Iron painted of a Braſs-colour and
gilt.

Here I ſaw an *Apple-Tree* potted, as the
Figs and *Oranges* uſe to be; it was the
White Queenen, (or *Calvil d'Eſte*) the Stem
of the bigneſs only of my Thumb, full of
Fruit the firſt of *June*.

Many Pots of *Sedum Pyramidale*, now a
moſt elegant Ornament. But nothing is
here ſo pompous as *double red and ſtrip'd*
Stockes; which they multiply with care;
and their Pains are juſtly rewarded : with
a thouſand other things, which my ſhort
turn in the Garden would not give me leave
to remember.

O 4   There

There are great numbers of thefe private Gardens in *Paris*, which deferve feeing ; but the Seafon of the Year not much favouring our Curiofity, we did not much enquire after them.

Hitherto I have given a fhort Account of what I faw moftly in *Paris*, as to the People, abroad and at home : The Country round about it, is full of populous and neat Towns, and many Palaces of the King and Princes of the Blood; which are not to be equalled with any thing we have in *England*. But I am unwilling to lead you any further, it being much out of my way and humour to go to Court ; but becaufe it was my fortune to be at *Verfails*, *St. Clou*, *Marli*, and *Meudon*, I will venture to fay fomething of each.

These four Royal Palaces and their Gardens poffefs a barren and hilly Country, as big as moft Counties in *England :* Two of them *Meudon* and *St. Clou*, have the Profpect of *Paris* under them; but the former hath it much more open and fully than the latter.

This Diftrict may be faid to be *Le Berceau des Roys*, or the Nurfery of Kings ; for the chief of the Blood-Royal are lodged here, *viz.* the King, Monfeigneur the Dauphin, and the three Grandfons, the Dukes

Dukes of *Burgundy, d'Anjou,* and *Berry,* Monfieur or the King's Brother, and his Son the Duke of *Chartres,* and Madamoifelle his Daughter. All thefe are, or will be (as it is eafie to guefs by the growth and proportions of the youngeft) very large and well-fhaped beautiful People. The other Branch of the Blood Royal, of the Houfe of *Bourbon,* as the Prince of *Conde,* the Duke of *Bourbon,* and the Princeffes his Daughters, the Prince of *Conti,* are all of lefs Stature, but very well fhaped and handfom.

The Duke *du Maine* and the *Conte de Toulouse* I did not fee; but the Princefs Dowager of *Conti* often, who is without difpute one of the moft graceful, and handfomeft Women in *France,* and methinks exceedingly like the King her Father, as I remember him in his full beauty, when I firft faw him in the Year —65.

Thefe four Palaces are all intirirely built and furnifh'd in this King's time, and all the Gardens, and what belongs to them.

St. *Clou* is the neareft *Paris,* and the Caftle is very magnificent, and moft commodious. The great *Salon* and the *Gallery* are extreamly well painted. St. *Clou.*

The Gardens are of a vaft extent, twelve or fifteen Miles in compafs.

The

The Natural *Woods* on the South-weſt ſide the Houſe, are well husbanded, and cut into ſmall and bigger Alleys, to ſave the Trees; which they have had ſo great a care of, they have kept them ſtanding not only in the Alleys, but in the very *Steps of Stone*, which are made to deſcend into the Alleys.

In the other parts of the Garden the Alleys are moſtly treble, and well ſhaded, run out in vaſt lengths of ſeveral Miles, every where *Baſins and Jets d'eau*; but there is a *Caſcade*, which I ſaw ſeveral times play, and is ſaid to be the moſt beautiful and beſt furniſh'd with Water of any in *France*. In the middle of the large Baſin amongſt the Woods, I ſaw a *Jet d'eau*, which threw up a Spout of Water ninety Foot high, and did diſcharge it ſelf with that force, that it made a miſt and coolneſs in the Air a great compaſs round about, and gave now and then cracks like the going off of a Piſtol; ſuch force the vent of Wind in the Pipes had.

The Pipes which convey the Water are compoſed of Iron Cylinders ſcrew'd together, three Foot long, ſome ten, ſome twenty Inches diameter, till they divide; and then they are of Lead.

I was once kindly invited to St. *Clou* by Madam's Phyſician, Monſieur *Arlot*, who

who fent his Coach for me to *Paris*, and nobly treated me : Before Dinner he carried me in his Coach (for this Priviledge is granted him) into all Parts, and round the Gardens; which were well furnifh'd with Alleys and Walks, adorned with Cyprefs, Pines, and Firrs, cut into Pyramids; and Water-works every where playing in abundance, particularly the *Gerbes d'eau* were very fine, that is, great and thick feeming Streams of Water thrown up into the Air. This is done to husband the Water by a great number of fmall Pipes like a *Sheaf*, to reprefent a folid Pillar of Water.

Monfieur has added, and taken into this vaft Garden, a new acquifition of a *Mountainous Plain*, which over-looks all the Country round; and will, no doubt, when it is modelled by that admirable Contriver Monfieur *le Noftre*, make one of the moft delightful places in the World.

From the Baluftrade in the upper Garden, the River *Seine* and a vaft plain bounded by *Paris*, is to be feen, and makes a moft delightful Profpect.

Thefe vaft *riding Gardens* are unknown to us in *England*, and *fe promener a cheval, ou en caroffe*, is not *Englifh*. We cannot afford to lofe fo much Country as thofe Gardens take up. I faw in fome of the Quarters

ters

ters not only Partridge and Hares plentifully, but, which I wonder at, five *Bitches*, or Female Red Deer feeding.

The *Orangery* belonging to this Garden is very large and magnificent, paved with Marble, and was filled with vaſt Trees in Caſes, not to be brought in or out without proper Engines, but in it there was nothing but thoſe Orange-Trees, Oleanders, and *Laurus Tinus's*. He goes out of the end of his Apartment, that is, the noble painted Gallery is continued upon a level with the Orangery, which leads directly into an aſcending Walk of a vaſt length ; and alſo fronts or flanks all along the Parterre or Flower-Garden ; where they are diſpoſed of in Summer. At this Treat I eat of a Preſerve or wet Sweetmeat, made of Orange Flowers, incomparable ; and the Lady obliged me with the manner of making it.

Though there were high and proper Walls for Fruit in many parts of the Garden, yet nothing of that nature was to be found, only ordinary and *infructiferous Greens* were faſtned to the Treillage, which are the Linings of moſt Walls here. In the Garden are many Arbours of Treillage, Pavillons, *&c.* of Iron mixt with Wood, painted Green, with Honeyſuckles running up them. Theſe Gardens have a-
bove

bove 150 People always imployed to keep them in order; which ſtands in 4000 Livres a Year.

Another time I din'd with the Captain of the Caſtle, who ſhewed me all the Apartments at leiſure. I eat here of the Red-legg'd Partridge taken here upon theſe Hills: They are much leſs here than in *Languedoc*, but yet far better taſted than the Grey Partridges taken in the ſame place. This was the beginning of *April*, and we drank our Wine in Ice, which I was not aware of, till I found the bad effect of it in my Throat; and the next Day much more; but it went off again without any great trouble. There is no Animal that abuſes it ſelf in Meat and Drink as Man does: we daily drink exceſſive hot and exceſſive cold; in other Creatures it is Inſtinct that guides them, but as for us we neither act by Inſtinct nor Reaſon; but betwixt both *looſely*, and therefore oftner are catch'd to our own Deſtruction.

At the end of the Apartments of *Monſieur*, are a fine Sett of Cloſets: The firſt you enter is furniſh'd with great variety of Rock Cryſtals, Cups, Agats upon ſmall Stands, and the ſides of the Rooms are lined with large Panes of Looking-glaſs from top to the bottom, with

with Japan Varnish and Paintings of e-
qual breadth intermix'd ; which had a
marvellous pretty effect.   The other Room
had in it a a vaft quantity of *Bijou*, and
many of very great price ; but the *Siam
Pagods*, and other things from thence, were
very odd.

There was alfo one very fmall *Roman
Statue* of White Marble, not ten Inches
high, which coft 20000 Crowns; one Leg
of it was a little injured.   It feemed a Piece
of admirable Workmanfhip.   It was a *Boy*,
who had in the Skirt of his Tunic *a Litter
of Puppies*, and the *Bitch* lying at his Feet
and looking up.

Meudon.   I cannot fay much of *Meudon*, becaufe
I was not within the Houfe or Park ; it
will require yet fome time to bring it to
that Perfection which is defigned ; for that
Monfeigneur has been but lately poffeffed
of it.   The Road from *Paris* to it is yet unpaved ; but the Situation is admirable, and
the *Splanade* before the Houfe is like a vaft
Baftion, and commands the full view of all
the Campagne, and *Paris* under it.   The
Gardens are very great, but I only coaft-
ed them and the Houfe.

Verfailles.   As to the Palace of *Verfailles*, (which is
yet fome Miles further within the Moun-
tainous Country, not unlike *Black-Heath*,
or *Tunbridge*) 'tis without difpute the moft
                                              magnifi-

magnificent of any in *Europe* : Yet what
of it was firſt built, and much admired
thirty Years ago, is now no longer reliſht.
However this King intends to rebuild it
where it is faulty. 'Tis, as I ſaid, plac'd
in a very ungrateful Soil, without Earth
proper for Herbs, or Water ; but he hath
brought that to it in abundance, and made
the Ground too to be fruitful.

There are Books writ to deſcribe this
famous Palace in every part ; to which I
refer the Reader. The way to it is new,
and in ſome places the Mountains are cut
down forty Foot, ſo that now you enjoy it
a Mile in Proſpect, before you come to it ;
it opens and cloſes in three Courts, the more
remoteſt, narrower and narrower ; which
is a fault ; and is, as I was told, deſigned
to be pulled down, and made into one
noble large ſquare Court of the ſame order of Building, as that magnificent Front
is which looks upon the Gardens. The gild-
ded Tiles and Roof have a marvellous effect in Proſpect. The Splanade towards
the Gardens and Parterres are the nobleſt
things that can be ſeen, vaſtly great, with
a very large Baſin of Water in the middle,
low walled round with white Marble, on
which are placed a great number of incomparable brazen Vaſa, and large Braſs
Figures *Couchant,* of the beſt Maſters in
Sculpture ;

Sculpture; it were endlefs to tell all the Furniture of thefe Gardens, of Marble Statues, and Vafa of Brafs and Marble; the multitude of Fountains, and thofe wide Canals like Seas running in a ftreight Line from the bottom of the Gardens, as far as the Eye can reach.

In a word, thefe Gardens are a Country laid out into Alleys and Walks, Groves of Trees, Canals and Fountains, and every where, more efpecially the chief Walks, adorned with ancient and Modern Statues and Vafa innumerable.

May the 17th. the Waters were ordered to play for the Diverfion of the *Englifh* Gentlemen. The playing of the Spouts of Water, thrown up into the Air, is here diverfified after a thoufand fafhions. The *Theatre des eaux*, and the *Triumphal Arch* are the moft famous Pieces. But in the Groves of the Left Hand, you have *Æfop's Fables*, in fo many Pieces of Water-Works, here and there in Winding-Alleys. This might have been faid to be done *in ufum Delphini*. 'Tis pretty to fee the Owl wafh'd by all the Birds; the *Monky* hugging her young one, till it fpouts out Water with a full Throat, and open Mouth, *&c.*

The *Orangery*, or Confervatory for Tubs of Winter Greens, is what correfponds
to

to the greatnefs of the reft. 'Tis a ftupendious *half Square* of under-ground
Vaults, like the Naves of fo many Churches
put together, of exquifite Workmanfhip
in hewn Stone, well lighted and open to
the South Sun.   It contains 3000 **Cafes of**
Greens; whereof near 2000 are Orange-
Trees, and many hundreds of them are as
big as generally they naturally grow in the
Earth.   Hence amongft them are fome,
which are faid to be in Cafes from the
time of *Francis* the Firft.

They did not think fitting to put them
out this Year till the latter end of *May;*
and indeed the Oleanders, Laurels, Lentifcus's, and moft other Greens, had fuffered miferably.

In the *Pottagerie* (which is part of thefe
Gardens, and hath its magnificence alfo)
there are 700 Cafes of *Figs,* befides Wall-
Fruit of all other kinds.   By all the Gar-
dens in and about *Paris,* I perceived they
are very fond of this Fruit.
   I obferved in fmall Fiance or Painted
Pots a vaft number of the narrow-leaved
Laurus Alexandrina; alfo *Thlapfi flore albo,*
Leucoii folio, latifolium; alfo the *Sedum Py-*
ramidale.   Thefe are not yet Ornaments
in our Gardens, that I know of, nor a
                    P   great

great many other Plants, which I obferved
in Flower there; and at my return gave a
Catalogue of them to Mr. *London* that he
might fend for them, if he pleafed. The
Plants I obferved were Vivace or Perennal.

Marli.

The 15*th* of *May* my Lord Ambaffador
went to *Marli*, where the Waters played
for his Diverfion.

I muft needs fay it is one of the pleafanteft Places I ever faw, or, I believe, is
in *Europe*; it is feated in the Bofom or
upper end of a high Valley, in the midft
of and furrounded with Wooddy Hills.
The Valley is clofed at the upper end,
and gently defcends forwards by degrees,
and opens wider and wider, and gives
you the profpect of a vaft plain Country,
and the River *Seine* running through it.

Marli is a fquare Houfe raifed upon
Steps, and Terraffed on all fides: The four
Fronts all alike; and the Doors opening
into the Garden all the fame. In the
middle an *Octogon-Hall*, running up Dome-
wife, in which all the fide Rooms meet;
which are all Rooms of State. Above are
12 Lodgings, with a narrow Gallery leading to them. In the lower Rooms at *Marli*,
particularly in the *Octogon Salon*, are extraordinary large (fix foot at leaft) Marble,
or rather *Agat Tables*; To the beft of
which

which they may be compared. They are veined like Wood, and of an Amber colour; Thefe are the admirable effect of Petrif-cation. Of this very Stone I have feen great Blocks in the Banks of the *Dropping-Well* at *Knaresborough* in *York-fhire.* I forgot to ask here whence they had them.

In one of the Ground Rooms was a Semicircular *Gilt Bar* or Rail, which took off and inclofed the upper end of the Room : Within the Bar was difpofed feveral Rows of Procellain or fine China on Gilt Shelves. Here at the Corners, within the Bar, opened two fmall Doors, whence the Ambaffador and his Retinue were plentifully ferved with Chocolate, Tea, and Coffee, in a moft obliging manner. Many of the Nobility and Gentlemen of *France* were ordered to attend him there.

The two fide Fronts of the Houfe have in profpect great Alleys cut through the Woods, and paved for the more commodious coming down to the Houfe ; which is defcending all the way.

On each fide the Valley, clofe under the Woods, run along in a line, fix fquare Pavillons or fmaller Palaces of the very fame figure and beauty with the *Mother-Houfe* ; at equal, but large diftances, as 500 Paces. The fix on the right hand the Garden are for the Men; The other fix on the left are for the Women of Quality whom the King weekly appoints, upon a Lift given, to attend him, and enjoy the Pleafure of this Retirement, as I may fay, from Court. Before thofe Pavillons, and betwixt them, are the fineft Alleys and Walks imaginable, with Fountains, and all the Decorations of Treillage and Flowers. Such a Shew of *not ordinary Tulips* in broad Beds, of 1000 Paces long, every where, all this vaft Garden over, in their full beauty, was a moft furprifing fight. I could not forbear to fay to the Duke *de Villeroy*, who was pleafed much to accompany me in this Walk, That fure all the Gardens in *France* had contributed to this Profufion of Flowers; which he took fo well, that the *Marifhal his Father*, afterwards detached himfelf to fingle me out, and very obligingly embraced and faluted me, and followed it with very kind and familiar Difcourfe.

The *Cafcade* coming down from the brow of the Hill, on that Front of the Houfe which refpects and ftands near it, was new and fingular, and of the King's own invention, as, indeed, all the Garden befide. From the Houfe it appeared a *Broad River*, quietly gliding down the Hill; but when I went near it, I found it compofed of 52 large fquare and fhallow

low

low Bafins of Water, difpofed at right
Angles, and not declining, but falling over
one into another.

In the Garden were many Fountains,
nobly adorned, and had variety of Water-
Pipes playing up into the Air in them.
Here are fome *Gerbes* of a fingular fafhion,
with a Circle of a great number of large
Pipes, within at leaft two Foot diameter;
which made the appearance of a vaft Pillar of Water. There was one *Jet d'eau*
in the Bottom of the Garden, which we
were told threw up Water 120 foot high;
for of 50 and more Fountains, we faw
but thofe on the fide Alleys to play; moft
of the great Bafins in the middle were
mending and dry. To furnifh all this
Water, there is a moft ftupendious *Machine*, which was invented by two *Liegois*.
This Machine forces the Water up 560
foot, from the River *Seine*, to the top of
the Tower or Aqueduct. It throws up
500 Inches of Water by almoft continued
Ructations or quick Pulfes. It is wrought
by 14 Wheels of 32 feet diameter each,
fet in the River, and carried about Night
and Day by its Stream.

This Invention is the fame with what
is practifed in the deep Coal-pits about
Leeds in *Lower-Germany*; fo that to fee
the Engines, and a great number of Iron

P 3　　　　　Cylin-

Cylinders or Water-Pipes lying bare *above ground*, and running up a vaſt Mountain, is to imagine a deep Coal-Mine turned wrong-ſide outward.

The Tree moſt in uſe here, was the ſmall-leaved *Horn-Beam* ; which ſerves for *Arcades, Berceaus* ; and alſo *Standards* with Globular Heads : At the foot of which they have planted little *Sprigs* of the ſame of a foot and half high ; and alſo in ſome places in like manner, whole *areas* full of them ; which cut ſmooth and level, make the fineſt *green Hedges* I ever ſaw ; Some of theſe low Hedges were 12 foot broad, and in a barren and dry Climate ſupply very artificially the uſe of *Graſs-plots*.

'Tis certainly very commendable in the King, who pleaſes himſelf in Planting and Pruning the Trees with his own Hand, to make uſe of no other Trees, but what the Neighbouring Woods afford ; ſo that 'tis admirable to ſee whole Alleys of *Pole-Hedges* of great height, and long Rows of goodly Standard Globes of 18 months growth only.

If this great King, as he grows older, ſhould take a fancy to place himſelf in a *warmer Climate*, (and he has a good one of his own, as any under the Sun , in *Languedoc*) as he does his Winter Greens in proper Houſes ; and, methinks, this

Inſtance

Inftance alone fhould be fufficient, to convince him of the neceffity there is to cherifh decaying Nature, and that a Naturally warm Air is a better Fence, than Cloaths or Fire) what Wonders would not his Purfe and Paffion for Planting do there?

The next Woods in *Languedoc* would afford *Laurel*, and *Myrtles* for Pole-Hedges; *Lentifcus's* and *Phylarea's* in as great abundance, as Hazel or Thorn with us. Alfo *Jafmins* for Arbors and *Treillage*; *Ciftus's* and *Rofmary*, and a hundred other fweet fmelling Wooddy Shrubs grow every where in the Fields, to furnifh the *Pots* and *Vafa*.

There the tall *Cypres's* grow of themfelves, to 60 and 100 foot high, like fo many Towers; and alfo *Tonfil* at pleafure, for the moft beautiful Pole-Hedges imaginable. The very Fields are moft Excellent, and well furnifht Parterrs of Flowers, and are Naturally Pottageries, or Kitchin Gardens. The Vineyards are very Orchards; and all the moft tender Fruits with us are there *Standards*; as Figs, and Grapes of all forts, Apricocks, Peaches, Nectorins, Jujubs, &c. The delicious and large Cherries; and, whatever has been faid to the contrary, Pipins and Pears there are in far greater perfection, than with us, or in in any parts of *France* elfe, befides that happy Climate.

What was it for fo great a King to make a Walk from *Marli* to *Montpelier*, or (if I might choofe) to *Pefcenas*, feated in the bofom of a well-watered Valley, inclofed with *perfumed Hills*. 'Tis not half fo far as betwixt *Labor* and *Agria*, two Seats the *Mogul* has thus joined. This would Eternife his Name, above any Palace he has yet built, and bring to himfelf much Health in his old Age. The Gardens of the *Hefperides*, and the *Labyrinths of Cande* , fo famous in Hiftory, would be nothing to fuch wonderful Performances, as his Abilities and Happy Genius is capable of. For befides the Natural Product of the Country, the Climate alfo is capable of producing, and nourifhing with fmall Art and Expence, whatever Plants both the *Indies* can afford. Whereas, at this end of the World, we drudge in vain ; and force a Pleafure which is dead, and gone before we can well enjoy it : We have indeed a kind of Shew of the Summer Delights, but all on a fuddain we drop into a long and tedious Winter again. But we love the Places we are ufed to, or born in. Man, to fay the truth, is a very Animal, as any Quadrupede of them all ; and moft of his Actions are refolveable into Inftinct, notwithftanding the Principles which Cuftom and Education have fuperinduced.　　The

The pleafure of feeing is fcarce to be tired; but yet after two or three hours Walk in fo fine and great a Garden, I was forc'd to make a halt behind the Company, and glad to retire to the gilt *Bureau* in the Palace again, to refrefh my felf; where I found fome of the King's Officers waiting, and fome other Gentlemen of the Houfhold, who had made feveral Campagnes in *Flanders*. I had now more a mind to a Glafs of cool *Burgundy*, than the infignificant *Indian* Liquors; which though I knew was againft the fanctity of the place, yet nothing was denied me a Stranger. Here being alone, we fell into difcourfe of the *Englifh*, and of their King. They willingly allowed the *Englifh* to be truly Brave; and now in Peace they found alfo, that they were as Civil, and well Bred, as Brave; That no Nation had given the King and his Court that fatisfaction, that the *Englifh* had done; being curious and inquifitive after all good things; They did fee a great difference betwixt them and other Nations; They did not ftare, and carelefly run about, or hold up their Heads, and defpife what they faw; but had a true relifh of every good thing, and made a good Judgment of what was Commendable; and therefore the King took pleafure to have them fhewed every thing.

thing. This Difcourfe of the *Englifh* they concluded with a great Encomium of K. *William*.

As for their own King they were much in the Praife of him, as one may eafily imagine : That his Retirement hither was moftly for his Health; That he left *Ver- failles* every *Tuefday* Night, and came hither with a felect Company of Lords and Ladies; That he returned not till *Saturday* Night, and fometimes intermitted ten or fourteen days; fo that he fpent half of his time here in Repofe; That he was the moft affable Prince in the World, and never out of Humour, of a pleafant and open Converfation where it pleafed him; eafie of accefs, and never fent any one away difcontented; The moft Bountiful Mafter in the World, of which there were Ten thoufand Inftances; nothing of Merit in any Kind, but he moft readily and chearfully Rewarded, ever, of late years at leaft, preferring the Virtuous; fo on the other hand, he never fpared the Rebellious and Obftinate; That the Government of his People could not be carried on with lefs feverity and ftrict- nefs; nor the Taxes which was neceffary to fupport it, raifed; That he delighted not in Blood or Perfecution; but that the Art of Government had different Rules, according

according to the Climate and Nature of the People, where and upon whom it was to be put in practice. His great *Wisdom* appeared in nothing more, than in preserving himself amidst his Troops, his Converts, his Court and numerous Family, all in a manner fit for the Throne. The greatness of his Mind, and Magnificence, in his Buildings. This was the Sum of the Discourse these Gentlemen were pleased to entertain me with.

At my return to *Paris* I was to see the *Pipinerie*, or *Royal Nursery of Plants*, in the *Fauxbourgh* of *St. Honorie*; where I met the Master or Controuler of it, Monsieur *Morley*, one of the Ushers of the Bed-Chamber to the King. *The Pipinerie.*

He, like the rest of the *French* Nation, was Civil to me; and shewed me a Written Almanack of Flowring Plants for the whole Year, which he said was an Original; it might, indeed, be so in *French*, but we have had Almanacks for Fruit and Flowers, for every Month in the Year, printed divers times, for above this 30 Years, thanks to Mr. *Evelyn.*

This Ground inclosed with high Walls, is vastly big, as it ought to be, to supply the King's Gardens; Here are several Acres of young Pines, Cypresses, Vues, &c. also vast Beds of Stock July-Flowers, of

all

all forts of Bulbes, as Tulips, Daffadills, Crocus's, &c. and therefore I could eafily believe him, when he told me, he had fent from hence to *Marli* alone, in four years time, eighteen Millions of Tulips, and other Bulbous Flowers; for which he offered to fhew me his Memoires.

He further told me, that the furnifhing the *Trianon*, (a peculiar Houfe of Pleafure, with its Parterrs at the end of the Gardens at *Verfailles*) with Flower-Pots in feafon, every 14 days in the Summer, took up no lefs than 92000 Pots from hence.

Alfo from hence he could plant and furnifh in 14 days time, any new Garden the King fhould caufe to be made.

Here befides the Plants common to us and them, I faw a multitude of Pots well conditioned of *Stæchas citrina folio latiufculo*.

Alfo a fort of *Cotila*, which bore large Sun-Flowers of Marigolds, propagated by Slips, called by him *Amaroutre*.

In this Ground are feveral Houfes to lodge the tender Winter Greens; amongft the reft there is one very large, which I may call the *Infirmery of fick Orange-Trees*; which coming from *Genoa* by Sea, are here depofited in a peculiar Green Houfe; and there were in it, and then actually carrying out into the Air, (it was the 22*d.*

of

of *May* our Style) 300 Trees in Cafes as thick as a Man's Thigh; but after 10, and fome after 17 years cherifhing, had not yet got Heads decent enough to be removed, and to appear at Court , they being often forc'd to lop both Tops and Root, that they might recover them.

After all , it muft be faid, that this Magnificence, and the number of thefe Palaces and Gardens , are the beft and moft commendable effect of *Arbitrary Government*. If thefe Expences were not in time of Peace, what would be this Kings Riches, and the extream Poverty of the People? For it is faid, that every three years, fome fay much oftner, he has all the Wealth of the Nation in his Coffers; fo that there is a neceffity he fhould have as extravagant and incredible ways of expending it , that it may have its due circulation amongft the People.

But when this vaft Wealth and Power is turned to the Difturbance and Deftruction of Mankind, it is terrible; and yet it hath its ufe too: We and all *Europe* have been taught , by the Induftry of this great King, mighty Improvements in War; fo that *Europe* has been thefe twelve Years an Over-match for the *Turk*; and we for *France* by the continuation of the War. The Forty Millions *Sterling* which

which the late War hath, and will coft *England*, before all is paid, was well be-ftowed, if it had been for no other end, than to teach us the full ufe and practice of War; and in that Point to equal us with our Neighbours.

It was obferv'd by *Polybius* of the *Romans*, that wherever they met with an Enemy, that had better Weapons than themfelves, they changed with them; This Docility gained them the Empire of the World. On the contrary, thofe late Eaftern Ty-rants have defpifed Learning, and confe-quently muft fubmit to the more refined Valour of *Europe*. I fay, the Effects of Arbitrary Government, both in War and Peace, are Stupendious.

The *Roman Emperors*, becaufe abfolute Lords of the People, far out-did the Com-monwealth in Magnificent Buildings, both Publick and Private. *Auguftus* left *Rome* a Marble City, which he found of Brick only. *Nero* burnt it and rebuilt it, and a *Golden Palace* for himfelf, like a City. *Vefpafian* and *Titus* built Amphitheatres and Baths far furpaffing any Buildings now upon the face of the Earth; in one of which 120000 Perfons might fee and hear, and be feated with more conveni-ence, than upon our Stages *Adrian* vi-fited moft parts of the World, on purpofe

to

to build Cities. *Trajan* had his Name on every Wall, which he either reſtored, or built. His Pillar and Bridge over the *Danube* are Stupendious Monuments of his Expences.

The *Ægyptian* Kings built them Monuments, wherein they ſlaved their whole Nation, and which are the Wonders of the World to this day, the *Obelisks* I mean, and *Pyramids.*

The *Aſiatick Emperors* of *China* and *Japan* have outdone the *Europeans* in this kind of immenſe Buildings, as the Wall in *China*, the Cut Rivers and Sluces and Bridges there. In *Japan* the Buildings are no leſs incredibly great.

Of this Abſolute Dominion we have Examples even in thoſe two *American* Empires, of *Mexico* and *Peru.* In this laſt, meer Nature forc'd Impoſſibilities without Art, Tools, or Science. The *Cuſco* Fortreſs was a Maſter-piece, where Stones were laid upon Stones, which no Engine of ours could carry, or raiſe up ; or Tools better polliſh, and fit together ; where a Country near as big as all *Europe,* was turned into a Garden, and cultivated better than *Verſailles,* and Water-Works brought to Play and overſpread ſome thouſands of miles, where it never Rains. This was the only Arbitrary Government well

well applied to the good of Mankind,
I ever met with in History; where Roads
and Store-houses of Food and Raiment
were the Guides, and numbred the miles
for the Travellers, and the whole Empire turned into an useful and intelligible
Map.

As for the *Turks, Perfians,* and *Mogul,*
the whole Empire is intended solely for
the Pleasure of one Man; and here even
Tyranny it self is foully abused.
Yet I should be loth to see them in
any kind exemplified in *England.* In our
happy Island we see such Palaces and
Gardens, as are for the Health and Ease
of Man only; and what they want in
Magnificence, they have in Neatness.
There is not such a thing as a *Gravel
Walk* in or about *Paris,* nor a *Rowler* of
any fort; when it Rains the Tuilleries
are shut up, and one walks in Dirt some
days after. The Grass-Plots, or, as they call
them, *Bowling-Greens,* are as ill kept: they
clip them and beat them with flat Beaters
as they do their Walks. This puts me in
mind of what I saw in the Garden of the
Prince of Conde in *Paris* ; where there was
a Grassy Circle of about four foot wide,
round one of the Fountains in the middle
of the Garden; to keep this down, and
make

make it of a finer Turf, the Gardner had Teathered two *Black Lambs*, and two *White Kids*, at equal diſtances, which fed upon it. Whatever the effect was, I thought it look'd pretty enough ; and the little *Animals* were as ornamental as the Graſs.

All the Paintings and Prints made of late Years of the King make him look very old ; which in my mind is not ſo ; for he is plump in the Face, and is well coloured, and ſeems healthy, and eats and drinks heartily, which I ſaw him do : This is certainly an Injury to him, and poſſibly in complaiſance to the Dauphin, or worſe. This is the meaneſt Compliment I have known the French guilty of towards their Prince ; for there are every where Expreſ-ſions of another nature all over *Paris*. See *the Deſcription of Paris*, where they are collected and at large. The *Romans* un-der *Auguſtns*, (the firſt abſolute Maſter of that People, as this King is of the *French*) had upon this Subject from the People a much finer Thought and Wiſh, De noſtris *annis tibi Jupiter augeat annos.*

However it be,the King ſeems not to like *Verſailles* ſo well as he did ; and has an O-pinion, that the Air is not ſo good as elſe-where ; he leaves it (as I ſaid) every Week on *Tueſday* night, and goes moſtly to *Marli,* or *Meudon,* and ſometimes to the *Trianon,*

which

which is but at the end of the Gardens, and returns not to *Verfailles* till *Saturday* night : Befides his extraordinary removes to *Fontainbleau.* I wonder no body puts him in mind of that Paradife of *France*, *Languedoc*, where he may be with eafe in 4 days, at the rate that Kings ufe to travel. I had this Difcourfe at Table with one of the Introducteurs to the Ambaffador at *Ver- failles* ; but he could not bear it, it being againft the Intereft of all fetled Courts to remove, though it were never fo good for their Princes Health. I remember but of one Inftance in Hiftory, and that was *Auren- zebe* the *Great Mogul*, who in his middle Age fell defperately fick, and long languiflht at *Lahor* ; but took Advice of fome body about him, and went in his own Kingdom a progrefs of 1000 Miles to *Cafimire*, a very mild and temperate Climate, where he re- covered, and lived to above 100 years old, and is yet alive for ought I know.

The King now feldom or never plays, but contents himfelf fometimes with look- ing on ; but he hath formerly been enga- ged, and has loft great Sums. Monfieur *S.* rookt him of near a Million of Livres at Baffet, by putting falfe Cards upon him ; but was imprifon'd and banifh'd for it fome years.

Before

Before I give over the bufinefs of Gardens and Country, I will add fome Remarks, which feemed particular and new to me.

In the Kitchen-Gardens at and near *Paris*, are a great number of *Apricock Standards*; but kept low; very full of Bloffoms and good Bearers.

They make a Conferve of the Fruit; which I like above any of their wet Sweetmeats; it was made by cutting them into thin Slices, and throwing away the Stone; which our People fpare fometimes, and leave in the Flefh intire, and fpoils the Sweetmeat, and fets it a fretting.

They imploy the Stones in Brandy, and diftil them in Spirits.

In the beginning of *April* we had ftore of *Afparagus*; but they were often fo bitter, to me at leaft, that there was little pleafure in eating them. 'Tis certain they were much worfe than ours in *England* in that particular. Which puts me in mind of the *wild Afparagus*, which grows plentifully with us on the *Sea-Coaft* in *Lincolnfhire*. This is very fair to the Eye; yet no Culture of our Gardens, by often tranfplanting, could make it eatable. I fancy the *Afparagus* recovers fomething of its natural force in a warmer Climate; for the fweet tafte is as it were a mark of degeneration. If they would

Q 2　　　　　have

have them good here, they muſt renew the Seed from *England* or *Holland*.

The *wild Aſparagus* of *Languedoc* is another Plant called *Corruda*.

I procured out of *Languedoc* a ſort of *Præcox Vine*, about fifty Plants, by the *Clermont* Carrier ; the which I gave to Mr. *London*, our King's Gardner, for my Lord Ambaſſador. This Grape is white, very thin skinn'd, and clear as a drop of Water ; it is uſually ripe at St. *John's-maſs* in *July* at *Montpellier*, where it is called *Des Unies*.

There are alſo in this Town *Præcox Grapes*, as Dr. *Turnfort* told me, in the Phyſick Garden ; but whether the ſame with the *Unies*, I know not.

I have ſaid they delight much in Figs in Pots or Caſes ; but here is another way of preſerving the Fig Trees ſet in the Ground; which is much practiſed ; and that is to lap and tie them up in long Straw, from top to bottom ; for which they are placed at a little diſtance from the Walls. This alſo is practiſed to ſuch Trees as ſtand in the middle of the Parterre ; they did not open them till Mid-*May*.

The Exotic Trees, which the *Pariſians* moſt delight in, for their Garden Walks, and for the Shade in their Courts, are the *Maroniers*, or *Horſe Cheſnuts*, of which they have innumerable ; for the Fruit ripens very

ry well here, and comes up of it felf. Alfo the *Acacia Rovini*, which is very common, and makes pretty Alleys, and which
they *lop and turn to Pollards, with good effect* : but of thefe laft the Leaves are late in
putting forth, it being the 15th of *May* our
Style, when thefe Trees were fcarce green.

May 25. when I took my leave of Monfieur *Valliant*, I found him in his Flower-
Garden ; he fhewed me a parcel of *Ranunculus's* in full Flower, which he had receiv'd
but two years before from *Conftantinople :*
They were very beautiful and rare, at leaft
fuch as I had never feen ; as pure White,
White and Green, White and ftrip'd with
Carnation, pure Carnation or Rofe-colour,
ftrip'd Carnation, *&c.*

Of thefe he had fold fome a Piftol a Root,
and hoped in a year or two to be more
plentifully ftock'd with them, that he might
afford them cheaper. I did fee afterwards
a few of them in the Royal *Pipinerie,* and
alfo in the Seedfman's Garden, Monfieur
le Febre ; but both came from him.

I alfo took notice of his Iron Cradles or
Hoops over his Beds, which were removable
and to be made higher and lower, according to the height and nature of the Flowers
they were deigned to cover. This, me-
thoughts, was far beyond all the Inventi-
ons of woodden Covers, and might with

Sail-Cloths and Mats well ferve for a fort of portable Green-houfe, to the lefs tender Plants.

I faw *Le Febre's* Flower-Garden *May 9.* The Tulips were in their Prime; indeed, he had a very large and plentiful Collection. The Panacheé or ftrip'd Tulips were many, and of great variety. He obferved to me, that from his large and numerous Beds of *felf-flowered Tulips*, that is, of one colour, as Red, Yellow, *&c.* they expected yearly fome ftrip'd ones; which *if perfect*, that is, ftrip'd in all the fix Leaves, would but doubtfully continue, and perhaps return to their former ftate the next year; but if they laboured, or did not finifh the Stripings of all the fix Leaves the firft year, there were better hopes of their continuing in that ftate.

Stone Quarries. Though I had no mind to defcend into the *Stone-Pits*, which are like our Mines, Well-fafhion, and the Stones wound up with great Wheels to husband the Soil over them : Yet I went to *Vanre*, three Miles from the Town, which is a ridge of Hills that runs along to the *Obfervatoire.* Here the Quarries are open on the fide of the Hill, as with us. In thofe I obferved two or three Layers of Stone, two or three Foot thick, moftly made up of Shells, or *Stones*

in

in the fashion of Shells. Amongſt theſe
Shell-ſtones the moſt remarkable for bigneſs was a certain ſmooth and long *Buccinum,* tapering with very many Spires. I
meaſured one whoſe firſt ſpire was eight Inches diameter, the full length I could not
ſo well come at ; yet holding proportion
with thoſe of the kind which lay flat, and
which we could ſee in their full length,
it muſt have been a Foot long at leaſt.
There is no *Buccinum* in any of our Seas a
quarter ſo big. Here are many of this Species. Alſo other large turbinated Stones,
which come near ſome of the *Weſt-India*
Kinds of *Muſick Shells,* of which *Genus* yet
there are none in the *European* Seas.

Theſe Layers of Stone mix'd with Shell-
figur'd Bodies, are at certain diſtances in
the Rock, and other Rocks void of Shells
interpoſed.

Fanciful Men may think what they pleaſe
of this matter ; ſure I am, until the Hiſtory
of Nature, and more particularly that of
Minerals and Foſſils is better look'd into,
and more accurately diſtinguiſh'd, all Rea-
ſoning is in vain. It is to be obſerved,
where Men are moſt in the dark, there Impudence reigns moſt, as upon this Subject :
They are not content fairly to diſſent, but
to inſult every body elſe. In like manner
upon the Subject of Mineral Waters : How

Q 4　　　　many

many *Scriblers* have there been, without any knowledge of Foſſils?

I know not whether it be worth the noting, but it ſhews the Humour of the *French,* that I ſaw in ſome Country Towns near *Paris,* the Church-Wall near the top, had a two-foot broad Mourning Liſt, which compaſſed the whole Church like a Girdle, and on this was at certain diſtances painted the Arms of the Lord of the Mannor, who was dead.

I ſhall conclude, what I have to ſay further, with the Air of *Paris,* and the State of Health and Phyſick there.

Air. The *Air* of *Paris* is dryer than that of *England,* notwithſtanding the greateſt part of the City is placed in a dirty miry Level : The muddy Banks of the River *Seine* witneſs this ; alſo the old *Latin* Name of *Paris, Lutetia* ; but ſome of them are unwilling to derive it from *Lutum* ; though there are ſeveral other Towns in *France,* formerly more conſiderable than it, of that very Name ; but from the *Greek* Original, as *Tolon, Toloufa,* which in that Language ſignifie *Black Dirt.* We have have an undoubted Experiment of the different Temper of the Air in our *Philoſophic Tranſactions,* where it is demonſtrated, that there falls twice as much Rain in *England,* as at *Paris* : Regiſters fters of both having carefully been kept, for fo many years, both here and in *France*.

From this quantity of Rain with us, our Fields are much greener; and it was a pleafing furprize to me at my return, failing up the River of *Thames* to fee our green Fields and Paftures on every fide; but we pay dearly for it, in Agues and Coughs, and Rheumatick Diftempers.

The Winter was very rude and fierce, as was ever known in the Memory of Man; the cold Winds very piercing; and the common People walk the Streets all in Muffs, and multitudes had little *Brafs Kettles* of Smallcoal kindled, hanging on their Arms; and yet you fhould fcarce hear any one cough.

I never faw a Mift at *Paris* in the fix Months I ftaid there, but one; though a very broad River runs through the middle of the City, nor any very ftrong Winds; but this may be accidental, and the Temper of fome one year by chance.

We were very fenfible by the 20th of *February* our Style, tho' the Nights were cold, and the White Frofts great in the Mornings, that the Sun at Noon had a much ftronger force and heat, than with us, at that time of the year.

Another Argument of the Drynefs of the Air at *Paris*, we had from the alteration

on of Health; fuch as were thick breath'd, and cough'd and fpit much, foon recovered; and the infenfible perfpiration of the Skin was fo clear and free, that the Kidneys had little to do; fo that it was obferved by moft, that tho' we drank pretty freely of the thin Wines of *Champagne* and *Burgundy*, yet they never broke our fleep to get fhut of them; and that very little paffed that way in the Morning.

Laftly a fign of the drinefs and great goodnefs of the Air of *Paris* is, the vaft number of Iron Bars all over the City; which yet are moftly intire, and the leaft decayed with Ruft I ever faw in any place; whereas ours in *London* are all in a few years all over rufty, and miferably eaten.

Water. We were fufficiently alarmed at our firft coming to *Paris*, with the unwholfomenefs of the *River Water*, and cautioned againft drinking it; and yet it was almoft impoffible to avoid the bad Effects of it; for within the Month two thirds of the Family fell into Fluxes, fome into Dyfenteries, and fome very ill of it. The *French* that come out of other remote Countries fuffer as well as the Strangers. We were told boiling it was a good Remedy to prevent its griping Quality; but that is a meer Notion; for we know
Mine-

Mineral Waters boiled have a ſtronger effect, and this Quality can proceed from
nothing leſs.

The *Well-Waters* here are much worſe
than the River Waters, becauſe more Mineral. But our ſafety was in the Water brought from the *Maiſon des Eaux,*
where the Aqueduct of *Arcueil* empties it
ſelf to ſerve the great Palaces and City
Fountains.

The Diſeaſe of the *Dyſentery* being one *Dyſentery.*
of the moſt common in *Paris,* the moſt
celebrated Drug for its cure is now the *Hy-* *Hypopecou-*
popecouana; though I never once made uſe *ana.*
of it to any of our People, but cured
them all as ſoon, and as well with our u-
ſual Remedies. Indeed they have great
need of it here, for the poorer ſort of People, through ill Diet, this Water, and Herbs,
are very ſubject to it : This Root is ſaid to
cure it with as much certainty, and as readily, as the Jeſuits Powder an Ague : Of this
moſt of the Phyſicians and Apothecaries a-
greed. They give it in Powder from ten
Grains to forty, which is the largeſt Doſe.
It moſt commonly Vomits, and ſometimes
purges, but both gently. 'Tis ſold here
from twenty to fifty Crowns a Pound.
They divide it into four ſorts according to
its goodneſs.

Ano-

The Stone. Another popular Difeafe here is the *Stone*; and there are Men well practifed in the Cutting for it. There are alfo two Hofpitals, where great numbers are cut yearly, as *La Charite*, and *Hoftel-Dieu*; in both of thefe are wired Chefts full of Stones cut from Human Bodies; and in the Cheft of *La Charite* is one, which exceeds all belief; it was cut from a Monk, who died in the very Operation; it is as big as a Child's Head. It is but the Model or Pattern of the Stone which is kept in the Cheft; which has this Infcription on it.

Figure & groffeur de la pierre, pefant 51 ounces, qui font trois livres trois ounces, qui a efté tirée dans cet Hofpital au mois de Juin 1690. & que l'ou conferve dans le Couvent de la Charité.

But that which I fhall here moft infift upon is the *new way*, practifed by *Pere Jaques*, a Monk. About the 20th of *April* he cut in the *Hoftel dieu* ten in lefs than an hours time: The third day after, all were hearty and without pain but one.

He cuts both by the grand and little Appareil; in both he boldly thrufts in a broad Lancet or Stilleto into the middle of the Mufcle of the Thigh near the *Anus*, till he joins the Catheter or Staff, or the Stone betwixt

twixt his Fingers ; then he widens the Inci-
fion of the Bladder in proportion to the
Stone with a Silver *Oval Hoop* ; if that
will not do, he thrufts in his four Fingers,
and tears it wider; then with the *Duck's-
Bill* he draws it out.

I fee him cut a fecond time in the *Hoftel-
Dieu* ; and he perform'd it upon nine Perfons
in three quarters of an Hour, very dexte-
roufly. He feemed to venture at all ; and
put me into fome diforder with the cruelty
of the Operation, and a ftouter *Englifhman*
than my felf. However I vifited them all
in their Beds, and found them more ama-
zed than in pain.

Pere Jaques cut alfo his way in the other
Hofpital *La Charite*; much about the fame
time, eleven at twice. Here Monfieur *Marfhal*, the beft of the Surgeons for this Operation now in *Paris*, harangu'd againft him
before the Governors ; who coldly anfwered,
they would be determined by the Event
which way was beft.

*Atque hac ratione Fæminis Calculi omnium
facillime exciduntur ; nempe fcalpello intra
vaginam uteri in veficam adacto.*

Of thofe cut in *La Charité* one died ;
and being diffected, it was found he had
his Bladder pierced in four or five places ;
alfo

alfo the *Mufculous Pfous* fadly mangled; alfo the left *Veficula Seminales* cut.

Notwitftanding this, if this Method was
well executed by a skilful Hand, it might
be of good ufe to Mankind.

This way of Cutting for the Stone, puts
me in mind of what I formerly writ and
publifh'd in the *Phil. Tranfactions*, about
cutting above the *Os Pubis*, in the Fund of
the Bladder.

Alfo of that Experiment of Cutting for
the Stone of an Alderman of *Doncafter* in
the *Gluteus Major* ; he was twice cut in the
fame place, and out-lived both. I faw the
firft Stone, which was very large, and in
fome meafure tranfparent, Cryftal like. This
Experiment is printed in Dr. *Willies Scarborough Spaw*, fourteen Years ago at leaft, and
is a fair hint for this new Method.

Since my return I had a Letter from
Mr. *Probie*, a very learned and induftrious young Gentleman, who was with me
to fee the Operation : That part relating to
this matter I fhall here tranfcribe.   Indeed I mightily longed for an account of
this Matter, the Succefs of which I came
away too foon to learn any thing for
certain.

Paris, Aug. 2. 98.

PEre Jaque's *Reputation mightily flackens,*
　　out of forty five that he cut at the Hoftel-Dieu, *but fixteen of them furvive; and
of nineteen in the* Charite, *but eleven. He
has practifed at the Hofpital at* Lyons, *but,
'tis faid, with worfe fuccefs than at* Paris.
*I am fenfible he has got abundance of Ene-
mies, which makes me very often queftion,
what I may hear faid of him.* Dr. Fagon,
the King's Phyfician, told Dr. Turnfort,
*when he went to prefent his Book to him, that
he had cut feven at* Verfailles, *and that fix
of them are alive, and as well as if never
cut. The Perfon that died was fo diftem-
pered, that he was not expected to live, and
'twas thought, if he had not been cut, he
had not lived fo long: The Surgeons have a
great mind to cry down the Man, though they
practife his Method. For* Marfhal *has fince
cut after* Pere Jaque's *manner, only with this
difference, that* Marfhal's Catheter *was can-
nulated.* Le Rue, *the fecond Surgeon of the*
Charity Hofpital *cut after the old manner,
at the fame time when* Marfhal *cut* Pere
Jaque's *way, but had not fo good fuccefs as*
Marfhal *had; for all that* Marfhal *cut are
alive and very well, whereas the other loft one
or two of his number; befides, thofe that lived*
were

were not ſo ſoon cured, no, not by a Month or ſix Weeks. Thus far Mr. *Probie.*

Pox.

 The *Pox* here is the great Buſineſs of the Town; a Diſeaſe which in ſome meaſure hath contributed to the ruin of Phyſick here, as in *London.* This ſecret Service hath introduced little contemptible Animals of all ſorts into Buſineſs, and hath given them occaſion to inſult Families, after they had once the Knowledge of theſe Misfortunes. And it is for this Reaſon the Quacks here, as with us, do thrive vaſtly into great Riches beyond any of the Phyſicians, by treating privately theſe Calamities.

 It was a pleaſant Diverſion to me to read upon the Walls every where about the Town, but more particularly in the *Fauxbourg* of St. *Germain,* the Quacks Bills printed in great Uncial Letters.

As,

De par l' Ordre du Roy.

Remede infallible & commode pour la geriſon des maladies ſecretes ſans gardar la chambre.

Ano--

Another,

Par permiſſion de Roy.

Manniere tres aiſee & tres ſure pour guerir ſans incommodite, & ſans que perſone en appercoive, les maladies veneriennes, &c.

Another,

Par privilege du Roy.

L' Antivenerien de medicin Indien, pour toutes les maladies veneriennes, telles quelles puiſſent eſtre, ſans aucun retour, & ſans guarder la chambre. Il eſt tres commode & le plus agreable de monde.

Another,

Remede aſſure de Sieur de la Brune privilege du Roy, &c. ſans qu'on ſoit contraint de guarder la chambre, &c.

By theſe Bills it is evident, there is yet a certain Modeſty and Decorum left in the Concealing this Diſeaſe, even amongſt the *French*; They would be Cured ſecretly, and as though nothing were doing ; which thoſe Wretches highly promiſe.

R

But

But this is that Handle which gives thofe mean People an occafion to infult their Reputation, and injure them in their Health for ever.

Every body here puts their helping Hand, and meddles with the Cure of this Difeafe, as Apothecaries, Barbers, Women, and Monks; yet I did not find by all the inquiry I could make, that they had other Remedies than we. Nay, there is fomething practifed in the Cure of this Diftemper in *England*, which they at *Paris* know nothing of; but this old Verfe forbids me to fay any thing further.

Artem pudere proloqui, quam factites.

Apotheca-ries Shops. The *Apothecaries Shops* are neat enough, if they were but as well ftored with Medicines; and fome are very finely adorned, and have an Air of greatnefs, as that of Monfieur *Geofferie*, who has been *Provoft des Merchands*, in the *Rue Burtebur*, where the Entry to the *Baffe Cour* is a *Port-cochier*, with Vafa's of Copper in the Niches of the Windows; within are Rooms adorned with huge Vafa's and Mortars of Brafs, as well for fight, as for ufe. The Drugs and Compofitions are kept in Cabinets difpo-fed round the Room. Alfo Laboratories backwards in great perfection and neat-nefs.

nefs. I muſt needs commend this Gentleman for his Civility towards me ; and for his Care in Educating his Son, who came over with Count *Tallard*, a moſt Hopeful and Learned Young Man ; whom our Society at *Greſham-College*, at my Requeſt, honoured with admitting him Fellow, according to his Deſerts.

I had the opportunity of Converſing *Phyſicians.* with many of the Phyſicians in this City ; who all agree in the low Condition and Difeſteem it was in, from the boundleſs Confidence and intruding of Quacks, Women, and Monks. Monſieur *d' Achin*, the late chief Phyſician, has been ill thought on for taking Money, and giving protection to theſe ſort of Cattle; but the chief Phyſician now, Monſieur *Fagon*, is a Man of great Honour and Learning, and very deſirous to promote the Art.

It is here as with us, ſome practiſe out of meer vanity, others to make a Penny any way to get Bread. The cauſe of all this is, I think, the great Confidence People have of their own Skill, an arrogance without thinking. To paſs a Judgment upon Cures, and the good and evil practice of Phyſick, without doubt is one of the niceſt things, even to Men of the Faculty; but a Jury, that is, the very ordinary

Men in *England*, are fuffered now to undertake the Queftion; when I may truly fay, that I have ever found, no difparagement to them, the moft Learned Men of the Nation, the moft miftaken in thefe Matters; and can it be otherwife in fo Conjectural an Art, when we our felves fcarce know, when we have done ill or well.

Another caufe of the low Efteem of Phyfick here, are the forry Fees that are given to Phyficians; which makes that Science not worth the Application and Study. The King indeed is very liberal, as in all things elfe, in his Penfions to his chief Phyfician, and gives his Children good Preferments.

Alfo Mr. *Burdelot*, who is alfo well Penfioned, and lodged at *Verfailles*, Phyfician to the Dutchefs of *Burgundy*, a Learned Man; he is perfectly well skill'd in the Hiftory of Phyfick; and we may fhortly (as he told me) expect from him, another Supplement to *Vauder Linden*, of many thoufand Volumes which have efcaped that Catalogue, and are not accounted for.

Monfieur, and the Dauphin, and all the Princes of the Blood, have their Domeftick Phyficians; fome of whom I knew, as Monfieur *Arlot*, Monfieur *Minot*, to the Prince

Prince of *Conty*, of my acquaintance formerly at *Montpelier*. The Two *Morins* very Learned Men; alſo Monſieur *Grimodet*, &c.

Others have the practice of Nunneries and Convents, which gives them Bread; others have Pariſhes; and ſome ſuch Shifts they make; but all is wrong with them, and very little incouragement given to the Faculty.

April 14. the *Prince of Conty* ſent his Gentleman and Coach at mid-night to fetch me to his Son, and to bring with me the late King *Charles's Drops* to give him. This was a very haſty call. I told the Meſſenger, I was the Prince's very humble Servant; but for any Drops or other Medicines I had brought nothing at all with me, and had uſed only ſuch as I found in their Shops, for all the occaſi-ons I had had to uſe any. I deſired he would tell him, that I was ready to Con-ſult with his Phyſicians upon his Sons Sickneſs, if he pleaſed to command me, but for coming upon any other Account I deſired to be excuſed; but I heard no more of the Matter, and the young Prince died. By this it is evident, there is as falſe a Notion of Phyſick in this Coun-try, as with us; and that it is here alſo thought a Knack, more than a Science or

Method

Method; and little Chimical Toys, the Bijous of Quacks, are mightily in requeſt. This Hereſie hath poſſeſſed the moſt thinking, as well as the ignorant part of Mankind; and for this we are beholden to the late vain Expoſitors of Nature, who have mightily inveighed againſt and undervalued the ancient *Greek* Phyſicians, in whoſe Works only this Art is to be learnt, unleſs ſingle Perſons could live over as many Ages, as thoſe Wiſe Men did.

Men are apt to preſcribe to their Phyſician, before he can poſſibly tell what he ſhall in his Judgment think fitting to give; 'tis well if this was in Negatives only; but they are prejudiced by the impertinence of the Age, and *our Men*, who ought to Converſe with the Patient and his Relations with Prognoſticks only, which are the honour of Phyſick; and not play the Philoſopher by fanciful and precarious Interpretations of the Nature of Diſeaſes and Medicines, to gain a ſort of Credit with the Ignorant; and ſuch certainly are all thoſe that have not ſtudied Phyſick thoroughly, and in earneſt.

Thoſe Drops were deſired of me by other Perſons of Quality, as the Princeſs *d'Eſpinoy*, the Dutcheſs of *Boullon*, Monſieur *Seſac*, &c. and having bethought my ſelf how my Maſter, the late King *Charles* had

had communicated them to me, and shewed me very obligingly the Proceſs himſelf, by carrying me alone with him into his Elaboratory at *Whitehall*, while it was diſtilling. Alſo Mr. *Chevins* another time shewed me the Materials for the Drops in his Apartment newly brought in, in great quantity, that is, *Raw Silk*. I cauſed the Drops to be made here. Alſo I put Dr. *Turnefort* upon making of them; which he did in perfection, by diſtilling the fineſt Raw Silk he could get. For my part I was ſurpriſed at the Experiment often repeated, having never tried it before. One Pound of Raw Silk yielded an incredible quantity of Volatil Salt, and in proportion the fineſt Spirit I ever taſted; and that which recommends it is, that it is when rectified, of a far more pleaſant ſmell, than that which comes from Sal-Armoniack or Hartſhorne; and the Salt refined and cohobated with any well-ſcented Chimical Oil, makes the *Kings Salt*, as it's us'd to be called. This my Lord Ambaſſador gave me leave to preſent in his Name; and the Doctor now ſupplies thoſe which want. Silk, indeed is nothing elſe, but a dry Jelly from the Inſect Kind, and therefore very Cordial and Stomachick no doubt. The *Arabians* were wiſe, and knowing in the *Materia Medica*, to have put it in their *Alkermes*.　　This

This muſt be ſaid for the Honour of this King, that he has ever given great Encouragements for uſeful Diſcoveries in all Kinds, and particularly in Phyſick. 'Tis well known he bought the Secret of the Jeſuits Powder, and made it publick; as he lately did that of the *Hypococana.*

To Conclude, it was my good Fortune here to have a Bundle of Original Papers of Sir *Theodore Mayerne,* and his Friends, who Correſponded with him, preſented me by the Reverend Dr. *Wickar,* Dean of *Wincheſter,* who Marrying his Kinſwoman, found them amongſt other Writings of Law Matters. I have not yet had the leiſure to peruſe them, but thoſe who know the Worth of that greāt Man, will deſire they may be made publick; which if they are, they ſhall come forth intire, and not diſguiſed, as ſome of his other Papers have been, to the great detriment of Phyſick; and I think it is the firſt Example of this Nature, that Poſthumous Papers were ever abreviated, and made what they never were, before an intire and full publication.

F I N I S.

E R R A T A.
PAGE 147. line 15. r. *Hair.* p. 180. l. 20. r. *ſa.*

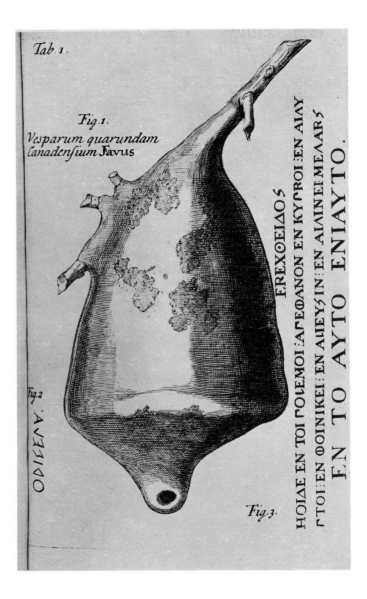

Tab. 1.

Fig. 1.

Vesparum quarundam
Canadensium Favus

Fig. 2.

Fig. 3.

Zenobia

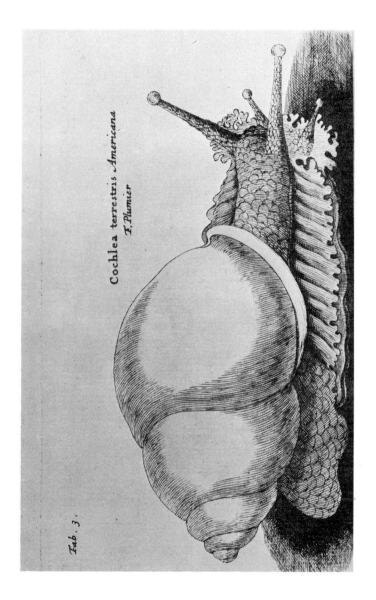

Tab. 3.

Cochlea terrestris Americana
F. Plumier

Tab. 4.

Purpura Americana
F. Plumier

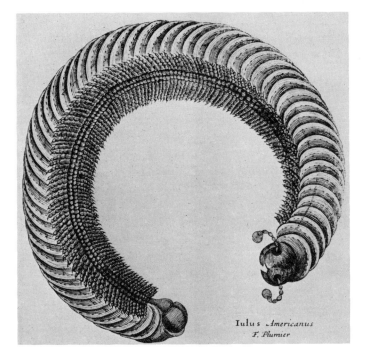

Iulus Americanus
F. Plumier

Tab. 6

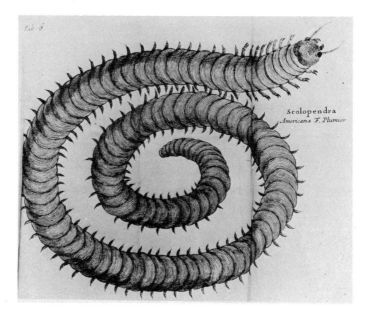

Scolopendra
Americana F. Plumier

APPENDICES

A. Notes to *A Journey to Paris*

P. 2, l. 9. *L'État de la France* first appeared at Paris in 1649. About forty different editions followed, with variations in titles, publishers, and places of publication until 1749. Lister may refer to the English translation and revision, entitled *The Present State of France. Containing a general discription of that Kingdom. Corrected and purged from many gross mistakes in the French copy, enriched with additional observations and remarks of the new compiler, and digested into a method conformable to that of the State of England.* By R.W.M.A. (London, 1687).

P. 2, ll. 9-10. Lister refers to Germain Brice (1652-1727), who published *Description nouvelle de ce qu'il y a de plus remarquable dans la ville de Paris* (2 vols. in 1, Paris, 1684). An edition appeared at The Hague in 1685, a second Paris edition in 1694, and, with variations in titles, at least eight editions appeared during the author's lifetime, the last at Paris in 1725. A subsequent "Nouvelle édition" appeared at Paris in 1752. The book had grown to two volumes by 1698, to three by 1713, and to four in 1725 and later. No English edition is recorded.

P. 3, l. 2. "Monsieur *Breman*": Jean Brémant (d. 1702), royal gardener, said to have assembled as many as 5,000 plants from all parts of the world — a task in which, no doubt, he profited from the efforts of many others, such as Joseph Pitton de Tournefort (1656-1708), France's most renowned botanist at the turn of the eighteenth century, in whose correspondence Brémant appears. E.-T. Hanny, "Jean Brémant, Jardinier du Jardin Royal (1672?-1702)," *Bulletin du Muséum d'Histoire Naturelle* (Paris, 1898), pp. 130-32.

P. 3, l. 20. The "Embassy" refers to that of the Earl of Portland (William Bentinck, 1649-1709), William III's favorite, who helped to negotiate, but did not sign, the Treaty of Ryswick (Sept. 30, 1697), negotiated in France for William concerning the Spanish succession in 1698, and signed the First Spanish Partition Treaty in that year (Oct. 11). Unhappily, the peace did not last "our Days" (l. 28). It was broken in 1701 and the War of Spanish Succession followed to 1713. Lister attended Portland as physician in the latter negotiations. Probably he was "on call" at all times, but clearly his noble patient demanded little of his time and medical talents.

P. 4, l. 14. Lister's pass for passage from Dover to Calais was issued December 9, 1697. *Calendar of State Papers, Domestic Series, William III, 1697*, p. 505.

P. 4, l. 28. The "three several times" when Lister had visited France before cannot be determined with precision. One had been in 1663-66, when he was associated with other Englishmen and Frenchmen in an academy at Montpellier. Cf. Harcourt Brown, *Scientific Organizations in Seventeenth Century France, 1620-1680* (Baltimore, 1934), pp. 208 ff.

P. 5, l. 6. The good friend was probably Dr. John Wickart, Dean of Winchester. Cf. pp. 195, 248. John Wickart or Wicourt (d. 1722) was educated in France and at Cambridge. He was Chaplain in Ordinary to Charles II (1684), Canon of Windsor (1684-1721), and Dean of Winchester (1693-1721).

P. 6, l. 28–p. 7, l. 1. One of the French editors wrote that "It was a matter of honoring the ambassador, and not at all of curiosity. Besides, a number of persons crowded the entrances to give themselves importance and to make one believe that they were of a rank that would make their presence desired." *Voyage de Lister À Paris* . . . (Paris, 1873), p. 21n.

P. 8, l. 7. *"Pont St. Bernard,"* say the French editors, is that of la Tournelle. *Ibid.,* p. 22n.

P. 10, l. 20. Henri Justel (1620-93), wealthy French amateur scientist and promoter of letters and the new science, served from about 1664 on as a self-appointed liaison between the Royal Society of London and French scholars and scientists. Cf. Harcourt Brown, "Un cosmopolite du grand siècle, Henri Justel," *Bulletin de la Société Historique Protestante Française,* LXXX (1933), 187-201; René Ternois, "Les débuts de l'anglophile en France: Henri Justel," *Revue de Littérature Comparée,* XIII (1933), 588-605; Gabriel Bonno, *Les Relations Intellectuales de Locke avec la France* (University of California Publications in Modern Philology, XXXVII, Berkeley, 1963), pp. 107 ff.

P. 13, l. 29. "Fiacres": hackney coaches said to have been named after a barefoot Augustinian monk who died February 16, 1684, almost as a saint ("en odeur de sainteté"), and whose portraits were hung widely over

Paris, particularly on the doors of carriages for hire.
See Joachim-Christolphe Nemeitz, *Séjour de Paris,
C'est-à-dire, Instructions fidèles pour les voyageurs de
Condition . . . durant leur séjour à Paris . . .* (2
vols. in 1, Leiden, 1727); also *Voyage de Lister À
Paris,* p. 26n.

P. 14, l. 31. *"Roullions,"* which Lister indicates is a French
word, escapes the French dictionaries. Obviously an
outgrowth of the verb *rouler,* it may have been local
Parisian speech, perhaps slang, lost to later literate
circles.

P. 15, l. 16. "the *Cour de la Reyne*": the Cours-la-Reine
was laid out and planted in 1616 for Marie de Médici.
It was replanted in 1724. See also p. 183, ll. 23 ff.
Lister repeats himself somewhat. *Voyage de Lister À
Paris,* p. 161n.

P. 16, ll. 7-24. This paragraph was considered unjust by
the French editors. They pointed out that the French
episcopate of the time included Huet, Bossuet, Féne-
lon, Fléchier, Mascaron, "the virtuous cardinal de
Coislin," Colbert, Bishop of Montpellier, and Cardinal
Rohan, "the friend of du Foy, the bibliophile and pos-
sessor of de Thou's books." Also, Mgr. Le Tellier,
Archbishop of Rheims, "whose catalogue has been
printed in folio, was certainly not an ignorant man."
Ibid., p. 29n.

P. 18, ll. 1-5. Lister's conjecture is probably baseless. Was
he confusing the English word "hostel" with the
French *hôtel?*

P. 18, ll. 16-17. English monarchs had reflected this
opinion. Queen Elizabeth attempted (vainly) to forbid further construction in London, and the first two
Stuarts threatened members of the nobility who

sought to live in London and urged them to return to their landed properties. Godfrey Davies, *The Early Stuarts, 1603-1660* (Oxford, 1937), p. 272.

P. 18, l. 26. Lister's "Workmen" were in error. Such houses were far more durable. *Voyage de Lister À Paris*, p. 31n.

P. 19, l. 25–p. 20, l. 10. Lister added this paragraph to his third edition, perhaps to clarify his concern for the welfare of Parisians and his implied support for the "*Basin* for a Winter Harbour" as opposed to the less socially oriented policies of mercantilism fostered by the government of Louis XIV.

P. 20, ll. 11-24. Probably this paragraph should be related to Lister's sour comment on p. 19: "Farming [of offices] is admirably well understood here." The sale of offices was widespread in the seventeenth century, especially in France. Although much earlier in origin, a decree of Henry IV (1604) conceived by the financier Paulet made many French offices essentially hereditary. The practice became enormously profitable to the monarchy and served to open office-holding to the wealthy bourgeoisie to the relative exclusion of the nobility. It was argued, also, that the practice helped to insure the independence of the magistracy. The sale of offices was by no means unknown in England, especially in Stuart times, although the reformers of the Interregnum and of the Glorious Revolution generally opposed it. Lister appears to be among the critics of the practice. Cf. Sir Stanley Leathes in *The Cambridge Modern History*, eds. A. W. Ward *et al.* (13 vols., New York, 1934), III, 695; K. W. Swart, *Sale of Offices in the Seventeenth Century* (The Hague, 1949), pp. 1-18 *et passim*.

P. 20, ll. 25 ff. Lister well reflects the anti-Catholic view of most Englishmen of his day, especially that of the supporters of William III during and after the Revolution of 1688.

P. 24, ll. 1-11. The French editors of *Voyage de Lister À Paris* reprint one of these "Advertisements," which offered a reward for the return of silver stolen from the Prince de Rohan. Cf. pp. 35-36n.

P. 25 *passim*. Paris street lighting, consisting of 6,500 reflecting candle lanterns, was set up in 1667 by the Lieutenant Général de Police, La Reynie. Lister's statement of its cost is in error. The system was financed by a property tax on the inhabitants which yielded only 300,000 livres. Cf. *Voyage de Lister À Paris*, p. 37n; F. L. Carsten, ed., *The New Cambridge Modern History* (12 vols., Cambridge, 1957——), V, 187. The method continued until gaslights were installed in the nineteenth century.

P. 28, l. 5. "Surfeit": twentieth-century equivalent would be "indigestion."

P. 28, l. 25. "Mons. *Girardon*": François Girardon (1628-1715), French sculptor who designed and cast the equestrian statue of Louis XIV.

P. 30, l. 16. "M. *Auzout*": probably Adrien Auzout (d. 1691), the French astronomer.

P. 31, l. 3. This grill was removed about 1835. Cf. *Voyage de Lister À Paris*, p. 41n.

P. 31, l. 19. "the Duke *de Mazarin*": Charles-Armand de la Porte, Marquis de la Meilleraye, Duc de Mazarin, who married Hortense Mancini, favorite niece of Cardinal Mazarin, whom he subsequently hounded with insane jealousy and forced her to flee to England. After her death (1699), the Duke was reported to have carted her body about Europe in a casket for a year or so, unable to part with her remains. Cf. Élisabeth Charlotte, Duchesse d'Orléans (1652-1721), *The Letters of Madame . . . 1661-1708* (New York, 1924), p. 20.

P. 32, l. 19. "were taken out hence": that is, from the Palais Mazarin.

P. 35, l. 10. "Steel Remedies": ferruginous preparations.

P. 35, l. 12. Bathing was generally frowned upon in Lister's time as being too enervating — although the Abbé de Marolles declared that he had never taken a bath because of modesty! See *Voyage de Lister À Paris*, p. 45n.

P. 36, ll. 18-19. "Monsieur *Viviers*": the French editors state (p. 46n.) that the name was properly M. du Vivier but they supply no Christian names and I have found none. Germain Brice, in the 1698 edition of *Description nouvelle de . . . Paris* (I, 376), refers to Vivier as one of the most famous and knowledgeable collectors of art. The editions of 1715 and 1717 speak of his remarkable clocks. He no longer appears in the edition of 1725.

P. 37, ll. 1-17 (and cf. p. 133, ll. 1-11). Reluctantly, I must agree with the French editors (*Voyage de Lister À Paris*, pp. 47n., 122n.) that it is impossible to identify the paintings which Lister attributes to Rembrandt. Titles of paintings have been changed, the number of works attributed to Rembrandt has been variously estimated, some of Rembrandt's works have been lost to public view, and, in the case of *"The Nativity of our Saviour"* (p. 133), there were two Nativity scenes known to have been done by Rembrandt and it is impossible to determine which one may have been at "the Closet or Cell of *P. Hochereau*" (p. 133). And it is possible that some of these cited by Lister (such as *"The Massacre of the Innocents,"* p. 133) were not by Rembrandt at all. Lister's evaluation of Rembrandt, whose personal and professional reputations were at a low ebb in the 1690's, is unusual for the time and more in keeping with present-day opinion.

P. 37, l. 22. *"Philibien"*: André Félibien, Sieur des Avaux et de Javercy (1619-95), French architect and author of books on painting, sculpture, and architecture.

P. 37, l. 27. "Monsieur *le Nostre*": André Lenôtre (1613-1700), the French landscape architect who designed, in whole or in part, many famous gardens, such as the Versailles, Fontainebleau, and Kensington gardens, St. James Park (London), and the Quirinal and Vatican gardens (Rome). He was eighty-five years old in 1698, not eighty-nine, as Lister asserts on p. 38.

P. 41, ll. 4-6. Lister errs. Rubens' pupils took a large part in the paintings in the Galerie de Médicis. Destined for the decoration of the gallery of the Luxembourg Palace, these paintings were rapidly done between February, 1621, and June, 1623. See *Voyage de Lister À Paris,* p. 50n.

P. 41, l. 23. *"Cornelius Johnson"*: Cornelius Janssen van Ceulen (1593?-1664), known in England, his adopted country, as Cornelius Johnson.

P. 43, ll. 21-22. The Louvre was about four centuries a-building. Francis I began the "Old Louvre" under the direction of Pierre Lescot (*c.* 1510-78), architect, and Jean Goujon (*c.* 1510-68), sculptor. Henry IV connected it with the Tuileries, and Louis XIV added the lovely colonnade by Claude Perrault (*c.* 1613-88).

But the King's attention was soon afterward diverted to the construction of the Palace of Versailles. The Louvre was not completed until the nineteenth century.

P. 44, l. 13. *"Le Brun"*: Charles Le Brun (1619-90), French historical painter. The "Battles of *Alexander*" were at Fontainebleau; Le Brun later worked for eighteen years on the decoration of the Palace of Versailles.

P. 44, l. 18. *"Paulo Verenese"*: Paolo Cagliari or Caliari, 1528-88, Venetian painter born in Verona (whence *"Verenese"* [Veronese]). The painting referred to by Lister was of "La Chananéenne."

P. 44, l. 29. "Monsieur *Gerardon*": François Girardon. See note for p. 28, l. 25.

P. 47, l. 17. "Monsieur *Baudelot*": Charles-César Baudelot de Dairval (1648-1722). His *Treatise on the Utility of Voyages* was *De l'Utilité des Voyages et de l'avantage que la recherche des Antiquités procure aux scavans* (2 vols., Paris, 1686). His other works included *Lettre à M. Lister, de la Société royale de Londres, médecin de S.E. mylord Portland . . .* (Paris, 1700), on the generation of stones in animals.

P. 51, ll. 17-18. "Monsieur *Thevenot*": Melchisédec Thévenot (1620-92), distinguished by his wide travels [cf. his *Relations de divers voyages curieux* (2 vols., Paris, 1663-72)] and interest in early science, served as Royal Librarian to Louis XIV. At his house in Paris met one of the private "colleges," or society of scholars, which presaged the founding of the Académie des Sciences (1666). See Brown, *Scientific Organizations in Seventeenth Century France,* pp. 135 ff.

P. 52, l. 13. The French editors take exception to Lister's explanation and write: "The digamma borrowed by Claude[?] from the Aeolien dialect did not express the consonant γ . . . but it expressed an aspiration, or rather a harsh expiration, represented by our *F*, which has kept the form of the Greek διγαμμχ, that is to say the two Γ (γαμμα) placed one on top of the other." See *Voyage de Lister À Paris*, p. 58n. Actually, the digamma was a letter in the original Greek alphabet which early fell into disuse, except in western dialects. Its form corresponded to the English *F*, and in regard to its physical properties the French editors are correct. There is dispute among classical scholars as to its phonetic values, but the Aeolian *F* was probably approximated by the English *W*. Whether this sound was *wa* or *va* is uncertain. If *va*, then perhaps Lister was correct as to its phonetic value. But it was not "new invented" by Baudelot or anyone else in the seventeenth century.

P. 53, ll. 22-23. I have found no evidence that Lister actually published this letter.

P. 53, ll. 24-25. Jean Dominique Cassini (1625-1712), Italian-born astronomer and mathematician, was virtually Director of the Paris Observatory (although he never held the title officially). Cf. C. Wolf, *Histoire de l'Observatoire de Paris* (Paris, 1902), chapter 13.

P. 54, l. 25. "Monsieur *Roman*" presents a problem in identity. Brice's various editions of *Description nouvelle de . . . Paris* list no French astronomer whose name resembles Roman. Perhaps Lister refers to Olaus Roemer (1644-1710), the Danish astronomer. Roemer had been in Paris in the early 1680's; where Lister saw him "afterwards" is uncertain.

P. 55, ll. 6-7. That is, Cassini's nephew and son Jacques (1677-1784), who later took a leading part in the fruitful French efforts to determine the figure of the earth.

P. 55, ll. 13 ff. Planned by Perrault and begun in 1670, the arch was never completed as intended. As Lister states, "it is finisht in *Plaister* [and wood]" to give an idea of it. It was demolished in 1716.

P. 56, ll. 8 ff. The French editors praise Lister's account of the qualities of the building stones around Paris and state that "they are confirmed by all the contemporary architects, particularly by M. Viollet-le-Duc in his *Dictionnaire d'Architecture* under the titles 'Construction and Building Stone.'" *Voyage de Lister À Paris*, p. 61n.

P. 57, l. 1. Jules Hardouin-Mausart (1646-1708), court architect to Louis XIV, designed the chapel of the Hôtel des Invalides, which soon became a landmark in Paris. Lister saw it before it was completed in 1704.

P. 57, ll. 20-21. Cf. *Philosophical Transactions*, XIII, no. 149 (July 10, 1683), 238-42.

P. 59, l. 3. "Monsieur *Buco*": Nicholas Boucot (d. 1699?), one of the four keepers of the records since 1685. Lister errs, however, in associating the office with the *Parliament;* rather, it was attached to the great Chancellery of France to keep the records and registers of all the offices which had been officially sealed.

P. 59, ll. 24-25. "my *Synopsis Conchyliorum*": *Historia sive Synopsis Methodica Conchyliorum* (2 vols., London, 1692). See the Lister bibliography herein, no. 12 under "Books."

P. 60, ll. 13-14. "*Hippocampus*": the common sea horse.

P. 60, l. 30. "*Vespetum Canadense*": a wasps' nest from Canada. See Fig. 1 herein.

P. 61, ll. 13-14. *"African* Ass": the zebra.

P. 62, ll. 2 ff. "Dr. *Tournefort":* Joseph Pitton de Tournefort (1656-1708), France's greatest botanist in Lister's
day. A systematist, he published *Élémens de Botanique* (Paris, 1694) among other works. He became
head of the Jardin du Roi in Paris and, as a great
professor, taught many visiting Englishmen, including
Tancred Robinson and Hans Sloane. He visited England in 1687 but was curiously uncivil to John Ray.
James Petiver tried for years to engage him in scientific exchange, and repeatedly wrote to Lister to ask
him to serve as intermediary, but with little success.
See *Sloane 3333,* fols. 121b-22b, 126-27b, 160b, 181b-
82, 182-82b (British Museum). Still, Tournefort's
manuscript remains demonstrate his debt to English
scholars. Cf. *Tournefort 76,* pp. 196-261, *253 (Re-
gistre),* vols. 9, 16, 17, 18, 19, 20, 21 (Bibliothèque du
Museum National d'Histoire Naturelle, Paris); C. E.
Raven, *John Ray* (Cambridge, 1950), p. 288 *et passim;* Raymond P. Stearns, "James Petiver, Promoter
of Natural Science," *Proceedings of the American Antiquarian Society,* LXII (Oct., 1952), 243-365.

P. 62, l. 24. *"Buccina":* whelks.

P. 62, l. 25. *"Auris Marina Spisse echinata":* probably a
sea urchin.

P. 63, ll. 29-30. *"Vespetum Canadense Maximum":*
another Canadian wasps' nest.

P. 64, l. 17. " a very great *Julus":* a millipede, family of
myriapods (class Diplopoda). See Fig. 5 herein.

P. 64, l. 23. *"F. Plumier":* Father Charles Plumier (1646-
1704) was sponsored by Louis XIV to travel in the
French West Indies, where he made extensive botanical collections and described hundreds of plants,

especially in Martinique and Santo Domingo. He corresponded frequently with the English circle in the later seventeenth century, especially with James Petiver and Hans Sloane, but was known also to John Ray and others, with all of whom he appears to have excited unusual feelings of warmth. He published *Description des Plantes de l'Amerique* (Paris, 1695). A brief sketch of him is in *Sloane 2337* (British Museum).

P. 65, l. 2. "another *Peiresk*": Nicolaus-Claude Fabri de Peiresc (1580-1637), early French scientist, revered patron of letters and "experimental philosophy," promoted French societies of learned men both in Paris and at Aix-en-Provence. Cf. Brown, *Scientific Organizations in Seventeenth Century France,* pp. 1 ff., 208 ff.

P. 65, l. 6. "Monsieur *Verney*": Guichard Joseph du Verney (1648-1730), anatomist with an international reputation as teacher of anatomy. He gave lessons to the Dauphin and other courtiers as well as scores of foreign pupils. He published a treatise on otology in 1683.

P. 65, l. 11. "Mr. *Bennis*": an English pupil of Verney. See also p. 69.

P. 66, l. 6. "Monsieur *Merrie*": Jean Méri (1645-1722), First Surgeon at the Hôtel-Dieu.

P. 66, l. 13. "*Willis*": Thomas Willis (1621-75), English anatomist and distinguished physician; published works on the brain and nervous system (1664 and later).

P. 72, l. 29. "Monsieur *Litre*": Alexis Littre (1658-1725), member of the French Academy of Sciences.

P. 74, l. 8. "Monsieur *du Pes*": unidentified beyond Lister's statement.

P. 74, l. 23. "Monsieur *Poupart*": François Poupart (1661-1709), French physician and naturalist, author of works on insects, leeches, mussels, and osteology.

P. 74, l. 28. "*Francisco Redi*": Francesco Redi (1626-97), Italian physician, naturalist, and poet. In his *Esperienze intorno alla generazione degl'insetti* (Florence, 1668) he launched the first scientific attack upon the ancient idea of the spontanteous generation of insects.

P. 75, l. 7. "F. *Plumier*": Father Charles Plumier. See note for p. 64, l. 23.

P. 76, ll. 15-16. "*Scolopendra*": a multipede or centipede, genus of chilopods. See Fig. 6 herein.

P. 76, l. 22. "a Blood-red *Polypus*": an octopus.

P. 76, l. 24. "*acetabulated*": refers to the suckers on the legs.

P. 77, l. 2. "*Murex*": "the purple fish," a genus of marine gastropods (suborder Stenoglossa); a secretion from the animal was used as a purple dye.

P. 78, l. 4. "Monsieur *Dacier*": André Dacier (1651-1722), French classical scholar. His two-volume translation of Hippocrates was published in Paris in 1697. His wife Anne (née Lefebvre) was also a classical scholar.

P. 79, l. 21. "*Tanaquil Faber*": Tannegui Lefebvre, Mme. Dacier's father.

P. 79, l. 26: "Monsieur *Morin*": Louis Morin (1635-1715), French physician and botanist well known and highly esteemed by Tournefort, Father Plumier, Dr. Fagon, and others of the day.

P. 81, l. 4. "Mr. *Oldenburgh*": Henry Oldenburg (1615?-1677), first Secretary of the Royal Society of London (1663-77) and founder of the *Philosophical Transactions* (1664).

P. 81, l. 26. *"Abbot Bignon"*: Jean Paul Bignon (1662-1743), nephew of Louis de Pontchartrain and member of the French Academy (1696).

P. 82, l. 23. "Mr. *Butterfield"*: Michael Butterfield, instrument maker. His instruments were prized for their quality and delicacy by the astronomer Jean Picard, and he was repeatedly given payments by the King for instruments used in the construction of the Palace of Versailles.

P. 86, l. 16. "Mons. *de la Hire"*: probably Philippe de la Hire (1640-1719), author of *Mémoires de Mathématique et de Physique* . . . (Paris, 1694), *Traité de Mécanique* . . . (Paris, 1695), and other works.

P. 86, l. 17. "Mons. *de Vallemont"*: Pierre Le Lorrain de Vallemont (1649-1721), physician, numismatist, and author of *Description de l'aimant qui s'est formé à la pointe du clocher neuf de N. Dame de Chartres* (Paris, 1692).

P. 87, l. 18. *"De Fontibus Medicatis Angliæ"*: De Fontibus Medicatis Angliæ, Exercitatio Nova et Prior (York, 1682). See the Lister bibliography herein, no. 4 under "Books."

P. 87, l. 26. *"Gilbert of Colchester"*: William Gilbert (1540-1603), physician to Queen Elizabeth, whose book *De Magnete, Magneticisque Corporibus* . . . (1600) declared the whole earth to be a magnet and recounted many experiments he had made.

P. 87, l. 31. "Mr. *Hartsoeker"*: Niklaas Hartsoeker (1656-1725), Dutch physicist and histologist.

P. 88, l. 10. *"Des Cartes* of Screw-fashioned Particles": part of Descartes' general system of vortices; see Renée Des Cartes, *Principia Philosophiae* (1644). Descartes' and others' theories of magnetism in the seventeenth century are discussed in Abram Wolf, *A History of Science, Technology, and Philosophy in the 16th and 17th Centuries,* new ed. by Douglas McKie (London, 1950), pp. 298 ff.

P. 94, l. 9. "Abbot *Droine*": René Drouin, professor of the Sorbonne.

P. 94, l. 10. "Monsieur *Guanieres*": M. de Gaignières, who lived in the Hôtel de Guise up to 1692 and later on in Rue de Sèvres. His collections were described in the *Description nouvelle . . . de Paris* in 1706. See *Voyage de Lister À Paris,* pp. 89-90n.

P. 95, ll. 6-7. According to the French editors, this portrait was in the Louvre in the 1870's. See *Voyage de Lister À Paris,* pp. 90-91n.

P. 95, ll. 9 ff. The French editors, who found many of these drawings in the Bibliothèque Nationale, held a lower opinion of them than Lister, saying that they betrayed "une naïve simplicité." *Ibid.,* p. 91n.

P. 95, l. 21. Surely Lister meant to write "Charlemagne" instead of "*Charles* V"?

P. 95, l. 31–p. 96, l. 4. The French editors state that these cards "sans doute" can be attributed to Gringonneur and were reproduced in "notre volume sur les Cartes à jouer" (Paris, 1844). I assume that the pronoun refers to the Société des Bibliophiles François, but I have not seen the volume cited. Cf. *Voyage de Lister À Paris,* p. 91, n. 3.

P. 96, ll. 6-7. "*Mademoiselle de Scuderie*": Magdeleine de Scudéry (1607-1701), sometimes called Sapho, was a poet, novelist, and lady of fashion whose salons attracted most of the notable persons of her day. As Lister suggests, her day was about over.

P. 97, l. 3. "The Marquis *d'Hopital*": Guillaume-François-Antoine L'Hôpital (1661-1704), Marquis de Ste. Mesme et Comte d'Entremont, French geometer, associate of Jacob Bernoulli, and author of *L'Analyse des Infiniment Petits pour L'Intelligence des Lignes Courbes* (Paris, 1696) and *Traité Analytique des Sections Coniques* (Paris, 1707).

P. 97, l. 11. "Mr. *Isaac Newton*'s Preferment": refers to Newton's appointment, in 1696, as Warden of the Mint. He became Master of the Mint in 1699.

P. 98, ll. 12-16. The French editors identified these ladies (omitting those previously identified herein) as follows: "Mad. *de Vicubourg*": Anne-François de Harlay, wife of the late Louis, Marquis de Vieux-Bourg; "Mad. *d'Espernon* the Daughter": Elisabeth Regine Goth under the assumed name of Duchesse d'Épernon, the only daughter of J-B. Gaston Goth d'Albert, Marquis de Rouillac, better known as the Duc d'Épernon, and Marie d'Étampes de Valençay; "Mad. *Pres. de Ferrand*": Anne Bellinzani, daughter of François B., Intendant of Commerce in France, and wife of Michel Ferrand, President of the Parliament of Paris. See *Voyage de Lister À Paris*, pp. 94-95n.

P. 98, l. 18. "*Pere Pezaron*": Père Pezron, who died in 1706. The "*Origin of Nations*" mentioned as in progress (ll. 28-29) was published in 1703 as *d'Antiquités de la nation et de la langue des Celtes*. He labored to prove that Celtic was the original language from which Greek, Latin, and other European tongues sprang.

P. 99, l. 3. "Mr. *Ed. Floid*": Edward Lhwyd (1660-1709), Celtic scholar and Keeper of the Ashmolean Museum, Oxford, Fellow of the Royal Society of London, and close friend of Martin Lister. Lhwyd was delighted at the prospect of a correspondence with M. Pezron, but the latter failed to follow through. See R. T. Gunther, "Life and Letters of Edward Lhwyd" in *Early Science at Oxford,* XIV (Oxford, 1945), 378-79, 400, 412 ff.

P. 99, l. 6. "Monsieur *Spanheim*": Baron Ezechiel von Spannheim (1629-1710), Swiss-born German scholar-statesman; later Prussian minister to London (1702).

P. 99, l. 25. "Mons. *Vaillant*": Jean-Foi Vaillant (1632-1706), celebrated numismatist; his son was Jean-François-Foi Vaillant (1665-1708). Both are to be disinguished from Sébastien Vaillant (1669-1722), prominent French botanist.

P. 101, l. 13. "Mr. *Cunningham*": Alexander Cunningham (1654-1737), historian, tutor to John, Marquis of Lorne (1697); employed by William III to spy on French military preparations (1701); British envoy to Venice (1715-20). He wrote a Latin history of Great Britain in his own day (1688-1714) which was posthumously translated and published in English (1787).

P. 102, ll. 4-13. See p. 30, ll. 16-19. Lister repeats himself.

P. 102, l. 21. "Monsieur *l'Abbe Drouine*": René Drouin. See note for p. 94, l. 9.

P. 103, l. 28. "Monsieur *Gurnier*": no further identification available.

P. 103, l. 29. "Monsieur *Thevenot*": Melchisédec Thévenot. See note for p. 51, l. 18.

P. 105, l. 3. "*Swammerdam*": Jan Swammerdam (1637-80), a Dutch naturalist known for his early researches with the microscope. He was the first to describe red blood cells, and he did a vast amount of work on insects and on their anatomy.

P. 105, l. 16. *"Asilus"*: a large, voracious fly of the family Asilidae.

P. 105, ll. 17-18. *"Scarabœus Nasicornis"*: obviously a dung beetle with a horn on its nose — or so the title suggests. The *Scarabœus* is well known, but I find none labeled *"Nasicornis."* But nomenclature (and perhaps evolution) have altered things since Lister's day.

P. 106, l. 2. *"Michael Servetus"*: the Spanish theologian and physician (1511-53) executed for heresy — but not before, as some maintain, he had anticipated William Harvey's later work on the circulation of the blood.

P. 106, l. 7. "Mons. *l'Abbe de Brillac"*: Pierre de Brillac (1667-1734) became Sous Bibliothécaire of the Royal Library in 1692.

P. 106, l. 15. "Monsieur *Clement"*: Nicolas Clement (1647-1712).

P. 106, l. 24. *"Synopsis Conchyliorum"*: see the Lister bibliography herein, nos. 12 and 27 under "Books."

P. 107, ll. 5-6. *"Abbe Louvois"*: Camille Letellier (1675-1718), Librarian of the Royal Library.

P. 107, l. 20. "Monsieur *Barbesieux"*: Louis-François Marie Le Tellier, Marquis de Barbezieux (1668-1701), Secretaire d'État de la Guerre.

P. 107, l. 25. The Abbé de Louvois lived on Rue Vivienne in an apartment in one of the two houses Colbert had purchased in 1666 for the Royal Library, which previously had been on Rue de la Harpe. The Royal Library remained there (on Rue Vivienne) until 1731. See *Voyage de Lister À Paris,* pp. 102-3n.

P. 108, l. 30. Does Lister mean that he had two catalogues? If so, he may have had the catalogues of 1666 and 1672, now both rare and expensive items. *Ibid.*, p. 104n.

P. 111, l. 8. "Father *Beauvais*": identity uncertain; probably a Jesuit missionary recently returned from the Far East.

P. 111, l. 20. "Monsieur *Baluze*": Etienne Baluze (1630-1718), historian and librarian, professor of canon law at the Collège Royal.

P. 112, l. 7. "Monsieur *Huygens*": the famous Christian Huygens (1629-95), Dutch mathematician, physicist, and astronomer, who worked in Paris (1666-81) at the invitation of Louis XIV. He perfected the pendulum clock (1658) and a balance spring for watches (1675), although the balance spring developed by Robert Hooke about the same time proved to be more satisfactory.

P. 113, l. 25. "Mr. *Molyneux*": Dr. Thomas Molyneux (1661-1733), later Sir Thomas (1730). He was a prominent physician in Dublin, widely traveled and well known in his day, a Fellow of the Royal Society of London with which he was an active correspondent, President of the Irish College of Physicians, professor of medicine at Dublin. For Lister's "Paper from Mr. *Molyneux*," see *Philosophical Transactions*, XX, no. 241 (June, 1698), 209-23.

P. 114, l. 13. Lister's article appeared in *ibid.*, XVII, no. 203 (Sept., 1693), 865-70.

P. 114, l. 19. "Monsieur *Valentine*": Louis Bernin de Valentine d'Ussé, who married the second daughter of Vauban, Louis XIV's great military engineer. The tombs were moved to his Château d'Ussé (Indre and Loire) and were still there in 1868. See *Voyage de Lister À Paris*, p. 108n.

P. 115, ll. 11-12. *"Pere Hardouin"*: Jean Hardouin (1646-1729), French Jesuit scholar who edited Pliny's *Historia Naturalis*, to which Lister refers, and wrote *Nummi Antiqui* (1684), which obviously excited Lister's interest in old coins. The College of Clermont, founded in 1563 by the Bishop of Clermont, was bought by the Jesuits in 1660 and took the name of Louis-le-Grand College. Cf. *Voyage de Lister À Paris*, p. 109n.

P. 116, l. 13. *"Nicolo,"* according to the French editors, was Niccolò dell'Abbate (1512-1571), born at Modena. He took a leading part in the decoration of Fontainebleau. The painting to which Lister refers was still in the same place in 1786 but disappeared during the French Revolution. *Voyage de Lister À Paris*, p. 110n.

P. 118, l. 9. *"P. Daniel"*: Gabriel Daniel (1649-1728), Jesuit historian and theologian, "professeur de rhétorique, philosophie et théologie."

P. 118, l. 12. *"Monsieur Huetius"*: Pierre Daniel Huet (1630-1721), Bishop of Avranches, renowned as a mathematician, Hellenist, and Hebraist; editor of Origen's *Commentaria in Sacram Scripturam*; author of a critique of Cartesian philosophy entitled *Censura Philosophiae Cartesiane* and other works.

P. 119, l. 1. *"P. de la Chaise"*: Françoise d'Aix de La Chaise (1624-1709), sometime confessor to Louis XIV, learned antiquarian. The King appointed him to the Académie des Inscriptions et Belles-Lettres when it was founded in 1701. See also p. 189, ll. 22-25.

P. 119, l. 19. "Mons. *l'Abbe de Villiers*": Pierre de Villiers (1648-1728) became a Cluniac monk (1689) in the Priory of St. Taurin.

P. 121, l. 19. *"Pere Mabillon"*: Jean Mabillon (1632-1707), French Benedictine monk and scholar. He lived in the Abbey of St. Germain-des-Prés for many years. His work included a nine-volume *Acta Sanctorum Ordinis S. Benedict* (1668-1702) and *De Re Diplomatica* (1681), to which Lister refers.

P. 121, l. 30. "Dr. *Bernard*": probably Edward Bernard (1638-96), classical scholar and astronomer, Fellow of the Royal Society, Savilian professor at Oxford; as tutor in Paris to Charles II's bastard sons by the Duchess of Cleveland he probably became well known there.

P. 122, l. 2. "Dr. *Gale*": Thomas Gale (1635-1702), Fellow of the Royal Society of London, classical scholar and author, professor of Greek at Cambridge (1666-72), Master of St. Paul's (1672-97), and Dean of York (1697-1702).

P. 124, ll. 9-10. *"Cornu Ammonis"*: a fossil shell of cephalopods of the group of Ammonoidea; from the Mesozoic age.

P. 124, l. 14. "the *As*": the Roman pound or libra (10½ ounces, Troy weight); also a Roman coin originally the weight of an as.

P. 125, l. 3. "the *Noble Piersc*": Nicolaus-Claude Fabri de Peiresc. See note for p. 65, l. 2.

P. 127, ll. 2-4. Lister was pulling the good father's leg, but the joke may have been somewhat obscure. If Lister referred to the use of mummified flesh as a medicine (as it was, especially in France), then the joke is clear enough. But mummified flesh was not used as an antidote to poison, which *"Venice-Treacle"* was. Perhaps, then, Lister meant that the mummy, if viewed during Lent as an antidote to sin, was, being flesh, breaking the spiritual fast. Cf. A. C. Wootton, *Chronicles of Pharmacy* (2 vols., London, 1910), II, 23-25.

P. 128, ll. 5-6. "Monsieur *Colbert*": Jean Baptiste Colbert (1619-83), the great minister of Louis XIV. He was a generous patron of writers, scientists, and academies, and he persuaded the King to organize the French Academy of Sciences.

P. 128, l. 22. "Monsieur *Baluze*": Etienne Baluze. See note for p. 111, l. 20.

P. 128, ll. 25-26. "*Carolus Calvus*": Charles le Chauve or Charles the Bold (823-77), King of France (840-77) and Holy Roman Emperor (875-77).

P. 129, ll. 12 ff. "*Servieto*": Michael Servetus. See note for p. 106, l. 2.

P. 130, ll. 14-15. "*Peter Berchorius*": Pierre de Bressuire, later Bercheure.

P. 131, ll. 1 ff. "Cardinal *Richelieu*": Armand Jean du Plessis, Duc de Richelieu (1585-1642), the powerful cardinal-minister of Louis XIII from 1624 to 1642, during which time he practically controlled France, and entered into the Thirty Years' War to win the balance of power from the Hapsburgs, a policy which succeeded. His tomb, by François Girardon (see note for p. 28, l. 25), was completed in 1694 and may still be seen in the Church of the Sorbonne.

P. 132, l. 2. "Monsieur *Morin*": Louis Morin. See note for p. 79, l. 26.

P. 132, l. 9. "*Francis Willoughby*": Francis Willughby (1635-72), one of the original Fellows of the Royal Society of London, naturalist, and principal patron of John Ray, with whom he cooperated in the study of natural history. He wrote books on ornithology and ichthyology, but, as he died prematurely, Ray completed some of his works. See Raven, *John Ray*, pp. 308 ff.

P. 133, l. 2. *"P. Hochereau"*: this good father remains unidentified beyond Lister's comments.

P. 133, l. 12. *"Piere Mallebranche"*: Nicholas de Malebranche (1638-1715), French metaphysician, founder of Malebranchism, a philosophical system opposed by Bossuet and Arnoud on the question of grace, and author of *Recherche de la Verité* (4 vols., Paris, 1674——), *Traité de la Nature et de la Grâce* (Paris, 1680), *Traité de l'Amour de Dieu* (Paris, 1697), and other works.

P. 136, l. 1. *"F. P."*: for Father Plumier. See note for p. 64, l. 23.

P. 136, l. 9. *"Hypocochoana"*: obsolete name of ipecac, an expectorant and emetic.

P. 137, ll. 7-8. *"Nizolius"*: probably one of the works of Marius Nizolius (1498-1576), Italian humanist best known as a Cicero scholar.

P. 137, l. 17. *"Melans"*: Claude Mellan (1598-1688), French engraver.

P.139, l. 22. "the *Potterie of St. Clou*" brings to mind the current European efforts to imitate Far Eastern designs in china, textiles, lacquered wares, etc. Many Europeans — in Italy, the United Netherlands, and France — successfully imitated Chinese porcelain wares, but the best European porcelain was that of Meissen (Dresden) in 1710. The French editors of Lister's work state that Lister relates almost everything known about the porcelain manufactory at St. Cloud. *Voyage de Lister À Paris*, pp. 129-30n.

P. 140, l. 31. *"Gomron Ware"*: an obsolete English term

for porcelains, arising from the fact that the early trade of the East India Company was not carried on directly with India or China but through an intermediary set up in the harbor of Gombron, facing Ormuz, in the Persian Gulf. *Ibid.,* p. 129n.

P. 141, l. 27. "Mons. *Morin*": Louis Morin. See note for p. 79, l. 26.

P. 142, l. 1. *"Frit"*: the materials of which glass is made after having been calcined or partly fused in a furnace but before vitrification.

P. 143, l. 5. "Tamis": a strainer or sieve of woolen cloth.

P. 143, l. 27. *"Bioux"*: misprint for *bijoux,* jewels or trinkets.

P. 143, l. 30. *"Bleaks"*: a small European river fish (*Alburnus lucidus*); its scales are still used in making artificial pearls.

P. 145, l. 7. "the *Gobelins*": the famous French tapestry works which Louis XIV had made into a royal manufactory in 1662.

P. 145, l. 14. *"Tuby"*: Jean-Baptiste Tuby (1630-1700), Rome-born sculptor who made many of the statues in the gardens of Versailles.

P. 145, l. 16. *"Quoisivox"*: Charles-Antoine Coyzevox (1640-1720), employed by Le Brun to carve decorations for Versailles. He made portrait busts including those of Louis XIV, Richelieu, Mazarin, Bossuet, Condé.

P. 146, l. 16. *"Talke"*: talc.

P. 153, l. 7. *"Rockamboy"*: rocambole, a kind of leek.

P. 154, ll. 8-9. "Romain Lettice": romaine lettuce, brought from Rome (hence its name) by the popes to Avignon and thence to Paris. See *Voyage de Lister À Paris,* p. 138n.

P. 155, l. 22. "the bar of *Vaugerard*": the Barrière de Vaugirard, the Vaugirard Gate.

P. 157, ll. 1-3. Lister may refer to his "Description of an odd kind of Mushroom," *Philosophical Transactions,* VII, no. 89 (Dec. 16, 1672), 5116-18.

P. 158, ll. 29-31. The French editors state that Lister's account of oysters cut from the shell and sold in straw baskets is unique, and point out the popularity during the reign of Louis XIV of oysters with the shell (*huîtres à l'écaille*), for "We believe that oysters with the shell are much superior to those brought without the shell on straw. . . ." *Voyage de Lister À Paris,* p. 143n.

P. 159, ll. 4 ff. The *macreuse* had been a puzzle to English naturalists only a few years earlier, largely because the French referred to it as a fish which they were allowed to eat in Lent. Actually it is a scoter, a kind of duck *(Melanitta nigra).* Cf. Raven, *John Ray,* pp. 333-34. There is an amusing exchange of letters between Ray and Tancred Robinson in the 1680's over the identity of this creature. Cf. William Derham, *Philosophical Letters Between . . . Mr. Ray and . . . Correspondents* (London, 1718), pp. 160 ff.; and Robinson's observations on the *macreuse* before the Royal Society of London, *Journal-Book,* VI, 244 (Royal Society Library).

P. 162, ll. 15-16. The practice of carrying apples as a deodorant was very ancient. See *Voyage de Lister À Paris,* p. 146n.

Pp. 163 ff. *passim.* One would rather expect the French editors to react unpleasantly toward any Englishman's estimates of French wines — and they do! See *ibid.,* pp. 148-49n. It is fruitless to enter into the matter; Lister's knowledge of French geography was obviously at fault, and it seems probable that the names of wines and liquors have changed since 1698.

P. 166, l. 17. *"Ratafia's"* continued to be in style throughout the eighteenth century, and is still celebrated in song in the twentieth (e.g., "The Unfortunate Miss Bailey").

P. 169, l. 18. It seems likely that coffeehouses had been set up in Paris since Lister's earlier visits there. See *Voyage de Lister À Paris,* p. 152n.

P. 172, l. 18. "Monsieur *Geofrys"*: probably Mathieu-François Geoffroy, clever (and rich!) apothecary and high office-holder in the Apothecaries' Guild. His son Étienne-François (1672-1731) became a famous French physician. See also p. 242, l. 20.

P. 173, l. 22. *"De Calculo Humano"*: *Dissertatio Medicinalis de Calculo Humano* (London, 1696). See the Lister bibliography herein, no. 18 under "Books."

P. 174, l. 4. *"l'Europe Gallante"*: composed by André Campra (1660-1744) and first produced on October 24, 1697. Campra, though a composer of no lasting fame, was considered, in the 1690's, to be a distinguished successor to Lully. *L'Europe Galante* presaged the more recent spectacular ballet.

P. 175, l. 10. *"Vendage de Suresme"*: *Les Vendanges de Suresnes* was by Flourent Carton-Dancourt (1661-1725), not by Molière.

P. 175, ll. 27 ff. Lister presents an old, widely popular story of Molière's death. But the latter's biographers make clear that Molière had suffered from tuberculosis long before his final appearance on the stage, that friends had begged him to stay away from the theater on this particular occasion, and that Molière's exertions in the play only exacerbated a condition already far advanced.

P. 176, ll. 15 ff. Physicians of the day might well have viewed Molière with suspicion, especially in view of such comedies as *L'Amour Médecin* and *Le Malade Imaginaire.* However, one can sympathize with Dr. Lister's concern for the honor of his profession without condemning Molière for malice. After all there *were* quacks, as Lister recognizes, and it was even more difficult in the seventeenth century than it is to-day for an educated man such as Molière to distinguish between the quacks and the honorable practitioners of medicine.

P. 177, ll. 6 ff. Lister's comments on the French stage were remarkably judicious for an English observer, especially in view of the contemporary censure (on generally just grounds) of the English stage at the time — although it is probably true to say that the English Restoration stage collapsed from its inanity rather than its obscenity. Jeremy Collier's *A Short View of the Immorality and Profaneness of the English Stage,* published the year that Lister was in France, was far less judicious than Lister's brief comments.

P. 179, ll. 4-5. "the late Persecution" refers to the revocation of the Edict of Nantes in 1685 and the dispersion of French Protestants (Huguenots).

P. 180, l. 24. *"the Fair of St. Germain"* was located on the site which later (1813) became the market place of St. Germain. The fair dated from 1482, was suppressed in 1736. See *Voyage de Lister À Paris,* p. 161n.

P. 183, l. 23. "the *Cours de la Reyne"*: the Cours-la-Reine. See note for p. 15, l. 16.

P. 188, l. 9. "Dr. *Turnefort"*: Joseph Pitton de Tournefort. See note for p. 62, ll. 2 ff.

P. 188, l. 10. "Mr. *Breman*": Jean Brémant. See note for p. 3, l. 2.

P. 188, l. 26–p. 189, l. 6. One wonders why Lister "took particular notice" in these plants, as they were relatively commonplace. 1. "*Jasminum Asoricum flore albo viridarii Regis Lusitanici*": white jasmine from the King of Portugal (Portuguese East Indies?). 2. "*Marum Cortusii*": Teucrium (germander or cat thyme), family Lamiaceae. 3. "*Caryophyllus Creticus arborescens*": rose apple tree from Crete (Jambosa, genus *Eugenia*). 4. "*Smilax fructu nigro*": smilax (bindweed) with black berries. 5. "*Iris bulbosa florè luteo*": yellow flowering iris (family Iradaceae). 6. "*Symphytum minus Boraginis flore*": a species of borage (family Boraginaceae). 7. "*Fraxinus Americana florida*": American flowering ash (family Oleaceae). 8. "*Stæchas* [Stachys?] *folio serrato Bauhini*": horsemint?

P. 189, ll. 21-25. "Country-House of *Father la Chaise*": its site (Mont Louis, northeast of Paris) was later (1806 *et seq.*) that of the Père Lachaise Cemetery. Father La Chaise was Françoise d'Aix de La Chaise (1624-1709), French Jesuit priest, confessor of Louis XIV (1674 *et seq.*), who approved of the King's secret marriage to Mme. de Maintenon. See also p. 119, l. 1.

P. 190, l. 27. "*D'Aumont*": Hôtel d'Aumont, constructed by Mansard, was on Rue de Jouy. Le Brun painted on its ceiling a picture representing the apotheosis of Romulus. Later it became a pension, then the central pharmacy. See *Voyage de Lister À Paris*, p. 169n.

P. 191, l. 4. "The *Treillage*": latticework, or fence.

P. 191, ll. 5-6. "adorned with Gilding": gilded.

P. 192, l. 4. *"Junkills"*: jonquils.

P. 192, l. 5. *"Rastumculus's"*: Ranunculus.

P. 192, l. 7. *"Puissart"*: Hôtel Pussort. M. Pussort was father-in-law of Colbert. His mansion was near Rue d'Alger. *Voyage de Lister À Paris*, p. 170, n. 2.

P. 192, l. 17. "Jacobæa Maritima": ragwort; "Marum Syriacum": cat thyme.

P. 192, ll. 18-19. "The Walls were well covered with Fruit-Trees": that is, espaliered.

P. 193, l. 1. *"Bouvillier"*: Hôtel de Beauvilliers, located on Rue Sainte-Avoy almost across from Rue de Montmorency. *Voyage de Lister À Paris*, p. 171, n. 1.

P. 193, l. 4. *"Cormartin"*: not identified.

P. 193, l. 12. *"Les Diguieres"*: Hôtel Lesdiguières, on Rue de la Cerisaye, a dead-end street separating it from the little arsenal. Built under Henry IV for Sébastien Zamet, it later belonged to the families of Lesdiguières and Villeroi. Tsar Peter I of Russia stayed there in 1717.

P. 194, l. 2. *"Laurus Tinus"*: laurustine (*Viburnum tinus*).

P. 195, ll. 2 ff. Perhaps simpler in more recent French:

Ci gît une chatte jolie:
Sa maîtresse, qui n'aima rien,
L'aima jusqu' à la folie;
Pourquoi le dire? On le voit bien.

P. 195, l. 18. *"De Lorge"*: Hôtel de Lorges, on Rue Saint-Augustin, between Rue de Choiseul and Rue de la Michodière. Later (1706 *et seq.*) called Hôtel de Chamillart.

P. 195, l. 19. "the Marshal": Guy Aldonce de Durfort de Duras (1630-1702), Comte de Lorges and Duc de Quintin, Marshal of France since 1676. He was also father-in-law of Louis de Rouvroy, Duc de Saint-

Simon (1675-1755), famous for his *Mémoires* of the courts of Louis XIV and Louis XV.

P. 197, l. 15. *"Hostel Pelletier"*: Hôtel Le Peletier, on Rue Culture-Sainte-Catherine.

P. 198, l. 9. *"Abel Trees"*: white poplars.

P. 198, l. 13. *"Hostel-sullie"*: on Rue Saint-Antoine. This mansion was still "almost intact, at least on the exterior," in the 1870's. See *Voyage de Lister À Paris,* p. 175, n. 1.

P. 198, l. 16. *"Louvois"*: on Rue Richelieu, on the present location of the Place Louvois. The mansion was of the late *"Mons Louvois,"* or François Michel Le Tellier, Marquis de Louvois (1641-91), Louis XIV's war minister who, for a time, succeeded Colbert as a principal adviser to the King.

P. 199, l. 14. "Mr. *Furnier"*: probably Claude Fornier, Treasurer of France. The mansion was on Rue d'Enfer near the Convent of the Feuillants de l'Ange Gardien. See *Voyage de Lister À Paris,* p. 176n.

P. 200, ll. 16-17. More familiarly today: Versailles, St. Cloud, Marly, and Meudon.

P. 206, l. 16. The castle at Meudon was built by Louis XIV for the Grand Dauphin. It was burned during the siege of Paris in 1871 and its site is now occupied by an observatory.

P. 208, l. 19. "The *Theatre des eaux"* was destroyed in 1775. Its site is now that of the Rond Vert.

P. 208, ll. 19-20. "the *Triumphal Arch"* (l'Arc de Triomphe) was destroyed by Louis XV. The only part remaining is a lead grouping representing France Triumphant by Tuby and Coyzevox.

P. 208, ll. 21-25. The "Winding Alleys" were a labyrinth including thirty-nine rock basins ornamented with lead figures of animals taken from Aesop's *Fables*. It was also replaced in 1775 by the present Bosque de la Reine (Queen's Grove).

P. 209, l. 26. *"Laurus Alexandrina"*: laurustine (as the names indicate there are many varieties of this shrub, widely valued for its evergreen leaves and different colored flowers); *"Thlapsi flore albo"*: white flowered pennycress.

P. 209, ll. 27-28. *"Leucoii folio, latifolium"*: gillyflower; *"Sedum Pyramidale"*: a sedum, of which there are some 200 species.

P. 210, l. 3. "Mr. *London"*: probably George London, expert gardener to Henry Compton, Bishop of London, at his remarkable gardens at Fulham. See Raven, *John Ray*, p. 229.

P. 212, ll. 13 ff. "Duke *de Villeroy"*: son of François de Neufvillé, Duc de Villeroi (1644-1730), one of Louis XIV's most famous and favorite military commanders, who became a Marshal of France in 1693.

P. 213, l. 7. *"Gerbes"*: bundles.

P. 213, ll. 18 ff. Two of these water wheels continued to operate until the early 1840's. Cf. *Voyage de Lister À Paris*, p. 188n.

P. 213, l. 30. *"Leeds"*: Liége, now in Belgium.

P. 214, l. 6. *"Horn-Beam"*: also called horn beech and yoke elm (*Carpinus, C. betulus*).

P. 214, ll. 22-23. *"Pole-Hedges"*: also hornbeam.

P. 214, ll. 30 ff. *"Languedoc"*: here, it appears, Lister reverts to the scenes of his youth when he studied at Montpellier. His picture on p. 215 suggests that he had enjoyed it there.

P. 215, l. 9. *"Lentiscus"*: mastic tree (*Pistacia lentiscus*); *"Phylarea"*: Phillyrea, a flowering evergreen (family Oleaceae).

P. 215, l. 11. *"Cistus"*: rockroses (family Cistaceae).

P. 215, l. 17. *"Tonsil"*: tonsile or clip, meaning that the cypresses could be pruned at pleasure.

P. 216, l. 3. *"Pescenas"*: Pézenas, about twenty-five miles southwest of Montpellier in Hérault Dept. Molière lived there in 1655-56 and wrote *Les Précieuses Ridicules* there. Lister's reference suggests a youthful familiarity with Pézenas but further evidence is lacking.

P. 219, ll. 15-16. "Monsieur *Morley*": Noël de Morlaix, gardener at the nursery at Roule (established in 1670), Director of Plants and Trees for the royal mansions, and Usher in the King's Chamber. See *Voyage de Lister À Paris*, p. 192, n. 1.

P. 219, l. 26. "Mr. *Evelyn*": John Evelyn (1620-1706), one of the original Fellows of the Royal Society of London, authority on numismatics, architecture, and landscape gardening. His *Diary* is, perhaps, second only to that of Samuel Pepys for the latter half of the seventeenth century. Lister refers to Evelyn's *Kalendarium Hortense,* a gardener's almanac, of which there were many editions beginning in 1664, the tenth appearing in 1706.

P. 220, l. 19. *"Stæchas* [Stachys?] *citrina folio latiusculo"*: broad-leaved yellow mint?

P. 220, l. 20. *"Cotila"*: unidentified.

P. 220, l. 22. *"Amaroutre"*: amaranth?

P. 223, l. 22. *"Cusco"*: Cuzco, once capital of the Inca empire in Peru. Captured by Pizarro in 1533.

P. 226, ll. 14-15. *"Aurenzebe"*: Aurangzeb (1658-1707), sixth Emperor of Hindustan of the Mogul dynasty. His wars weakened the dynasty and opened the way for further European penetration in India. Lister may well have heard much of him from François Bernier at

Montpellier, as the latter had been to India and served as physician to the Mogul.

P. 226, ll. 26-27. "Monsieur S.": the French editors state that "without doubt" this was the Marquis de Saissac, of the House of Lodève. See *Voyage de Lister À Paris*, p. 198, n. 2.

P. 229, l. 2. "*Acacia Rovini*": the locust tree, genus *Robinia*.

P. 229, ll. 23-24. "Monsieur *le Febre*": Lefebvre? Unidentified except for Lister's indication that he was a "Seedsman."

P. 231, ll. 21 ff. Lister's unsure position on the origin of fossils has led to contradictory interpretations of his words. Sir Charles Singer holds that Lister "wrote the first book devoted to fossils which accepted their organic nature (1678)" [*The Story of Living Things, a Short Account of the Evolution of the Biological Sciences* (New York, 1931), p. 241], and the author of the biographical sketch of Lister in the *Dictionary of National Biography* takes a similar view. On the other hand, Abram Wolf [*A History of Science, Technology, and Philosophy in the 16th and 17th Centuries*, new ed. by Douglas McKie (London, 1950), p. 362] states that Lister's "views on fossil shells were reactionary. He regarded them as merely curiously shaped stones" that "never were any part of an animal"; and Karl Alfred von Zittel [*History of Geology and Palaeontology to the End of the Nineteenth Century*, trans. Maria M. Ogilvie-Gordon (London, 1901), p. 17] took a similar position. Other writers are similarly divided on the nature of Lister's views. Actually, Lister neither denied that fossils are organic remains of plants or animals which formerly lived in this world nor asserted categorically that they were. His final position appears to be well summed up in his *Journey to Paris*: he awaits further evidence, without which "all Reasoning is in vain." A larger treatment of this problem appears in my Introduction herein, pp. xxxvii-xxxix.

P. 232, l. 21. *"Lutum"*: mud.

P. 233, l. 25. "our Style": Lister refers to the fact that the English still followed the Julian calendar and continued to use it until 1751, whereas the French had adopted the Gregorian calendar.

P. 235, ll. 13-14. *"Hypopecouana"*: ipecac.

P. 235, l. 22. "Jesuits Powder": quinine.

P. 236, l. 20. *"Pere Jaques"*: Jacques Baulot or Beaulieu (1651-1720), a peasant boy whose skill in surgery was further developed by an army empiric. He adopted a fanciful religious costume and the name of Brother Jacques, and practiced in many parts of France as an itinerant, accepting no fees except food, lodging, and the upkeep of his cheap costume. He developed a wide reputation and was honored by both the Emperor and the Pope. But his reputation was severely eclipsed when Guy Aldonce de Durfort de Duras, Marshal of France (see note for p. 195, l. 19) died at his hands. Subsequently, he retired to Besançon and died obsecurely in circumstances of religious retreat. See *Voyage de Lister À Paris*, p. 207n.

P. 237, ll. 18-19. "Monsieur *Marshal*": M. Maréchal de Marsin (d. 1706), surgeon to Louis XIV.

P. 237, ll. 24-26. *"Atque hac ratione . . . adacto"*: "By this method all stones of women may be more easily removed. . . ." But the exact technique as set forth in the remainder of the Latin statement escapes this nonsurgical reader.

P. 238, l. 8. *"Phil. Transactions"*: I have not seen this in the *Philosophical Transactions*, and I suspect Lister erred. Actually "A Proposall of a New Way of Cutting for the Stone of the Bladder" was given before the Philosophical Society of Oxford, April 28, 1685, and was by the method of "cutting above the *Os Pubis*." See R. T. Gunther, "Dr. Plot and the Correspondence of the Philosophical Society of Oxford," in *Early Science at Oxford*, XII (Oxford, 1939), 291.

P. 238, ll. 17-18. "Dr. *Willies Scarborough Spaw*": perhaps Lister refers to Sir Charles Scarburgh (1616-94), anatomist and Royal Physician to Charles II, James II, Queen Mary, and Prince George of Denmark, and author of works on dissection and other items.

P. 238, l. 21. "Mr. *Probie*": unidentified.

P. 240, ll. 23-25. *"gerison"*: *guérison*; *"gardar"*: *garder*.

P. 241, ll. 3-5. This passage should read: "Mannière très aisée & très sûre pour guérir sans incommodité, & sans que personne s'en aperçoive, les maladies vénériennes, &c."

P. 241, ll. 8-12. This passage should read: "L'antivénérien du médecin indien, pour toutes les maladies vénériennes, telles qu'elles puissent être, sans aucun retour & sans garder la chambre. Il est très commode & le plus agréable du monde."

P. 241, ll. 14-16. This passage should read: "Remède assuré du Sieur de la Brune, par privilège du Roi, &c., sans qu'on soit contraint de garder la chambre, &c." As Lister comments below, it is interesting that the French displayed "a certain Modesty and Decorum . . . in the Concealing this Disease . . . ," i.e., venereal diseases. It is interesting, too, to find an old Indian remedy being touted so early.

P. 242, l. 15. Cicero, *Orator,* 43, 147: "Blush to own the art you practice" [trans. H. M. Hubbell, Leob Classical Library (Cambridge, Mass., 1952)].

P. 242, l. 20. "Monsieur *Geofferie*": Mathieu-François Geoffroy. He had been Échevin (Alderman) and not Prévôt (Marshal) des Marchands since 1685. See note for p. 172, l. 18.

P. 243, l. 3. "his Son": probably Étienne François Geoffroy, elected Fellow of the Royal Society July 6, 1698.

P. 243, l. 18. "Monsieur *Fagon*": Guy-Crescent Fagon (1638-1718), chief physician to Louis XIV.

P. 244, l. 18. "M. *Burdelot*": Pierre Michon (1610-84), also known as l'Abbé Bourdelot, a physician.

P. 244, l. 31. "Monsieur *Arlot,* Monsieur *Minot*": both unidentified.

P. 245, ll. 3-4. "Monsieur *Grimodet*": Grimaudet? Unidentified.

P. 245, l. 14. "King *Charles's Drops*": also known as "King Charles's salts," "the King's Drops," and "the King's Salts." Little more is known about this nostrum than Lister relates. A. C. Wootton, *Chronicles of Pharmacy,* II, 181-82, uses Lister as his only source.

P. 248, l. 10. "Sir *Theodore Mayerne*": Sir Theodore Turquet de Mayerne (1573-1655), physician (M.D. Montpellier, 1597); Royal District Physician at Paris (1600); condemned by the College of Physicians because of a treatise on chemical remedies (1603); moved to England, became physician to James I's queen; spent most of the rest of his life in England attending the royal family; knighted (1624); made

chemical and physical experiments and drew up pre-
cautions against the plague (1644). Many volumes of
his notes on cases reside in the British Museum.
P. 248, l. 12. "Dr. *Wickar*": John Wickart. See note for
p. 5, l. 6.

B. Bibliography of the Works of Martin Lister

I. MANUSCRIPT MATERIALS

Letters and other manuscript remains of Martin Lister
are largely concentrated in three repositories: the Bodleian Library, Oxford; the British Museum, London; and
the Library of the Royal Society of London, Burlington
House, London. The *Lister MSS* at the Bodleian is a considerable collection, including three volumes of letters
covering the period 1665-1710, addressed to Lister from a
wide variety of scientific correspondents from many parts
of the world. A few of these have been published by R. T.
Gunther in *Further Correspondence of John Ray* (London, Ray Society, 1928); "Dr. Plot and the Correspondence of the Philosophical Society of Oxford," in *Early
Science at Oxford*, XII (Oxford, 1939); and "Life and
Letters of Edward Lhwyd," in *ibid.*, XIV (Oxford, 1945).
The *Lister MSS* also contain other papers from Lister's
pen, including medical case histories, parts of some of his
scientific books in manuscript, and an unpublished (and
incomplete) book entitled "A Methode for ye Historie of
Iron," chapter 4 of which Lister appears to have published
separately as "The Manner of making Steel, and its
Temper" in *Philosophical Transactions*, XVII, no. 203
(Sept., 1693), 865-70. The *Ashmole MSS* (especially
1816), also in the Bodleian Library, contain further letters

to Lister by his scientific correspondents during the years 1680-1706.

Most of the Lister material in the British Museum is in the *Sloane Papers* of the Manuscript Division, especially *Sloane 1929, 3330, 3332, 3333, 3338, 4062,* and *4067.* But there is at least one letter to Lister from John Ray in *Stowe 746,* fol. 113. Much of the Lister-Ray Correspondence has been published by Edwin Lankester in *Memorials of John Ray* (London, Ray Society, 1846), and *The Correspondence of John Ray* (London, Ray Society, 1848); by William Derham, *Philosophical Letters Between . . . Mr. Ray and . . . Correspondents* (London, 1718); and by R. T. Gunther as cited above.

Manuscript materials by or relating to Lister exist in the Library of the Royal Society of London in four separate categories:

1. The *Letter-Books,* especially vols. IV, VIII, X, and XI. 2. The *Guard-Book* (*L 5-6*), which includes copies of most of Lister's letters to the secretaries of the Royal Society (especially Oldenburg and Grew), most of which were scientific communications read at meetings of the Society and, in the majority of cases, published in the *Philosophical Transactions.* These cover the years 1670-1701 and include the most significant contributions by Lister to the Society. 3. The *Journal-Books,* which are the minutes of the meetings of the Royal Society and which furnish specific information about Lister's relations with the Society, his attendance at meetings of the Society, his occasional participation in the discussions of the Fellows, and his services in the chair as Vice-President of the Society in 1685 (Samuel Pepys was President and was absent from the meetings very frequently; Lister served as chairman at twenty-six of the Society's regular meetings in 1685).

4. The *Council Minutes*, which record the activities of the
elected Council of the Society, the policy-making body and
the prudential overseers of the Society's affairs. Lister was
elected to the Council on November 30, 1683, immediately
upon his removal to Westminster from York, and he
served for three years (1684-86 inclusive). He was appointed a member of the Council's committee to audit the
Treasurer's accounts on November 10, 1684, and was
sworn in as Vice-President of the Society on January 14,
1684/85.

II. BOOKS

1. *Historiæ Animalium Angliæ Tres Tractatus: Unus de
   Araneis, alter de Cochleis tum terrestribus tum fluviatilibus; tertius de Cochleis Marinia.* . . . Published
   by the Royal Society, London, 1678-81. Reviewed in
   Philosophical Transactions, XII, no. 139 (April-June,
   1678), 982-85. Partially translated and republished,
   with illustrations of spiders, by Johann August
   Ephraim Goeze [ed.], *D. Martin Listers . . . Natur-
   geschichte der Spinnen Uberhaupt und der Engel-
   ländischen Spinnen insonderheit.* . . . Quendlinburg
   und Blankenburg, 1778.

2. *Historiæ Animalium Angliæ tres tractatus.* Eboraci
   [York], 1681.

3. *Johannes Godartius* [Goedaert] *of insects. Done into
   English, and methodized. With the addition of notes*
   [*by M. Lister*]. The figures etched upon copper by
   Mr. R. Pl[ace]. York, 1682. Reviewed in *Philosophical Transactions,* XIII, no. 143 (Jan. 12, 1682/83),
   22-23.

4. *De Fontibus Medicatis Angliæ, Exercitatio Nova et
   Prior.* Eboraci [York], 1682. Reviewed in *Philo-*

sophical Transactions, XIII, no. 144 (Feb. 10, 1682/ 83), 59-61.

5. *Letters and divers other Mixt Discourses in Natural Philosophy.* York, 1683. Dedicated to Robert Boyle. A reprint of letters and communications previously printed in the *Philosophical Transactions.*

6. *De Thermis et Fontibus Medicatis Angliæ.* London, 1684. Cf. no. 3 above and see also *De Fontibus Medicatis Angliæ, Exercitatio Altera.* London, 1684. 2 pts. in 1 vol. Both editions have illustrations of the crystals of various medical substances. Reviewed in *Philosophical Transactions,* XIV, no. 158 (April 20, 1684), 579-85.

7. *De Cochleis, tam Terrestribus, quàm Fluviatilibus Exoticis, seu, quæ non omino in Anglia inveniantur, liber [I].* London, 1685. Title also lists Susanna and Anna Lister (Lister's daughters) as engravers.

8. *De Cochleis, tam Terrestribus quàm Fluviatilibus Exoticis; item de iis quæ etiam in Anglia inveniantur, libri II.* London, 1685. Susanna and Anna Lister named as engravers.

9. *Exercitationes et descriptiones Thermarum ac Fontium Medicatorum Anglicæ.* London, 1685.

10. *De Cochleis, tam Terrestribus quàm Fluviatilibus Exoticis; item de iis quæ etiam in Anglia inveniantur, libri III.* London, 1687. Susanna and Anna Lister named as engravers.

11. ———, *libri IV.* London, 1688. Susanna and Anna Lister named as engravers.

12. *Historia sive Synopsis Methodica Conchyliorum,* vol. I: "Qui est de Cochleis Terrestribus," bk. I, London, 1685; bk. II, London, 1686; bk. III, London, 1687; bk. IV, London, 1688; Appendix, London, 1688. Pub-

lished in 2 vols., London, 1692. Copies vary in contents in accord with binders' practices. Beautiful illustrations by Susanna and Anna Lister with little descriptive text. A fine example of the fruits of scientific correspondence and exchange of specimens. See no. 27 below for later editions.

13. *Exercitationes et Descriptiones thermarum ac fontium medicatorem Anglia.* . . . London, 1689. See no. 9 above.

14. *Exercitatio Anatomica in quâ de Cochleis maximè Terrestribus et Limacibus agitur.* . . . London, 1694. 2 pts. in 1 vol. Illustrated.

15. *Sex Exercitationes Medicinales De Quibusdam Morbis Chronicis.* . . . 2 pts., London, 1694. Case histories in "Hydrope," "Diabete," "Hydrophobia," "Lue Venerea," "Scorbuto," and an appendix of 48 pp.: "De Arthritide Sexta Exercitatio Medicinalis." Republished in Richard Morton, *Opera Medica* (London, 1697).

16. *Dissertatio Anatomica Altera de Buccinis Fluviatilibus et Marinis.* . . . London, 1695.

17. *Exercitatio-Anatomica altera, in qua maximè agitur de Buccinis fluviatilibus et marinas* . . . *His accedit Exercitatio medicinalis de variolis.* 2 pts., London, 1695. The second part was published separately as *Disquisitio Medicinalis de Variolis* (London, 1696) and twice republished, first in *Tractatus de Variolis variis historiis illustratus* (Geneva, 1696), and second in Richard Morton, *Opera Medica* (2 vols., London, 1737), II.

18. *Exercitatio Anatomica Conchiliorum Bivalvium utriusque Aquæ. Huic Accedit Dissertatio Medicinalis de Calculo Humano.* London, 1696. See also *Conchyli-*

orum Bivalvium Utriusque Aquæ Exercitatio Anatomica Tertia: Huic Accedit Dissertatio Medica de Calculo Humano. 2 pts. in 1 vol., London, 1696. The *Dissertatio Medicinalis de Calculo Humano* also appears separately.

19. *Octo Exercitationes Medicinales.* . . . London, 1697. An enlarged and revised edition of no. 15 above.

20. *A Journey to Paris In the Year 1698.* London, 1699.

21. ———. The Second Edition. London, 1699. Corrected and revised.

22. ———. The Third Edition. London, 1699. Lister's *Journey to Paris* was twice republished in English but in neither case did the editor indicate which edition of the original was used. The first was in John Pinkerton [ed.], *A General Collection of the best and most interesting Voyages and Travels in all parts of the World* . . . (12 vols., London, 1809), IV, 1-76. Pinkerton appears to have used the second edition. George Henning [ed.], *An Account of Paris at the close of the seventeenth century* . . . *by Martin Lister, M.D., now revised* . . . (London, 1823), is so "revised" by the editor that the form of the original (though not its content) is unrecognizable as any one of the three original editions. It is probably the second edition, as it contains none of the additions which Lister added to the third edition. Unhappily, Henning's volume, rather than one of the original editions, was the basis of the French translation published as *Voyage de Lister À Paris en MDCXCVIII Traduit pour la première fois, publié et annoté Par La Société des Bibliophiles François* . . . (Paris, 1873). This volume also includes extracts from the works of John Evelyn relative to the latter's journey in France between 1648 and 1661.

23. *Hippocratis Aphorismi, cum commentariolo, Auctore Martino Lister*. . . . London, 1703. Reviewed in *Philosophical Transactions*, XXIII, no. 284 (March-April, 1703), 1373-76.

24. [Ed.], *De Opsoniis et Condiméntis sive Arte Coquinariâ* by Apicius Caelius. London, 1705. A second edition of this work appeared in London in 1709, in spite of the ridicule it excited from Lister's colleagues in medicine.

25. *Dissertatio de Humoribus in qua veterum ac recentiorum Medicorum ac Philosophorum opiniones et sententiæ examinantur*. London, 1709. Dedicated to Queen Anne after Lister had become Royal Physician.

26. *De Scarabæis Britannicus*, in John Ray, *Historia Insectorum*, London, 1710.

27. *Historiæ sive Synopsis Methodicae Conchyliorum et Tabularum anatomicarum editio altera. Recensuit et indicibus auxit G. Huddesford*. Oxford, 1770. Includes manuscript notes and observations by Lister on no. 12 above. Lewis Weston Dillwyn incorporated Lister's shells under Linnaean nomenclature in *A Descriptive Catalogue of Recent Shells arranged according to the Linnæan Method; with Particular attention to Synonymy* (2 vols., London, 1817); and the same author published *Martini Lister Historia sive synopsis methodica conchyliorum* with "An Index to the Historia Conchyliorum of Lister . . ." (Oxford, 1823).

III. ARTICLES

In 1669, upon the recommendation of John Ray, Martin Lister became a contributor to the *Philosophical Transactions*, published by the Secretary of the Royal Society of London. As was customary, many of the articles were transmitted to the Secretary in the form of letters and read at one of the meetings of the Society before appearing in the *Philosophical Transactions.* All of the following items appeared in that journal, therefore its name is omitted below.

1. "Some Observations Concerning the odd Turn of Some Shell-snailes, and the darting of Spiders, made by an Ingenious Cantabrigian and by way of Letter communicated to Mr. I. Wray [John Ray], who transmitted them to the Publisher for the R.[oyal] S.[ociety]," IV, no. 50 (Aug. 16, 1669), 1011-16. No comments were added by Ray.

2. "A further note on the darting of Spiders," V, no. 65 (Nov. 14, 1670), 2104.

3. "Extract of a letter on the Acid Liquor of Pismires and the Bleeding of the Sycamore," V, no. 68 (Feb. 20, 1670/71), 2067-69. Read before the Royal Society, Feb. 23, 1670/71 (*Guard-Book L 5-6,* fol. 24). Dated from York, Jan. 28, 1670/71.

4. "Extracts of divers Letters . . . Touching some Inquiries and Experiments the Motion of Sap in Trees, and relating to the Question of the Circulation of the Same," VI, no. 70 (April 17, 1671), 2119-26. Read before the Royal Society, Feb. 23, 1670/71 (*Guard-Book L 5-6,* fol. 26). Dated from York, Feb. 15, 1670/71 .

5. "On the Motion of Juyces in Vegetables," VI, no. 70 (April 17, 1671), 2126-28. Read before the Royal Society, April 20, 1671 (*Guard-Book L 5-6,* fol. 29). Dated from York, April 8, 1671.

6. "Touching Colours in order to the Increase of Dyes, and the Fixation of Colours," VI, no. 70 (April 17, 1671), 2132-36.

7. "An Observation Concerning certain Insect husks of the Kermes kind," VI, no. 71 (May 22, 1671), 2165-66. Read before the Royal Society, May 18, 1671 (*Guard-Book L 5-6,* fol. 27). Dated from York, March 4, 1670/71.

8. "Concerning a kind of Fly that is Viviparous together with a Set of curious Inquiries about Spiders," VI, no. 72 (June 19, 1671), 2170-75.

9. "Concerning an Insect feeding upon Henbain," VI, no. 72 (June 19, 1671), 2176-77.

10. "Extracts of Two Letters . . . concerning the kind of Insect hatched by the English Kermes . . . ," VI, no. 73 (July 17, 1671), 2196-97. Read before the Royal Society, June 22, 1671 (*Guard-Book L 5-6,* fols. 31, 33). Dated from York, May 22, May 31, 1671.

11. "A considerable Accompt touching Vegetable Excrescencies," VI, no. 75 (Sept. 18, 1671), 2254-57.

12. "About Musk sented Insects . . . ," VI, no. 76 (Oct. 22, 1671), 2281-84.

13. "About Vegetable Excrescencies and Ichneumon-Worms," VI, no. 76 (Oct. 22, 1671), 2284-85.

14. "Some Additions . . . about Vegetable Excrescencies and Ichneumon Wasps . . . ," VI, no. 77 (Nov. 20, 1671), 3002-5.

15. "An Ingenious account of Veins, by him Observ'd in Plants, analogus to Human Veins," VI, no. 79 (Jan. 22, 1671/72), 3052-55. Read before the Royal Society, Jan. 18, 1671/72 (*Guard-Book L 5-6,* fol. 42). Dated from York, Jan. 10, 1671/72.

16. "An Account of a Stone cut out from under the tongue of a Man," VII, no. 83 (May 20, 1672), 4062-64. Read before the Royal Society, April 10, 1672 (*Guard-Book L 5-6,* fol. 45). Dated from York, April 10, 1672.

17. "Concerning Animated Horse-hairs, rectifying a Vul-

gar Error," VII, no. 83 (May 20, 1672), 4064-66. Read before the Royal Society, May 1, 1672 (*Guard-Book L 5-6*, fol. 46). Dated from York, April 12, 1672.

18. "Enlarging and Correcting his former Notes about Kermes . . . ," VII, no. 87 (Oct. 14, 1672), 5059-60. Read before the Royal Society, Oct. 30, 1672 (*Guard-Book L 5-6*, fol. 47). From York, n.d.

19. "A description of an odd kind of Mushroom," VII, no. 89 (Dec. 16, 1672), 5116-18.

20. "A further account concerning the Existence of Veins in all kind of Plants," VII, no. 90 (Jan. 20, 1672/73), 5132-37.

21. "A Letter . . . partly taking notice of the foregoing Intimations [by Dr. John Wallis regarding veins in plants], partly communicating some Anatomical Observations and Experiments concerning . . . Chyle . . . ," VIII, no. 95 (June 23, 1673), 6060-65.

22. "A Description of certain Stones figur'd like Plants . . . ," VIII, no. 95 (June 23, 1673), 6181-91. Illustrated. A note added by John Ray argues "that these Stones were originally pieces of Vegetables" (p. 6191). Read before the Royal Society, Nov. 13, 1673 (*Guard-Book L 5-6*, fol. 61). Dated from York, Nov. 4, 1673, Jan. 7, 1673/74.

23. "Concerning the first part of his Tables of Snails," IX, no. 105 (July 20, 1674), 96-99. Lister was assisted by William Lodge. Read before the Royal Society, April 2, 1674 (*Guard-Book L 5-6*, fol. 70). Dated from York, March 12, 1673/74.

24. "Some Observations and Experiments," IX, no. 110 (Jan. 25, 1674/75), 221-26. Six items: "Of the Efflorescence of certain Mineral Glebes," "Of an odd figured Iris," "Glossopetra nonserrata," "Of certain Dactili Idæi," "Of the Flower and Seed of Mush-

rooms," "Of the Speedy vitrifying of the whole body of Antimony by Cawk."

25. "Observations of the Astroites or Star-Stones," X, no. 112 (March 25, 1675), 274-78.

26. "An Experiment made for altering the Colour of the Chyle in the Lacteal Veins," XIII, no. 143 (Jan. 12, 1682/83), 6-9.

27. "An Account of a Roman Monument found in the Bishoprick of Durham . . . ," XIII, no. 145 (March 10, 1682/83), 70-74.

28. "A Remarkable Relation of a Man bitten with a Mad Dog and dying of the disease called Hydrophobia," XIII, no. 147 (May 10, 1683), 162-70.

29. "Some Observations upon the Ruins of a Roman Wall and Multi-angular-Tower at York," XIII, no. 149 (July 10, 1683), 238-42.

30. "Some Probable thoughts of the Whiteness of Chyle . . . ," XIII, no. 149 (July 10, 1683), 242-44.

31. "Touching the use of the Intestinum Cæcum," XIV, no. 155 (Jan. 20, 1683/84), 455-57.

32. "Roman Inscriptions from Bath, with Illustrations," XIV, no. 155 (Jan. 20, 1683/84), 457.

33. "Certain Observations of the Midland Salt-Springs of Worcestershire, Stafford-shire, and Cheshire," XIV, no. 156 (Feb. 20, 1683/84), 489-95.

34. "Three Papers of Dr. Martin Lister, the first of the Nature of Earth-quakes, more particularly of the Origine of the matter of them, from the Pyrites alone," XIV, no. 157 (March 20, 1683/84), 512-19.

35. "The Projection of the Threds of Spiders . . . ," XIV, no. 160 (June 20, 1684), 592-96.

36. "Concerning Some Very Aged Persons in the North of England," XIV, no. 160 (June 20, 1684), 597-98. A manuscript with this title was sent to the Royal

Society on March 17, 1674, and read before the Society on March 30 following (*Guard-Book L 5-6*, fol. 28).

37. "An Ingenious proposal for a new Sort of Maps of Countrys together with Tables of Sands and Clays," XIV, no. 164 (Oct. 20, 1684), 739-46. Lister's famous article on a "*Soil* or *Mineral* map," where, were one with "great care . . . very exactly to note upon the *Map* where such and such *Soiles* are bounded . . . I am of the opinion such upper *Soiles* if natural, infallibly produce such *under Minerals,* and for the most part in such order."

38. "A Discourse concerning the rising and falling of the Quicksilver in the Barometer . . . ," XIV, no. 165 (Nov. 20, 1684), 790-94.

39. "Some Experiments about Freezing . . . ," XV, no. 167 (Jan. 28, 1684/85), 836-38. An account of this paper was read before the Philosophical Society of Oxford on Feb. 9, 1684/85. See R. T. Gunther, "Dr. Plot and the Correspondence of the Philosophical Society of Oxford," in *Early Science at Oxford,* XII (Oxford, 1939), p. 163.

40. "An Account of a Stone grown to an Iron Bodkin in the Bladder of a Boy," XV, no. 168 (Feb. 23, 1684/85), 882.

41. "A Letter of Dr. Lister's to Mr. Ray concerning some particulars that might be added to the Ornithology," XV, no. 175 (Sept.-Oct., 1685), 1159-61.

42. "Three Queries relating to Shells proposed by Mr. Samuel Dale and answered by Dr. Martin Lister," XVII, no. 197 (Feb., 1692/93), 641-45.

43. "An Account of certain transparent Pebbles . . . ," XVII, no. 201 (June, 1693), 778-80. Illustrated.

44. "The Manner of making Steel, and its Temper . . . ,"
XVII, no. 203 (Sept., 1693), 865-70. Corresponds in
part with chapter 4 of Lister's unpublished account of
"A Methode for ye Historie of Iron," in *Lister 1*.

45. "An Account of the Nature and Differences of the
Juices, more particularly, of our English Vegetables,"
XIX, no. 224 (Jan., 1696/97), 365-83. Written about
thirty years earlier.

46. "Part of Two Letters . . . concerning several Plants
. . . for Producing Grass or Hay," XIX, no. 225
(Feb., 1696/97), 412-17. Written "some time since."

47. "The Anatomy of the Scallop," XIX, no. 229 (June,
1697), 567-70.

48. "Of a Venomous Scratch with the Tooth of a Porpos,
its Symptoms and cure," XIX, no. 233 (Oct., 1697),
726.

49. "An Observation of Two Boys bit by a Mad Dog,"
XX, no. 242 (July, 1698), 246-48. Case histories of
1679-80.

50. "An Objection to the New Hypothesis of the Generation of Animals from Animalcula in Semine Mascu-
lino," XX, no. 244 (Sept., 1698), 337. In opposition
to Leeuwenhoek and continued by him in XXI, no.
255 (Aug., 1699), 270 ff., 301 ff.

51. "Of the origin of White Vitriol and the Figure of its
Crystals," XXI, no. 256 (Sept., 1699), 331.

52. "A Letter from Dr. Martin Lister . . . Concerning
pouder'd Blues passing the lacteal Veins, Etc.," XXII,
no. 270 (March-April, 1701), 819-20.

IV. SCIENTIFIC CORRESPONDENCE PUBLISHED

Like most of his contemporaries, Martin Lister main-
tained a wide correspondence with other virtuosi and,

also like his fellows, he often presented letters from his correspondents to the Royal Society of London, from whence they sometimes appeared in the *Philosophical Transactions.* All of the references below refer to that journal.

1. "An Account of two Uncommon Mineral Substances found in some Coal and Iron Mines of England . . . ," communicated to Lister by Mr. Jessop of Bromhal in Yorkshire, VIII, no. 100 (Feb. 9, 1673/74), 6179-81.

2. "An Observation of Dr. Johnston's of Pomphret, communicated by him to Mr. Lister, and by him sent in a Letter to the Publisher, concerning some Stones of a perfect Gold-Colour found in Animals," IX, no. 101 (March 25, 1674), 8-9. Dated from York, March 12, 1673/74.

3. Letter from Mr. Jessop with additions by Lister and "Observations about Damps, [and] Worms vomited by children," X, no. 117 (Sept. 26, 1675), 391-95.

4. Letter from Dr. Thomas Towne of Barbados with "Some Observations made at Barbados," X, no. 117 (Sept. 26, 1675), 399-400. Transmitted by Lister from York, June 27, 1675 (*Guard-Book L 5-6,* fol. 74).

5. Letter from Tancred Robinson about bridges in France, XIV, no. 163 (Sept. 20, 1684), 712-13.

6. "The Extract of Four Letters from Mr. John Banister to Dr. Lister, communicated by him to the Publisher," XVII, no. 198 (March, 1693), 667-72. Comments on plants, shells, insects, etc. which John Banister had sent from Virginia.

7. Letter from Dr. Nicholas Witzen, Burgomaster of Amsterdam, with "The Description of certain Shells found in the East Indies," XVII, no. 203 (Sept., 1693), 870-72.

8. "A Letter from Monsieur N. Witsen to Martin Lister, with two Draughts of the Famous Persepolis," XVIII, no. 210 (May, 1694), 117-18. Illustrated.

9. "Part of a Letter from Mr. Edw. Lhwyd to Dr. Lister" about "Fiery Exhalation" in Wales, XVIII, no. 213 (Sept.-Oct., 1694), 223.

10. "An Account of the upper part of the Burning Mountain in the Isle of Ternata according to the View taken thereof; written to the Right Worshipful Nicholas Witzen, Burgermaster of Amsterdam etc. And by him communicated to Dr. Martin Lister, F. R. S.," XIX, no. 216 (March-May, 1695), 42-48.

11. "An Account of the sad Mischief befallen the Inhabitants of the Isle of Sorea, near unto the Molucco's . . . ," in a letter to Nicholas Witzen, XIX, no. 216 (March-May, 1695), 49-51.

12. "A Letter from Mr. Ralph Thoresby . . . giving an Account of a Roman Pottery, near Leeds in Yorkshire," XIX, no. 222 (Sept.-Oct., 1696), 319-20.

13. "A Letter from Sir Robert Sibbald . . . containing an Account of several Shells observed by him in Scotland," XIX, no. 222 (Sept.-Oct., 1696), 321-25.

14. "Part of a Letter from Fort St. George in the East-Indies giving An Account of a long Worm . . . troublesome to the Inhabitants . . . ," XIX, no. 225 (Feb., 1696/97), 417-18.

15. "Part of a Letter from Mr. Nicolas Witsen . . . giving a further Relation of . . . the Molucco Islands," XIX, no. 228 (April, 1697), 529-32.

16. "Part of a Letter from Mr. Thoresby . . . concerning Two Roman Altars lately found in the North of England . . . ," XIX, no. 231 (Aug., 1697), 661-64. Illustrated.

17. "Part of two Letters of Mr. Thoresby . . . about Roman Antiquities found in Yorkshire," XIX, no. 234 (Nov., 1697), 738-70. The letter from Thoresby to Lister is dated from Leeds, Oct. 30, 1697.
18. Letter from Mr. Robert Clarke with "Two Observations . . . about the Death of a Dog . . . [and] about the Polypus of the Lungs," XIX, no. 235 (Dec., 1697), 779-80. Letter dated Nov. 8, 1697.
19. "A Letter from Dr. Thomas Molyneux . . . Containing some additional Observations on the Giants Causeway in Ireland," XX, no. 241 (June, 1698), 209-23.
20. "Part of a Letter from Mr. Edw. Lhwyd . . . concerning several regularly Figured Stones . . . ," XX, no. 243 (Aug., 1698), 279-80. Illustrated.
21. "Part of a Letter from Mr. [Michael] Butterfield from Paris . . . concerning Magnetical Sand," XX, no. 244 (Sept., 1698), 336.
22. "Part of a Letter from Mr. Witsen . . . concerning some late Observations in Nova Hollandia," XX, no. 245 (Oct., 1698), 361-62.
23. "Part of Two Letters from Mr. [Jonathan] Cay [Kay] . . . concerning some Mineral Waters," XX, no. 245 (Oct., 1698), 365-70.
24. "An Extract of a Letter from Leghorn . . . concerning Seignior Redi's Manuscripts, and the Generation of Fleas," XXI, no. 249 (Feb., 1698/99), 42-43.
25. "Part of a Letter from Mr. Dale . . . concerning several Insects," XXI, no. 249 (Feb., 1698/99), 50-51.
26. "Account of a young man slain with Thunder and Lightning . . . from Ralph Thoresby . . . ," XXI, no. 249 (Feb., 1698/99), 51-52.
27. "Of Coal-Borings . . . from Mr. Maleverer, of Arn-

cliffe in Yorkshire," XXI, no. 250 (March, 1699), 73-78. Notes by Lister from records of 1639-59.

28. "Part of a Letter from Dr. Cay . . . Concerning the Vertues of Ostracites . . . ," XXI, no. 250 (March, 1699), 81-85.

29. "A Letter from Mr. Christopher Hunter . . . concerning some Roman Inscriptions found near Durham," XXII, no. 266 (Sept.-Oct., 1700), 657-58.

30. "Part of Monsieur Pouparts' Letter . . . concerning the Insect called Libella," XXII, no. 266 (Sept.-Oct., 1700), 673-76.

31. "Part of some Letters from Mr. Christopher Hunter . . . concerning several Roman Inscriptions . . . in Yorkshire," XXIII, no. 278 (March-April, 1702), 1129-32. Dated from Stockton, April 12, May 15, May 29, 1702.